Satellite view of Crete (courtesy NASA)

THE AERIAL ATLAS OF ANCIENT CRETE

THE AERIAL ATLAS OF ANCIENT CRETE

Edited by   *J. Wilson Myers, Eleanor Emlen Myers, and Gerald Cadogan*

Geomorphology by   *John A. Gifford*

with contributions by   *Stylianos Alexiou, Philip P. Betancourt, William D. E. Coulson, Costis Davaras, Leslie P. Day, Antonino Di Vita, William R. Farrand, Edward Flaccus, Geraldine C. Gesell, Elpida Hadjidaki, Barbara J. Hayden, Athanasia Kanta, Vincenzo La Rosa, Angeliki Lebessi, J. Alexander MacGillivray, Vanna Niniou-Kindeli, Olivier Pelon, Olivier Picard, Nikolaos Platon, Jean-Claude Poursat, L. Hugh Sackett, Efi Sakellaraki, Yannis Sakellarakis, Joseph W. Shaw, Jeffrey S. Soles, Chiara Tarditi, Petros Themelis, René Treuil, Metaxia Tsipopoulou, Yannis Tzedakis, Henri Van Effenterre, Antonis Vasilakis, Peter Warren, James Whitley, Antonis A. Zois*

THAMES AND HUDSON

First published in Great Britain in 1992 by
Thames and Hudson Ltd, London

Printed and bound in Korea

9 8 7 6 5 4 3 2 1

The paper used in this publication meets
the minimum requirements of American
National Standard for Information Sciences—Permanence of Paper for Printed
Library Materials, ANSI z39.48-1984.
∞

Along the winedark sea, by water ringed,

there lies a land both fair and fertile: Crete,

the home of countless men, of ninety cities.

ODYSSEY *19:172–74*
(Trans. Allen Mandelbaum)

Published with the assistance of

the Getty Grant Program

The Press would also like to

acknowledge the support of a grant from

the National Endowment for the Humanities,

an independent federal agency

CONTENTS

This project had its beginnings in the Department of Humanities at Michigan State University, where J. W. and E. E. Myers organized a program to do fieldwork in aerial archaeology. The program enabled us to travel each year to make balloon photographs of archaeological sites for individual excavators and to assemble a photographic archive for comparative study. University Vice President John Cantlon and Provost Jack B. Kinsinger provided research initiation grants which enabled us to develop equipment and refine field techniques. Humanities Department Chairman F. DeWitt Platt and Vice Chairman Floyd Barrows encouraged the project and helped with further sources of funding. The Physics Department's machine shop made our precision camera gimbals, the backpack tether reels, and elements of the radio control system.

Members of the advisory committee for our project generously gave their time and counsel: Alan Fisher, William and Louise Mc-Cagg, F. DeWitt Platt, and, from the Rochester Institute of Technology, Nancy Stuart. William Harrison, of Custom Photographic Inc. in Lansing, Michigan, contributed much of the early color processing. The Millbrook Printing Company helped us produce an illustrated newsletter for friends of the project.

Particular thanks go to colleagues Lydia and Truman Woodruff of East Lansing, who organized a successful art auction—contributing works from their own collection and soliciting works from local artists—to raise matching funds for a National Endowment for the Humanities grant.

We are also grateful for the help and support of the Classics Department and the Semple Classics Fund of the University of Cincinnati during the time that Gerald Cadogan had his academic base there. As the project concludes, the Myerses are members of the Archaeology Department and the Center for Remote Sensing at Boston University, which have provided useful advice and assistance.

In Greece the American School of Classical Studies at Athens was the official base for our research and the source through which we obtained archaeological and flight permits from the Greek government. The School's Directors, James McCredie, Henry Immerwahr, Stephen Miller, and William Coulson, were most helpful, as were a succession of diligent Secretaries of the School, James Wright, David Romano, Halford Haskell, Murray McClellan, and Robert Bridges. Maria Pilali, Secretary to the Director, smoothed our way through many complexities.

Nothing could have been achieved without the official permission and active encouragement of the officers and former officers of the Greek Archaeological Service, many of whom we are delighted to have among our contributors. We thank especially the Director of the Service, Yannis Tzedakis, and his colleagues and former colleagues in Crete, Stylianos Alexiou, Costis Davaras, Elpida Hadjidaki, Alexandra Karetsou, Angeliki Lebessi, Stavroula Markoulaki, Vanna Niniou-Kindeli, Nikos Papadakis, Yannis Sakellarakis, Metaxia Tsipopoulou, Despina Vallianou, and Antonis Vasilakis, for their constant help, encouragement, and patience with our photographing sites they are excavating or sites under their control.

As Secretary of the Archaeological Society of Athens, the late George Mylonas was most gracious in giving us permission to photograph excavations of the Society. Mr. Moudakis of the Civil Air Service helped us to obtain permission for each flight of the balloon. Among friends in Athens, Lucy and Demetrius Krystallis helped expedite our work at critical times.

We also thank the University of Crete and the foreign schools of archaeology in Greece: the British School at Athens, its Managing Committee, its Director Hector Catling, its Curators at Knossos Sandy MacGillivray (generous there with hospitality and advice and later our host as the excavator at Palaikastro) and Alan Peatfield, and the housekeeper Steve Townsend; the French School of Athens, and its Directors Pierre Amandry and Olivier Picard; and the Italian School of Athens, its Director Antonino Di Vita and its Assistant Director Alberto G. Benvenuti.

We are indebted to the excavation directors and heads of research who permitted the aerial photographs and who have written the entries. Thirty-five contributors from six countries supplied entries in four languages to Gerald Cadogan for translation and editing. Authors who submitted their entries early were able to revise them to reflect discoveries at the sites through 1989, though later digging would not be shown in the photographs. Our thirty-sixth contributor is John Gifford, who made several expeditions to Crete, examining the geomorphology of the sites to prepare the chapter on Cretan geology and to write a section of the site entries. We are also indebted to Edward Flaccus, who, in addition to helping us in the field in 1983, wrote the chapter on the Cretan climate and vegetation.

The architects and surveyors Michael Clews, Mary Hood, David Myers, David Smyth, and William Taylor have drawn most of the plans and collaborated with us in the tricky decisions in interpretation that the plans—and the photographs—present. Nancy Cooper, Edward Flaccus, Sally Flaccus, Sandy MacGillivray, David Myers, Adam Stepan, and Nancy Stuart supplied ground photographs.

Marie-Louise Collard helped to edit as well as translate some of the site chapters. Rupert Housley assisted in the calibration of radiocarbon dates. We received additional editorial assistance from the site contributors as well as from Stelios Andreou, Anthony Bryer, James Coulton, Stella Chrysoulaki, Frank Frost, Sinclair Hood, Nicoletta Momigliano, Polly Muhly, Ronald Stroud, Lucia Vagnetti, and David Wilson. We are most grateful.

The Institute for Aegean Prehistory gave generous grants to Gerald Cadogan and the Myerses for editorial expenses.

At the University of California Press, James H. Clark, the director, has been a patient and wise supporter throughout; Eileen McWilliam and her assistant, Adele Grinnell, guided us through the acquisition process; Stephanie Fay has been a discerning copy editor, helping at every step to improve the text; Steve Renick's eye for design has closely interwoven text and illustrations.

Those who volunteered their time to work with us in Crete, tolerating blown-down tents, pouring rain, spring chill and summer heat, meals at odd times, predawn hours for inflations, and the neverending hauling of hydrogen tanks to and from Herakleion, deserve special and heartfelt thanks: in 1976, Stelios Andreou, Mary Hood, and John McEnroe; in 1981, Nancy Cooper, Andrea Deagan, Kathy Donahue, Andrew Sherwood, Tim Jarvis, and Margaret Walsh; in 1982, Gina Anderson, Doug and Lisa Cox, Katie Curry, John Gifford, Catherine Johnson, Sandy MacGillivray, Jean-Pierre Olivier, Marny Payne, Doug Price, Michael Quillinan, and Nancy Stuart; in 1983, Toby Baldwin, Ed and Sally Flaccus, Alan Ortega, Doug Price, and David Myers; in 1984, Toby Baldwin, Doug Price—for his third year of indispensable help—and Stan and Peg Myers; in 1987, Sophie Huxley, Sonya Laurence, Colin Macdonald, Sandy MacGillivray, and John McPhedran.

The late Marcos Peronikolis, the archaeological guard at Gournia, befriended us at the start of our 1981 season and did much from then on to instruct us in the ways of the island. From Marcos and his wife, Maria, we learned the full meaning of Cretan hospitality.

We are grateful to the many friends of the project who contributed to the matching funds offer of the National Endowment for the

Humanities: Edward G. Acomb, Walter Adams, Mr. and Mrs. Russell V. Allman, the late Joseph W. Alsop, Donald and Gina Anderson, James R. Anderson, R. E. Olds Anderson, Patricia C. Atkinson, Helen K. Baer, Mr. and Mrs. Charles A. Baryames, George and Ann Bass, Mr. and Mrs. Jack Bass, Mrs. Myron C. Beal, Judith Feinberg Brilliant, Mr. and Mrs. Theodore M. Brody, Ruth A. Bryant, Giovanna M. Burk, Margot C. Camp, Joan Tozzer Cave, Francisco Chang, Lorain D. and Sonya M. Cornell, Mary Critzas, Mr. and Mrs. Myles S. Delano, Mr. and Mrs. Robert Derleth, Joseph L. Druse, Larry R. Duerbeck, Mr. and Mrs. Surjit Dulai, Mr. and Mrs. Adolph K. Feinberg, Herbert I. Finch, Alan and Carol Fisher, Mr. and Mrs. Carl L. Foiles, Ford Motor Company, Dr. and Mrs. Silvio P. Fortino, Marjorie E. Gesner, Perry E. Gianakos, James P. Gillis, Stephen and Sandra Glass, Mr. and Mrs. Bruce A. Goodrich, Mr. and Mrs. Thomas H. Greer, Betty Grossman, Meryl Halpern, Elwood C. Hamsher, Elizabeth Hanks, Patricia C. Hecker, Joanne Heffelfinger, John and Carolyn Hoagland, Mr. and Mrs. John G. Hocking, George W. Hoddy, Robert L. Hohlfelder, Mr. and Mrs. John Howe, Mr. and Mrs. Henry Immerwahr, the Institute for Aegean Prehistory, Mr. and Mrs. Michael Jameson, Squire Jaros, Anne M. Johnston, Dr. David Kahn, Norma Kershaw, Elizabeth Kiefer, Mr. and Mrs. Edgar Knoebel, Mr. and Mrs. Henry C. Koch, Cleo Rae Lavey, Carol Lawton, George W. Loomis, Jr., Mr. and Mrs. Wilfred MacDonald, Carl Rennie Mandenberg, Jeff B. Marvig, Roy and LeeAnn Matthews, William and Louise McCagg, James R. McCredie, Sara L. Miller, Vivian Najar, Christy Nichols, Nora N. Mouradian, Martha J. Payne, Mr. and Mrs. Kenyon Payne, George J. Platsis, DeWitt and Dixie Platt, Dr. John Psaroutakis, Robert S. Quimby, the late Walter G. C. Ramberg, Ernest Rich, Sharon L. Rich, Alvin Lee Rogers, Harold and Gertrude Sadoff, Donna Grace Scheel, Mr. and Mrs. Robert J. Scheffel, George and Veronica Sionakides, Lyman and Doreen Spitzer, Alan P. Suits, Beverly Y. Suits, W. B. and Candace Thoman Foundation, Homer A. Thompson, Jane K. Veith, Mr. and Mrs. William Vincent, Mr. and Mrs. William J. Walter, Malcolm H. Wiener, Julian and Eunice Whittlesey, Jere Wickens, Dr. Thomas Wilensky, Kathleen L. Williams, James D. Wilson, Rachel Haines Wilson, Howard Wong, Jr.

Louise McCagg, Judith Brilliant, Patricia G. Hecker, Mrs. Edwin Grossman, Nancy H. Grove, and Mrs. Alberta S. Kalish also made contributions to support the book's publication.

The preparation of this volume was made possible in part by a grant from the National Endowment for the Humanities, an independent federal agency. The grant enabled us to record and preserve these images of the beginnings of Western civilization.

JOURNALS

AA	*Archäologischer Anzeiger*
AAA	*Archaiologika Analekta ex Athinon (Athens Annals of Archaeology)*
AJA	*American Journal of Archaeology*
AntJ	*Antiquaries Journal*
AS	*Anatolian Studies*
AR	*Archaeological Reports*
ArchDelt	*Archaiologikon Deltion*
ArchEph	*Archaiologiki Ephimeris*
ASAtene	*Annuario della Scuola Archeologica di Atene e delle Missioni Italiane in Oriente*
AthMitt	*Athenischer Mitteilungen*
BCH	*Bulletin de correspondance hellénique*
BdA	*Bollettino d'arte*
BICS	*Bulletin of the Institute of Classical Studies of the University of London*
BSA	*Annual of the British School at Athens*
CRAI	*Comptes rendus des séances de l'Académie des Inscriptions et Belles-Lettres*
CronCat	*Cronache di archeologia e di storia dell'arte, Università di Catania*
CrSt	*Cretan Studies*
ILN	*Illustrated London News*
IstMitt	*Istanbuler Mitteilungen*
JdI	*Jahrbuch des Deutschen Archäologischen Institut*
JFA	*Journal of Field Archaeology*
JHS	*Journal of Hellenic Studies*
JRGZM	*Jahrbuch des Römisch-Germanischen Zentralmuseums, Mainz*
KrChron	*Kritika Chronika*
MonAnt	*Monumenti antichi*
OJA	*Oxford Journal of Archaeology*
PAE	*Praktika tis en Athinais Archaiologikis Etaireias*
PP	*La parola del passato*
PPS	*Proceedings of the Prehistoric Society*
PZ	*Prähistorische Zeitschrift*

RA	*Revue archéologique*
RALouvain	*Revue des archéologues et historiens d'art de Louvain*
RdArchéom	*Revue d'archéometrie*
REA	*Revue des études anciennes*
RendLinc	*Atti dell'Accademia Nazionale dei Lincei. Rendiconti*
RivFil	*Rivista di filologia e d'istruzione classica*
RPhil	*Revue de philologie, de littérature et d'histoire ancienne*
SIMA	*Studies in Mediterranean Archaeology*
SIMA PB	*SIMA Pocket Book*
SMEA	*Studi micenei ed egeo-anatolici*
StRom	*Studi romani*
TechChron	*Technika Chronika*

CONFERENCES, CORPORA, ENCYCLOPEDIAS AND FESTSCHRIFTEN

Ancient Crete	Italian Archaeological School of Athens. *Ancient Crete: A Hundred Years of Italian Archaeology, 1884–1984* (Rome 1985)
Antichità cretesi	*Antichità cretesi: Studi in onore di Doro Levi 1, 2 (CronCat 12, 13 [1973, 1974])*
Aux origines de l'hellénisme	*Aux origines de l'hellénisme: La Crète et la Grèce. Homage à Henri Van Effenterre* (Paris 1984)
CMS	*Corpus der minoischen und mykenischen Siegel 1–.* Ed. F. Matz, H. Biesantz, and I. Pini (Berlin, 1964–)
COMIK	J. Chadwick, L. Godart, J. T. Killen, J.-P. Olivier, A. Sacconi, and Y. Sakellarakis, *Corpus of Mycenaean Inscriptions from Knossos 1. Incunabula Graeca* 88 (Cambridge and Rome 1986–)
Creta antica	Scuola Archeologica di Atene. *Creta antica: Cento anni di archeologia italiana, 1884–1984* (Rome 1984)
1 Cretological	*Pepragmena tou Protou Diethnous Kritologikou Synedriou 1–3 (KrChron 15–16 [1961–62])*
2 Cretological	*Pepragmena tou Defterou Diethnous Kritologikou Synedriou 1–3* (Athens 1968)
3 Cretological	*Pepragmena tou Tritou Diethnous Kritologikou Synedriou 1–3* (Athens 1973–75)

4 Cretological	*Pepragmena tou Tetartou Diethnous Kritologikou Synedriou* 1–3 (Athens 1980–81)
5 Cretological	*Pepragmena tou Pemptou Diethnous Kritologikou Synedriou* 1–3 (Herakleion 1985)
6 Cretological	*Pepragmena tou Ektou Diethnous Kritologikou Synedriou* 1–3 (Chania 1990–91)
EAA	*Enciclopedia dell'arte antica, classica e orientale* 1– (Rome 1958–)
Eilapini	*Eilapini: Tomos timitikos yia ton Kathigiti Nikolao Platona.* Ed. L. Kastrinaki, G. Orphanou, and N. Yannadakis (Herakleion 1987)
EtCr	*Etudes Crétoises* 1– (Paris 1928–)
The Function of the Minoan Palaces	*The Function of the Minoan Palaces.* Proceedings of the Fourth International Symposium at the Swedish Institute in Athens, 10–16 June 1984. Ed. R. Hägg and N. Marinatos (Stockholm 1987)
GORILA	L. Godart and J.-P. Olivier, *Recueil des inscriptions en Linéaire A* 1–5 (*EtCr* 21, nos. 1–5) (Paris 1976–85)
IC	M. Guarducci, *Inscriptiones Creticae* 1–4 (Rome 1935–50)
A Land Called Crete	*A Land Called Crete.* Smith College Studies in History 45 (1968)
Minoan Society	*Minoan Society.* Proceedings of the Cambridge Colloquium, 1981. Ed. O. Krzyszkowska and L. Nixon (Bristol 1983)
The Minoan Thalassocracy	*The Minoan Thalassocracy: Myth and Reality.* Proceedings of the Third International Symposium at the Swedish Institute in Athens, 31 May–5 June 1982. Ed. R. Hägg and N. Marinatos (Stockholm 1984)
1 Mycenological	*Atti e memorie 1° Congresso Internazionale di Micenologia. Roma 27 Settembre–3 Ottobre 1967* 1, 2 (*Incunabula Graeca* 25) (Rome 1968)
PECS	*The Princeton Encyclopedia of Classical Sites.* Ed. R. Stilwell (Princeton 1976)
Problems in Greek Prehistory	*Problems in Greek Prehistory.* Papers presented at the Centenary Conference of the British School of Archaeology at Athens, Manchester, April 1986. Ed. E. B. French and K. A. Wardle (Bristol 1988)
RE	*Real-Enzyklopädie der klassischen Altertumswissenschaft.* Ed. G. Wissowa et al. (Berlin 1894–)
Sanctuaries and Cults in the Aegean Bronze Age	*Sanctuaries and Cults in the Aegean Bronze Age.* Proceedings of the First International Symposium at the Swedish Institute in Athens, 12–13 May 1990. Ed. R. Hägg and N. Marinatos (Stockholm 1981)
Svoronos	J.-N. Svoronos, *Numismatique de la Crète ancienne* (Mâcon 1890)
2 Thera	*Thera and the Aegean World.* Proceedings of the Second International Scientific Congress, Santorini, Greece, August 1978, 1, 2. Ed. C. Doumas (London 1978, 1980)
3 Thera	*Thera and the Aegean World III.* Proceedings of the Third International Scientific Congress, Santorini, Greece, September 1989, 1–3. Ed. D. A. Hardy (London 1990)
TUAS	*Temple University Aegean Symposium* 1–10 (Philadelphia 1976–85)

CHRONOLOGY		MEASUREMENTS	
A	Archaic	cm	centimeter(s)
Arab		cu	cubic
Byz	Byzantine	d	diameter
C	Classical	ha	hectare(s)
E	Early	km	kilometer(s)
F	Final	m	meter(s)
G	Geometric	sq	square
H	Hellenistic		
L	Late		
M	Minoan		
MM	Middle Minoan		
MN	Middle Neolithic		
Med	Medieval		
N	Neolithic		
O	Orientalizing		
Ott	Ottoman		
PG	Protogeometric		
R	Roman		
SM	Sub-Minoan		
V	Venetian		

PART I

THE ATLAS AND CRETE

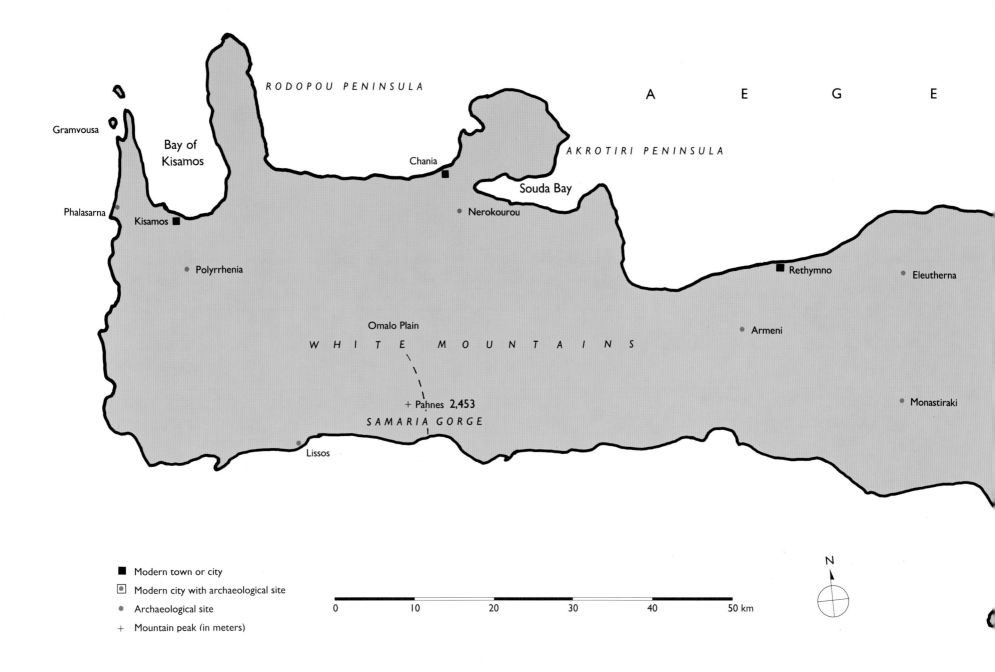

Gramvousa

RODOPOU PENINSULA

AKROTIRI PENINSULA

A E G E G E

Bay of
Kisamos

Chania

Souda Bay

Phalasarna

Nerokourou

Kisamos

Rethymno

Eleutherna

Polyrrhenia

Omalo Plain

Armeni

W H I T E   M O U N T A I N S

+ Pahnes 2,453

Monastiraki

SAMARIA GORGE

Lissos

■ Modern town or city

◉ Modern city with archaeological site

● Archaeological site

+ Mountain peak (in meters)

0   10   20   30   40   50 km

N

L   I   B   Y

S E A

Dia

Cape Sidero

■ Herakleion

Tylissos • • Knossos

• Mallia

• Dreros

Olous

Siteia ■

Ayia Photia

Mt. Juktas +
811

⊡ Archanes

• Karphi

Ayios Nikolaos ■

Pseira • Mochlos

• Chamaizi

Palaikastro

• Vathypetro

Bay of Mirabello

L A S I T H I
+ 2,148
M O U N T A I N S

• Lato

+ Ornon
1,237

• Achladia

• Kavousi

Zakro

Vrokastro •

• Gournia

• Praisos

• Vasiliki

+ Thripti
1,476

• Makryyialos

Kalonero Bay

• Syme

Chondros •

⊡

Ierapetra ■

Kouphonisi

Myrtos

S E A

Figure 1.1   Location of sites on Crete

AERIAL ARCHAEOLOGY AND THE ATLAS

J. WILSON MYERS AND ELEANOR EMLEN MYERS

At the mention of aerial archaeology, one thinks immediately of open-cockpit planes and those old photographs made during World War I over the deserts of the Middle East. In the raking light of early morning or late evening, the pilot has discovered the faint but unmistakable pattern of an ancient city whose walls of sun-dried brick have all but melted away. The low sun creates defining shadows paralleled by highlighted ridges, a combination that forces ground contours into high relief. The aerial observers were quick to learn that a high vantage point with raking light gives one the peculiar ability to make sense of larger patterns that confuse the viewer or go unnoticed on the ground.

The impressive record of airplanes and now of satellite imaging in aerial archaeology may obscure the pioneer achievements of the balloon camera and make its continued use seem anachronistic. But the balloon still offers a simple and relatively inexpensive way of making low vertical photographs that show impressive detail. It seems appropriate to share with the reader some of what we have learned about the history and current application of the tethered unmanned balloon we used to produce the aerial images in this atlas.

Above 800 m one would do best to use a plane, especially for extended surveys, and up to 10 m a photo tower or bipod is useful; in the range between 10 and 800 m, however, the camera balloon continues to occupy its own evolutionary niche. Without the most sophisticated military equipment, low-flying planes cannot make sharp and detailed images since speed blurs the photographs; helicopters are expensive and, because unstable in their hovering mode, require special mounts to produce true vibration-free vertical photographs. The powerful downwash from the rotors can damage fragile excavations and ruffle the surface over underwater sites.

Certainly for mapping and aerial surveying the airplane provides an appropriate platform, but the balloon camera from its lower vantage point can best reveal the immediate details of human activity. Starting low and moving up by letting out the tether cord, one can show the mosaic floor of an excavated room; the shape, through foundations or stubs of walls, of a large room or complex; the relationship of rooms in a large building; and the shape of a group of buildings: a village or a town. Near the practical upper limit, a square-kilometer frame can include an entire ancient city.

In practice, balloon photographs serve several archaeological purposes, the most vital being to record the details of a site against the inevitable process of erosion. Information is saved that will be lost as mud-brick structures weather or as rain washes the clay packing out of stone walls. Even the most solid of stone structures can be undermined by rainwater where ancient drains no longer function, and fig trees growing tightly wedged in the cracks between laid blocks can tumble buildings. Though modern excavators work hard to stabilize their sites, and government agencies with limited budgets try to guard and maintain them, a slow deterioration is inevitable. Thus even for previously published excavations the photograph, like a time capsule, can save information for the archaeologists of a future when ancient cultures will be better understood and the technology for image analysis may be far advanced.

For recording purposes, photographs and excavators' drawn plans, though both important, have separate, complementary functions. No photograph can substitute for the information that experienced archaeologists, after close observation, can put into a drawn plan. Where the excavation itself is complex and confusing, they can and must decide which details and continuities to emphasize and which to eliminate as irrelevant. A drawn plan, usually an orthographic projection, is always an interpretation, a skillful simplification of visible evidence. An aerial photograph, however, records all that can be seen and recognized from above: abundant and graduated detail in patterns, tones, shades, and colors. To trained observers, the photograph can provide nuances of fresh information difficult to represent in a plan and sometimes impossible to see on the ground; to those not accustomed to reading plans, a photograph establishes a convincing sense of perceived reality that drawings cannot, though its very wealth of detail may suggest that a supplemental plan beside it would help with interpretation. A recognition of the complementary functions of air photographs and drawn plans placed side by side led to the format of this atlas.

The word *plan* has two meanings: architects, ancient or modern, must begin with a conceptual scheme, an idea for a building—a plan in the primary sense. When the idea is reduced to paper, it is more properly a ground plan, indicating where lines on the ground must be marked out to start construction, but it can also include what lies just above ground level. In a plan made at an excavation, the location of foundation walls, room separations, doorways, column bases, and staircases are all indicated as though they were flattened and seen from a high vantage point. The excavation of an ancient site usually reveals these lower parts of buildings, the upper elements having eroded away or been deliberately removed. Thus archaeologists' drawings help recover the original concept, or ground plan, of the ancient builders. (The other major architectural view, the reconstructed side view, or elevation, is necessarily much more conjectural for a ruin.) Because a vertical air photograph over a level site makes a similar image, it has been called a photo plan. As long as the site is flat and the plane of the camera's film is parallel to the ground, drawing and photograph will correspond. The difference appears when a site is not on level ground; then perspective will magnify higher objects in relation to those at lower levels. If, to illustrate, we look directly below out of a high apartment window, the flower pot on a lower fire escape appears larger than an automobile down on the street. In an orthographic drawing made from the same window, the flower pot is "lowered" to the street and appears in its true size. But, this difference of perspective aside—and most of our atlas sites lie on level ground—both drawn plans and photo plans can lead us directly to the intention of the original builders. The photograph is all-inclusive; the drawing simplifies. The photograph lifts us for a bird's-eye view of all that the camera captures; the drawing, through selection, helps us interpret what we see.

Published air photographs sometimes depart from the convention of most maps and plans that north is at the top of the page. As experienced air photographers know—and we discovered for ourselves—shadows thrown to the left of objects (as when the top of an early morning photograph represents north) sometimes distort ground contours in a photograph so that pits become hills and hills turn into pits. The reader can experiment with this effect by rotating the Kamilari tomb photograph (Fig. 14.2). With the light coming from the left, the photograph appears to show a circular stone wall with a depression in the center. With the light coming from the right, the image can be read as stone paving in a circular trench. We suggest that those who experience problems with an image rotate the aerial photograph until the light appears to be coming from the upper left, with the shadows cast to the lower right. In professional shorthand, let "shadow stab stomach."

BEGINNING AT MEGIDDO

The first ascent by aeronauts was made in Montgolfier's balloon in 1783, and the first aerial photograph (over Paris) was made in 1858 by the early photographer and balloonist known as Nadar. In 1901 an archaeological site, megalithic Stonehenge in England, was for the first time the subject of a balloon photograph; a little later the Italians recorded both the Forum in Rome and the ancient port of Ostia. But not until 1930 were vertical balloon photographs used systematically at an ongoing excavation. The place was the tell, or city mound, of the biblical site Megiddo, the Armageddon of the Book of Revelation. The excavator was P. L. O. Guy, the field director for James H. Breasted, head of the Oriental Institute of the University of Chicago.

Well supplied with workers and well funded by John D. Rockefeller, Jr., Guy, whom Breasted had made director in 1927, was able to set a high standard for scientific excavation and careful recording. The mound occupied a half-kilometer square, and the problem of sorting out the internal walls of rubble and mud at different stratigraphic levels was unusually difficult.

"The excavation of Megiddo," Guy wrote in his 1932 article, "presented the opportunity of realizing an old desire—the use of air-photography as an aid to recording ruins progressively exposed, and as a help in the often puzzling task of distinguishing excavated buildings of one stratum from those of another." Ruling out the use of airplanes as too expensive and kites as too difficult to handle in eddying winds, he settled on a small unmanned rubber meteorological balloon and a light plywood camera with a holder for 5-by-7-inch cut film. When the balloon burst (on Guy Fawkes Day), he ordered a larger rubberized silk balloon and a camera with an 8-by-10-inch film holder. To inflate the balloon he used hydrogen tanks imported from France. This larger balloon appears to have been a great success through the 1930 campaign.

Using two opposing control cords, and an electric cable that went up to the shutter release, he was able to make a regular series of overlapping vertical photographs at 100 m. These were combined into a mosaic image of the city at each level before deeper digging erased the recorded overburden. The mosaics were then used both in preparing drawn plans and, on the ground, in comparing elements of buildings that are some distance apart: "having spotted a similarity on the mosaic, one can walk over and verify it (or not) on the ground."

Guy gives enough sound advice to allow others to profit by his experience. The area to be photographed should be carefully cleaned and weeded, the balloon should be inflated only when the air is still, the two line handlers must wear gloves, the work should go "as quickly as may be without hurrying" lest the weather not hold or the morning light be lost. He noted that since it was difficult to understand complex aerial enlargements published in the small standard format of a journal, it might be best to supply a set of "lantern slides" to go with the publication. He recommended that projected slides not just be used for lectures and then put away but studied quietly by the archaeologist at close range. Guy concludes his article with this comment about the air photographs: "the main point about them is this—and all diggers who have seen them agree about it—they have a high and lasting archaeological value."

It seemed strange to us as we read the accounts that the method so successful for Guy (1932) and Breasted (1933) appeared to have been abruptly abandoned. Years later, in discussions with John A. Wilson, who succeeded Breasted as director of the Oriental Institute, and with James H. Breasted, Jr., both of whom remembered Guy and his balloon at Megiddo, we learned that at the end of the 1930 season a sudden wind had destroyed the balloon and smashed the camera. We remembered that Guy had emphasized that the air *must* be still when the balloon is inflated. Lacking automatic film advance, his camera had to be lowered and reloaded after each individual exposure, a time-consuming procedure. We could infer more difficulty with the wind than the reports suggest; the balloon was in fact often difficult to handle. Unlike a kite, which rises in the wind, a spherical balloon will blow down as the lateral drag in a sudden breeze begins to overtake the lift. Because the vertical lift of the gas at a given altitude remains constant and the lateral force increases exponentially as the wind rises, we soon learned ourselves that a rising wind poses a danger to the small captive balloon, its gross lift already reduced by the combined weight of the balloon fabric, the cameras, and the tether cords. The angle of the tether with the ground is, in fact, an expression of the lift-drag ratio.

Though Philip Guy at Megiddo was clearly the pioneering archaeologist in systematic balloon photography, it was some years before more modern equipment made his system both less risky and practical enough to encourage its revival.

EARLY EXPERIENCE

Our own introduction to modern balloon photography came in Greece in 1973 when, following a sabbatical exploration of Roman cities in North Africa, we worked through the summer at Michael Jameson's undersea excavation of the Sanctuary of Apollo at ancient Halieis (Jameson 1974). At the end of the season Julian and Eunice Whittlesey of Wilton, Connecticut, flew their spherical balloon and radio-controlled, motor-driven Hasselblad camera from a rowboat to record building foundations on the harbor bottom. Working with the Whittleseys, we saw clearly that no other method could offer such comprehensive coverage of the temple and associated structures. Much credit is due to the Whittleseys for their energy and resourcefulness in demonstrating at sites in the Mediterranean that equipment more modern than Philip Guy's had greatly improved the efficiency of balloon photography (see Whittlesey 1975).

After several summers of association with the Whittleseys, who planned then to concentrate their own activities in North and South America, we established the Projects in Field Archaeology program at Michigan State University as our own academic base for further research and development in balloon photography. It was clear that expanded, systematic aerial documentation of Mediterranean sites would have immediate archaeological value while it also preserved vanishing data for future study.

With research grants from the university, we were able to design our own aerial equipment and develop new methods of operation as we went to the Mediterranean each year to visit both land sites and those submerged in shallow water. We were given an additional office and lab for organizing and storing the prints, negatives, maps, and plans of our growing archive, and we found funding for a computer—especially needed by our expanding program with its two-person staff—which made correspondence for project planning and fund raising easier, helped us to manage the finances, and, perhaps most important, enabled us to keep a database record of our work. Our overseas center of operation was the American School of Classical Studies at Athens, which helped with official permissions and offered storage space for our field equipment. At remote sites a specially fitted field van became camp headquarters, balloon tender, and an air-conditioned place for developing the morning's photographs under conditions where 100-degree heat outside would otherwise turn film to intractable flypaper.

By 1981, as individual excavators invited our collaboration, we had gained experience at over fifty sites and were ready to undertake a more comprehensive project: an atlas of related sites in a given region, or even, if things worked out, a series of regional atlases. We had become convinced that the archaeological value of our site photographs increased as they were grouped together for comparative study. At some sites we made visits in successive years to preserve data as the digging progressed to lower stratigraphic levels.

The maxim that excavation is the "systematic destruction of evidence" is a cautionary one understood by all.

In 1985 our academic base moved to Boston University, where we have positions in the Department of Archaeology and the additional advantage of access to the university's Center for Remote Sensing, with its computer programs developed by NASA for the enhancement and analysis of images.

CRETE AND THE ATLAS PROJECT

Though the first fieldwork deliberately done for the *Aerial Atlas of Ancient Crete* began in 1981 with major funding from the National Endowment for the Humanities, the idea for an atlas began to take shape, and some of the photographs were made, in 1976 during our first visit to Crete. At the invitation of Gerald Cadogan, we flew a spherical balloon and a single Hasselblad camera to record his excavation of a Minoan village and country house on the hilltop at Myrtos-Pyrgos (see Figs. 28.2–5). Next we went with Gerald and photographed, for the British School at Athens, Arthur Evans's great find, the Palace of Minos at Knossos (see Figs. 17.2, 17.4–5, 17.7). We ended the 1976 work on Crete by collaborating with Joseph Shaw to record, with the help of Stelios Andreou and John McEnroe, the barren beach and sand dunes at Kommos—where Shaw would soon uncover the remarkable Minoan port town, which now appears here in before and after photos (see Figs. 18.1 and 18.2).

In discussions that summer with Gerald and others, particularly with Costis Davaras, Ephor of East Crete, and Stylianos Alexiou, Director of the Herakleion Museum, the idea of a comprehensive aerial study of monuments and excavations across the whole 250-km length of the island was developed and encouraged. Helpful as low-altitude vertical photographs are to excavators at their individual sites, the potential for a comprehensive regional treatment, in which major archaeological sites related by both culture and geography could be presented in a single volume for comparative study, seemed even greater. We also saw that such treatment, if successful, could be extended to other regions: Sicily, mainland Greece, or Anatolia. As the specific plan for an atlas produced in partnership with Gerald Cadogan grew, we realized how fortunate we were to be able to draw on his experience in Crete. We agreed that each site entry should be simple, combining aerial photographs of legible size with brief tabular text and enough technical and bibliographic information to make the entry useful for professional research but not confusing for the educated layman. Gerald agreed to translate where necessary and to edit the site entries submitted by active excavators and researchers

to fit our concise format and to write the remainder himself, adding a general chapter on Cretan archaeology and chronology. We were also fortunate to enlist the help of John A. Gifford, an experienced Mediterranean geomorphologist at the University of Miami, to write accounts of the geomorphology of the sites and an introduction to the geomorphology of Crete in general. Edward Flaccus, a botanist/ecologist at Bennington College, traveled and worked with us in Crete in 1983; his chapter on climate and vegetation gives a valuable perspective on the environment.

The project had the cooperation of the Greek Archaeological Service and the Archaeological Society of Athens; of the American, British, French, and Italian schools of archaeology in Athens; and of the individual excavators. We received regular flight permission for the balloon from the Greek Civil Air authority.

With an outright grant from the National Endowment for the Humanities and an additional matching grant, we completed the fieldwork in four full seasons on Crete, returning for a fifth short visit in the fall of 1987 to photograph new work at Palaikastro and the newly discovered fortified Minoan building at Ayia Photia.

METHODS AND EQUIPMENT

The methods and equipment used in the field to make the atlas developed as we gained experience and improvised, modifying and adapting as the work progressed. We knew that a larger balloon would be more stable and less apt to blow down than a smaller one and that an aerodynamic blimp-shaped balloon with fins would head into the wind and have less drag for its lift than a spherical one. But we knew also that too large a balloon would be impossible to manage without heavy winching machinery, which we could not carry on foot to more remote off-road sites.

Consulting with engineers at the Raven Industries balloon factory at Sioux Falls, South Dakota, we determined that a four-finned inflatable blimp of 1,000-cubic-foot capacity and 34 feet long would be ideal, not too difficult to control yet still able to lift two cameras and their gimbal mount—the device that keeps them vertically positioned—to 800 m. The balloon was made of an unusually light fabric (polyurethane-coated rip-stop nylon at 3.2 ounces per square yard) that was not recommended by the factory for rough duty but provided us with much-needed additional lift and stability. We would have to avoid abrading the balloon on the ground, using canvas ground cloths for inflation and deflation, and would need to check regularly for punctures or abrasions. The balloon was fitted with a pleated dilation panel along the underside, crossed by stout elastic

Figure I.2 Balloon crew's camp

Figure I.3 Starting inflation

cords that allowed it first to expand without bursting as it rose into thinner air and then to keep its aerodynamic shape as it descended. A small spring-loaded emergency valve let gas escape before the increasing internal pressure, in ordinary ascents, could burst the fabric. International air regulations required, however, that should the balloon snap its tether cord and rise rapidly above its operating ceiling, it burst along the seams and fall to the ground, presenting no drifting hazard to other aircraft. We regularly checked the tether cord for fraying and replaced it when necessary—to avoid a fall that would end the useful life of the cameras.

The balloon, promptly named Daedalus, was small enough to be moved and managed from the ground by one person (wearing gloves), accompanied by another who carried the backpack tether reel, but large enough to be stable in winds up to about 12 miles an hour. A third person was always needed to operate the radio control of the camera, and others were usually required for aligning the balloon over the target and for the strenuous job of hauling down. Having used a kite successfully elsewhere to make aerial photographs, we tried this technique in Crete on days too windy for ballooning but found that a kite large enough to lift our twin cameras could drag two men across the ground as the wind rose. In lighter winds, sudden calms or eddies could cause the kite to fall, and we concluded that a kite is best used in a steady sea breeze or over a flat plain or desert.

To know exactly what the balloon cameras would be recording required some practice and careful calculation. We used two methods, one for the single-tether operations and another for the two-cord method (usually below 200 m). Given the film size, the focal length of the camera lens, and the area to be photographed on the ground, we used a pocket calculator to derive the proper altitude for the bal-

Figure I.4 Half-inflated at dawn

Figure I.5 Topping up the fins

Figure I.6   Climbing to excavation with balloon

Figure I.7   Twin cameras in gimbal

loon. The altitude of the balloon in turn was regulated by marks of colored yarn whipped to the tether cord at measured intervals. The framing of the target could be accurately controlled by using two tethers on opposite sides of the gimbal. It required only a little geometry to calculate and then measure and mark the stations on the ground where the two people holding the cords should stand to both center the camera at a known distance over the target and keep themselves and their tether lines from showing in the picture.

Above 200 m, we used a single tether and controlled the framing by other methods, having found that two cords added much weight and were difficult to manage when the camera was nearly out of sight. There was no way to keep the single tether from showing in the photograph, but it would virtually disappear through rotation when its shady side was toward the camera. In still air, the camera would be directly overhead, and the slow rotation of the gimbal (suspended at some distance below the balloon to isolate it from the balloon's slight rolling or pitching) would offer a choice of exposed frames. In a light breeze, however, the balloon, no longer overhead, would move off downwind. It could then be brought on target by three-way walkie-talkie communication between two people out a good distance from the center and the tether party. One person would be on the north–south axis of the site and the other on the east–west. Looking up, each in turn would direct the tether party to move the balloon into his sight line over the target; when both agreed, the camera was centered. Sometimes the operator of the camera-control transmitter would stand at the target and use a walkie-talkie to move the tether party until the balloon was judged to be directly

overhead. At lower altitudes, where the slow camera rotation on the single cord was still visible, it was possible to release the shutters when the framing appeared to be optimum.

Our radio control was the improved Hasselblad FM model (the old AM model had suffered from channel interference), rigged to operate not only the Hasselblad ELM/500 medium-format camera but also a second camera in the same gimbal, a 35mm Canon AE-1. We ran a short wire from the flash nipple of the Hasselblad to a small triggering device we had modified and fitted to the cable-release hole of the Canon. Thus a single radio impulse could make simultaneous photos, an important advance. Our aluminum and magnesium gimbal mount for the cameras was designed to be a lighter version of the previous model, every bit of reduced weight adding to our stability in a breeze.

A typical season began in April when, having obtained permission to make photographs from the Archaeological Service and other relevant authorities or excavators, we submitted a list of planned flights to the Civil Air Office. The request included maps and geographic coordinates for each site. When a copy of the government telex arrived giving us general flight permission, we could then give the name of the next site to Civil Air to have the permission activated with the broadcast of the standard radio Notice to Airmen, or NOTAM, thus reserving the air space for us. Some sites, including Amnisos, Aptera, Chania, Debla, Mt. Juktas, Lyttos, Nirou Chani, Prinias, Sklavokambos, Vai, and Zou, were impossible to photograph because of protective roofs, electric wires, or official restriction.

In the field, arriving with our crew and equipment at a typical site

Figure I.8   The backpack tether reel

Figure I.9   Preflight check

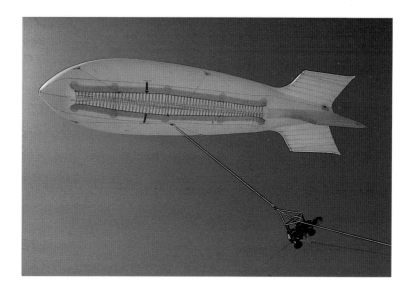

Figure I.10   Cameras rise with balloon

on Crete—and some of the more remote ones took time to find—
we had much to do before flying the balloon. Often cleaning and
weeding were needed, and it always took a day or two to plan the
order of the shots, mark on the ground the stations for double tether
positions, and make at least one dry run through the sequence.

Immediately before a flight, we were careful to go through an
eighteen-point checklist of mechanical adjustments, camera settings,
electrical connections, and battery tests—there were four different
battery types—to be sure that nothing was forgotten. More technical information on cameras and film is given at the end of this
chapter, but it might suffice here to say that we used the fastest shutter speeds possible to compensate for the gentle motion of the cameras, took careful readings of the incident light before setting the
openings, and, since we were using wide-angle lenses, could safely
set the focusing distance at infinity.

We inflated the balloon at sunrise, but only on days when the light
and wind conditions were favorable, using a sensitive anemometer to
be sure that a slight breeze was not gradually rising and in no case
inflating in winds of more than seven or eight miles an hour. Often
we released a small rubber trial balloon first and watched its flight
with binoculars as it rose to check for unsafe winds at our working
altitude. The winds on Crete rise gradually during a typical day.
It was important not to be flying too high as conditions changed.
A sharply rising breeze could draw the tether taut and set it hum-
ming as the tension approached the breaking strength of the tether, a
stout one-eighth-inch solid braided polyester cord. In rising wind
emergencies, one person can sometimes throw the snatch block (or

Figure I.11   Radio control

Figure I.12   Lowering to reload film

Figure I.14   Rolling up during deflation

Figure I.13   Hauling down with snatch block

open pulley) over the tether and walk from the reel toward the balloon; this brings the balloon rapidly to the ground but without the additional strain on the line that hauling in would cause. Unfortunately this simple rescue technique is possible only when one has a clear downwind path—without trees, fences, electric wires, or rivers in the way—for the whole length of the tether line. Above all we learned that when the wind velocity increased to about 15 miles an hour, the balloon could no longer keep its heading and, rolling broadside, would suddenly catch the wind's full force like a spinnaker and dive for the ground. When this happened—only twice in over two hundred flights—we saved the balloon by running toward it with the tether reel, giving it sufficient slack to rise and recover, and then playing it like a fighting fish, letting cord out in a new gust and hauling in whenever the wind slackened. From this experience caution became ingrained.

We used a variety of techniques for hauling down the balloon either to deflate it or to reload the cameras. At low altitudes, with no wind, one person could pull straight down with gloved hands, or two could stand facing each other and alternate with "swimming strokes." The backpack reels, made light enough to be carried easily, were used only to wind up the slack and were not intended to crank down the balloon. At higher altitudes, with the balloon up hundreds of meters, the cord was run down through an open pulley, or snatch block, and then out horizontally so the crew, with gloved hands, could get a grip and take turns walking it toward the take-up reel, now placed on the ground at a good distance, downhill if possible to make the exhausting work easier.

Since the angle of the sun is critical in aerial photographs, the time of day for each flight had to be carefully planned. The first few hours after summer sunrise are usually the best in Crete, for though low raking light is also available later in the day, an afternoon breeze usually prohibits flying. At a site with trees, tall shrubs, or standing ruins, the first long shadows after sunrise can cause confusing patterns; by noon, however, the necessary defining shadows and highlights have disappeared, and the flat photograph, almost without contrast, is virtually useless. A 45-degree sun angle is best for subjects where shadows of a standing column or the corner of a building will provide an accurate sense of height, and the sharper topographic contours are still obvious. Over low, level sites where long shadows would not cause confusion, a low sun angle can best reveal the slightest undulations in the ground.

In the afternoon after each flight, we developed the black-and-white photographs to check on the morning's work. Lacking a darkroom and working in whatever shelter we could find, we loaded the film tanks in a changing bag and used cold spring water or ice (when available) to keep the chemicals at 20 degrees C. We studied the negatives with magnifiers to be sure they were sharp and properly framed. If so, we could also be sure of the corresponding color image made at the same instant.

The more delicate process of printing custom enlargements, with careful dodging and burning to control areas of contrast, was handled back in our lab during the winter. For the prints used in the atlas, the source was usually the $2\frac{1}{4}$-by-$2\frac{1}{4}$-inch color transparency made by the Hasselblad camera and only very occasionally the 35mm slide, when the higher shutter speed of the Canon camera made for a sharper image. Prints, as the work progressed, were also furnished to the excavators and to archaeological officials for immediate study.

The early distribution of the air photographs to excavators confirmed their many uses. They were valuable for publication, for lectures, and—as Philip Guy had pointed out—for thoughtful study. Some photographs of sites that had never been excavated were studied in advance to help plan the digging priorities, and some were used to help with new surveys at old sites. At Palaikastro it was useful for each archaeologist on foot survey to carry balloon prints of the site. Sherd scatterings and artifacts seen on the ground could be located and marked on the photos in relationship to shrubs, clumps of grass, and other ephemera; and anomalies first spotted in the prints could be easily located on the ground and examined at close hand. Later it was not difficult to transfer the reference marks on the photographs to a proper map. The excavators J. A. MacGillivray, L. H. Sackett, et al. have described the process (1984). We have found too that close comparison of photographs of a site with the original drawings sometimes reveals inaccuracies in measurement or undetected relationships. At some sites, such as Chamaizi, Lissos, Monastiraki, Nerokourou, Olous, Phalasarna, and Polyrrhenia, the aerial photographs were an invaluable help in drawing our maps or plans.

A recent grant from the National Endowment for the Humanities has allowed us to make our aerial images available to all scholars. We have produced two sets of five hundred prints (indexed for computer search) including balloon work on sites in Greece, Italy, Yugoslavia, Israel, and Turkey for two research collections: the Blegen Library of the American School of Classical Studies at Athens and the Center for Remote Sensing at Boston University.

In the future it is likely that low-altitude photography and other forms of aerial remote sensing, and the associated techniques of image analysis and comparison made possible by the computer, will find increasing application in our investigation of the past. As the cost of archaeological excavation continues to rise and higher standards of scientific investigation dictate caution and restraint in all investigative digging, it is more important than ever that nondestructive methods be developed for archaeological exploration and recording and that accurate visual records be kept of surface patterns. Excavation and salvage priorities can be established more easily where low-altitude photographs of various sites can be compared. Though some completed excavations can be better stabilized than others, fragile sites must necessarily suffer when the overburden of protecting earth has been removed and the remains of now roofless buildings are exposed to the wind and rain. Thus we see the atlas project and all other recorded image collections as works of conservation, saving for future investigation patterns of association that must inexorably deteriorate.

For us the atlas fieldwork was a most rewarding and remarkably varied activity. Long days of deliberate preparation and occasional delays as we camped at remote sites waiting for better weather or official permits alternated with challenging physical activity and emergency judgments. A major reward of the project was, of course, the opportunity we had to record and save for the future a bird's-eye view of a people long vanished from Crete. But in our five seasons as visitors, there was much else for us to admire on the island itself and to learn from those who live there now. As we visited each region, we heard local people reveal their attitudes toward the land—its plants, birds, and animals as well as its topographic features—and found that remnants of ancient culture still survive in the back country. The combination of coastal cliffs and broad beaches, of snow-topped mountains and fields lush with wildflowers, was always fascinating; and we will not forget our many friends among the people of Crete who were so generous with their hospitality and help. There is a sense in which all of us in Europe and America whose work involves the study of Western civilization look to Greece and especially Crete as our ancient homeland. It has been a great satisfaction to participate in the investigation of this common past.

TECHNICAL NOTES ON THE PHOTOGRAPHY

The Canon AE-1 35mm camera was usually flown with a 28-mm wide-angle lens and the Hasselblad ELM/500 with a 60-mm lens, also wide-angle and—allowing for the square shape of the larger negative and the rectangle of the slide—covering similar areas on the ground. For extended coverage (1 sq km, made from 800 m) we used the much heavier 40-mm wider-angle lens and flew the Hasselblad alone in the gimbal to reduce weight. Shutter speeds were always set at maximum to reduce blur or spin caused by motion of the suspended cameras, 1/1000 of a second for the Canon and 1/500 for the Hasselblad. The Canon diaphragm was set for automatic light metering and control, but for the Hasselblad it was necessary to make an incident light reading on the ground and set the opening in advance—allowing a half-stop down for the rapidly rising sun of the morning's first flight. With wide-angle lenses, focusing distance could safely be set at infinity.

Experimenting with many types of film, we eventually settled on Kodachrome ASA 64 to make 35-mm slides in the Canon, and Agfa Isopan and Agfapan ASA 100 for 120-size black-and-white negatives in the Hasselblad, developed with Rodinal. We had tried Kodak Panatomic X and Technical Pan films and used H & W VTE (very thin emulsion) with some success, but we found that the slower speeds of fine-grained film did not always allow us to use the fast shutter speeds that were necessary to stop the effects of camera movement. At most sites we also switched films, making 120-size Ektachrome ASA 200 color transparencies (the source of most of the plates in the Atlas) with the Hasselblad and putting black-and-white film in the Canon for daily proof development.

BIBLIOGRAPHY

Balloon Archaeology

Breasted, James H. 1933. *The Oriental Institute.* The University of Chicago Survey 12:249. Chicago.

Cooper, Frederick A., and J. Wilson Myers. 1981. "Reconnaissance of a Greek Mountain Village," *Journal of Field Archaeology* 8:124–34.

Guy, P. L. O. 1932. "Balloon Photography and Archaeological Excavation," *Antiquity* 6:148–55.

Jameson, Michael H. 1974. "The Excavation of a Drowned Greek Temple," *Scientific American* 231, no. 4:110–19.

MacGillivray, J. A., L. H. Sackett, et al. 1984. "An Archaeological Survey of the Roussolakkos Area at Palaikastro," *BSA* 79:129–59.

Myers, J. Wilson. 1978. "Balloon Survey Field Season, 1977," *Journal of Field Archaeology* 5:145–59.

Myers, J. Wilson, and Eleanor Emlen Myers. 1980. "The Art of Flying: Balloon Archaeology," *Archaeology* 33:33–40.

———. 1985. "[Making] an Aerial Atlas of Ancient Crete," *Archaeology* 38:18–25.

———. 1990. "Low-Altitude Aerial Photography in Crete," *Expedition* 32.3:31–33.

Whittlesey, Julian. 1975. "Three Balloon Systems." In *Photography in Archaeological Research*, ed. Elmer Harp, Jr., 239–58. Albuquerque.

Aerial Archaeology

Bevan, Bruce W. 1975. *Aerial Photography for the Archaeologist: A Report from the University Museum Applied Science Center for Archaeology.* Philadelphia.

Deuel, Leo. 1969. *Flights into Yesterday: The Story of Aerial Archaeology.* New York.

Riley, Derrick N. 1987. *Air Photography and Archaeology.* Philadelphia.

St. Joseph, J. K. S. 1977. "Air Photography and Archaeology." In *The Uses of Air Photography*, ed. J. K. S. St. Joseph, 135–53. London.

Schmidt, Erik F. 1940. *Flights over Ancient Cities of Iran.* Chicago.

Schoder, Raymond V., S.J. 1974. *Ancient Greece from the Air.* London.

Wilson, David Raoul. 1982. *Air Photo Interpretation for Archaeologists.* New York.

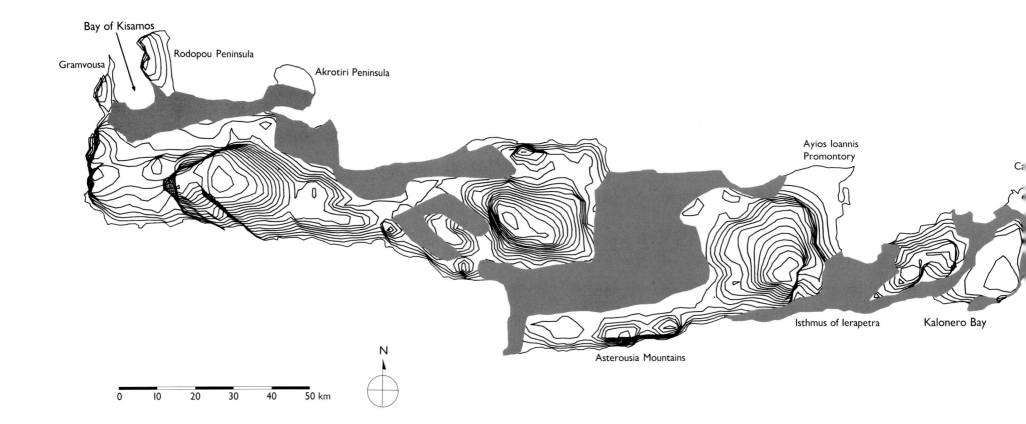

Bay of Kisamos

Gramvousa

Rodopou Peninsula

Akrotiri Peninsula

Ayios Ioannis
Promontory

Ca

Isthmus of Ierapetra   Kalonero Bay

Asterousia Mountains

N

0   10   20   30   40   50 km

Figure I.15 Computer-generated view
of Crete with perspective
from the south at 89 de-
grees. The gray areas
represent Neogene- and
Quaternary-age rocks and
sediments; the rest of the
island is composed of pre-
Neogene nappe sequence.
Contour interval: 100 m.

THE GEOMORPHOLOGY OF CRETE

Although Crete's geological history covers several hundred million years, its entire prehistory, beginning with the earliest cultural deposits underlying Knossos, occupies only the latter half of the youngest and shortest interval of geological time, the Holocene (or Recent) epoch. Human activity—settlement locations, agriculture, mining—has been circumscribed by the island's distinctive geology, which in turn accounts for some geographic elements of its prehistory, especially the location of sites in the landscape. Two geological processes—neotectonics and the recent rise in sea level—have affected the archaeology of Crete's coastlines, while human-induced erosion may have contributed to the burial of sites throughout the island.

THE GEOLOGICAL SETTING

Crete is the keystone of the Hellenic (or Southern Aegean) Arc, a tectonic zone of transition between the Hellenides mountain range of mainland Greece and the Taurides of southern Anatolia. Crete's geomorphological structure is characterized by an east–west trending series of horsts—uplifted blocks of primarily metamorphic and sedimentary rocks—separated by downfaulted blocks called grabens. The uplifted blocks represent discontinuous linear fragments of the Hellenides, extensively deformed by the tectonism that thrust them southward during the Alpine orogeny that formed the present Mediterranean Sea. This mountain-building activity was concentrated in the earlier half of the Tertiary, the late Eocene to the early Miocene epochs of about 40–20 million years ago (Aubouin et al. 1976). The grabens often are filled with younger marine sediments that are now lithified, for the most part, into limestones and marlstones.

The crustal blocks forming Crete have linear dimensions averaging between 10 and 100 km; they are tilting intermittently and independently. In Flemming's general summary (1978) of the regional tectonic framework of the southern Aegean, Crete is divided into three tectonic units, each consisting of several crustal blocks. The eastern block is fault bounded at the isthmus of Ierapetra and is tilt-

ing north, the central block shows no tilt, and the western one, bounded by a fault from Rethymno through the western Mesara, is tilting northeast. As is true in other mountainous regions, Crete's tectonism has exposed at many localities unrivaled views of its complex bedrock stratigraphy. Often one can look at a topographic feature—Mt. Juktas, west of Archanes, for example—and associate it with a particular rock type identified on the geological map of the region.

It is helpful in explaining the stratigraphy of Crete to divide its rocks into a pre-Neogene group, overthrust on top of and around the autochthonous rock core of the island before the beginning of the Miocene epoch (about 24 million years ago), and a Neogene sedimentary group deposited in the shallow seas that covered the island during much of the subsequent geological past: the late Tertiary and Quaternary periods. While the younger Neogene rocks are defined in conventional stratigraphic terms (lithology and fossil content), the pre-Neogene rocks are defined as tectonic units on the basis of structural relationships mapped in the field. Most of the following description of Crete's general geology is based on Bonneau et al. (1977) and Wachendorf et al. (1975) for the pre-Neogene, and on Meulenkamp et al. (1977) and Fortuin (1978) for the Neogene.

The pre-Neogene rocks of Crete include a sequence of nappes, blankets of rock several hundred square kilometers in area but less than a few kilometers thick, that have been overthrust or recumbently folded over the basement rock (the autochthon) that forms the island's core. On Crete the autochthon consists of the Plattenkalk series, a sequence of dark gray, coarsely crystalline and slightly metamorphosed limestones with intercalated bands of chert. Rocks of this formation are of Jurassic (beginning about 210 million years ago) to early Tertiary (beginning about 65 million years ago) age; they are capped in some places with low-grade metamorphic rocks—phyllites—of early Tertiary age. The Plattenkalk series includes the east–west ranges of the White Mountains (or Lefka Ori), Psiloriti (or Mt. Ida), Talea Ori, Lasithi mountains, Ornon mountains, and the Ayios Ioannis promontory between the Bay of Mirabello and the Bay of Mallia.

Archaeological, geomorphological, and other technical terms are defined in the Glossary.

Geological Periods of Crete

Era	Period	Epoch	Age	Event	Million Years Ago
CENOZOIC	QUATERNARY	Holocene		(local tectonism)	0.01
		Pleistocene		(fluctuating world sea level) (marine terraces) (continental clastic deposits)	1.7
	TERTIARY	Pliocene	Late Early	(flooding of Mediterranean basin)	5
		Miocene	Messinian Tortonian Serravalian Langhian Burdigalian Aquitanian	Late Early (salinity crisis; dry Mediterranean)	24
		Oligocene			37
		Eocene			56
		Paleocene			65
MESOZOIC	CRETACEOUS	Late			98
		Early			145
	JURASSIC	Late			160
		Middle			185
		Early			210
	TRIASSIC	Late			230
		Middle			244
		Early			250

The first nappe is the Trypali unit, massive shallow-water limestones and dolomites emplaced primarily in the western part of the island (White Mountains and Akrotiri peninsula) during late Triassic to early Jurassic time (210–180 million years ago). Above this lies the Phyllite-Quartzite series (or Phyllitic series), which includes the bedrock of extreme southwestern Crete and the periphery of Ornon just east of the isthmus of Ierapetra, as well as dozens of smaller nappe fragments a few square kilometers in area scattered across the island. The Phyllite-Quartzite series has been dated to between the Permian (beginning about 290 million years ago) and the Triassic (ending about 210 million years ago) periods.

Limestones of the third tectonic unit, the Tripolitza series, or the Gavrovo-Tripolitza (Tripolis) series on the official 1:200,000 map (N. Kreutzberg et al., 1977), form peaks and lower ranges from the eastern end of the island (near Zakro, Fig. I.16) to the western end (the Gramvousa and Rodopou peninsulas), as well as flanking Psiloriti and the Lasithi mountains. The calcareous sediments of this series were deposited during late Triassic to middle Eocene time, roughly 220–45 million years ago. Some geologists define as an upper (unnamed) subunit within the Tripolitza series a flysch commonly found south of Psiloriti and along the Asterousia mountains on the central south coast.

Overthrust four is termed the Pindos-Ethia nappe (the Pindos series on the geological map by Kreutzberg et al., 1977) and is characterized by relatively small disjoint fragments of overthrust rock tens of kilometers in average dimensions. They may be seen across the island, but the most topographically distinct exposure is Mt. Kedros, southwest of Psiloriti in central Crete. Rocks of the Pindos series also were deposited between late Triassic and middle Eocene time and consist of pelagic limestones, cherts, and an upper flysch subunit.

Lying above the Pindos-Ethea nappe is a collection of heterogeneous intermediary nappe fragments called the Subpelagonian series by Baumann et al. (1976); three subunits are distinguished by Bonneau et al. (1977): the Arvi and Miamou nappes, and the Vatos schists. These were once defined by a single term—the Asterousia nappe—but on the geological map of Crete they are combined into the system of Ophiolites. Yet another term for the same group is the Serpentinite-Amphibolite association, which more precisely describes the predominant rock types they contain.

An impressive and easily observed example of how such tectonic units are expressed in the present-day landscape exists between Mallia and Ayios Nikolaos. The traveler driving along the national highway through the Neapolis valley is in fact surrounded by a landscape formed by the overthrusting of tectonic rock units that is characteristic of Crete. To the northeast lies the Plattenkalk limestone,

Figure I.16   Gorge of Zakro eroded into massive Tripolitza limestone

which has always been there, while the valley itself represents a narrow slice of the overlying Phyllite-Quartzite series tectonic nappe. Finally, the high mountains bounding the valley to the southeast, west, and northwest represent limestones of the younger Tripolis series nappe that was thrust over the earlier two units. In structural geological terms the Neapolis valley is a fenster, or window, through the upper Tripolis series nappe onto the Phyllite-Quartzite series nappe below. Thus this natural route of travel linking the Bay of Mirabello with the Bay of Mallia is a product of Crete's turbulent geological history.

The mountain (and island) building of the Alpine orogeny peaked in late Eocene to Oligocene time, approximately 40–30 million years ago. In the process of shaping the general geological character of Europe and the Mediterranean region, it closed most of the Tethys Sea, the precursor of the Mediterranean. After the Alpine orogeny, Crete was still connected to Europe as part of the southern Aegean landmass. The pile of nappes that was to become Crete was fractured by extensive high-angle north–south and east–west faulting into numerous horsts and grabens. The isthmus of Ierapetra, along with the Bay of Mirabello just to the north, is a good example of a graben structure.

During Neogene time (equivalent to the Miocene and Pliocene epochs, from 24 to 1.7 million years ago) the geology of Crete was dominated by marine and terrigenous sedimentary deposition in the grabens around the pre-Neogene nappe fragments. On the Kreutzberg et al. geological map of Crete, all the areas marked Postorogenic Upper Tertiary represent these units. Most are now lithified sediments that were deposited on the nappe flanks, sometimes above the contemporary sea level (producing terrigenous rocks), but more commonly at or below sea level to produce brackish-water or marine sedimentary rocks. When the paleo-Mediterranean's only link with the Atlantic Ocean was blocked by tectonic uplift in the area of the present Strait of Gibraltar, the lack of freshwater inflow combined with intense evaporation to produce, in only a few hundred thousand years, a depression containing shallow brine lakes and salt playas.

This event is known as the Mediterranean salinity crisis (Hsu et al. 1978). During its two-million-year timespan—the Messinian age of the late Miocene epoch—cyclical sequences of evaporite minerals (gypsum, halite, potash salts) accumulated in the basins of the paleo-Mediterranean depression. The area that is now Crete consisted of numerous islands and shoals separated by shallow embayments. Algal reefs grew in shallow waters along bathymetric highs, while fine-grained dolomitic muds accumulated in the intermediary basins.

A paleogeographic reconstruction of Crete during this time, based on micropaleontological studies of the rocks, is given in Meulenkamp and Zachariasse (1973).

Understanding the genesis of Messinian deposits on Crete is important because these deposits form the bedrock of the Mesara plain, the largest depositional basin on the island, along with that of all the island's smaller coastal plains, from the Bay of Kisamos through Chania and Rethymno to the vicinity of Koulokonas, as well as the undulating hills between Herakleion and the Mesara plain, the isthmus of Ierapetra, and the low interior valley stretching from Siteia to the south coast along Kalonero Bay.

The Messinian deposits are highly calcareous (Fig. I.17), consisting of bioclastic (usually reef) limestones that grade into alternating finely laminated and homogeneous marls. The finely laminated marls are commonly very rich in siliceous microfossils (especially sponge spicules) and plant and fish remains; the homogeneous marls contain these attributes to a much less conspicuous degree. Within these rocks are layers and lenses of gypsum, often well crystallized; it is from such deposits that the Minoans quarried the gypsum slabs used in many of their buildings in the central part of the island (e.g., Knossos, Ayia Triada, Phaistos, and Myrtos-Pyrgos).

Toward the end of the Messinian age, parts of the eastern Mediterranean were submerged beneath shallow brackish lakes, and the entire basin eventually was reflooded by Atlantic Ocean water at the beginning of the Pliocene epoch, about five million years ago. In late Pliocene time (three million years ago), regional tectonism uplifted an island approximately the shape of today's Crete, although several surficial rock units had yet to be deposited. The late Pliocene sedimentary record is relatively uniform across the island (see Fig. I.15), with deposits of the paleo-Mediterranean filling the grabens and forming about one-third of the island's surface. Subsequent regional faulting and folding during the late Pliocene and Pleistocene epochs have deformed these rock units. For example, Phaistos and Ayia Triada are sited on a Plio-Pleistocene horst fault block that rises some 80 m above the lower Mesara plain.

There is a direct correlation between the distribution of the Neogene rocks (Fig. I.18) and prehistoric archaeological sites, not only because the Neogene rocks are soft and easily quarried for tabular building stone but also because of the type of soil that develops on them (see below). Angelier et al. (1982) outline the late Neogene development of Crete and the southern Aegean region, which has been dominated by large-scale normal faulting related to extensional tectonic processes.

Figure I.17   White Neogene marl bedrock; possible ancient source of clay

Figure I.18   Low Neogene bedrock hills east of Kommos

During the most recent interval of geological time—the Quaternary period, beginning about 1.7 million years ago—the earth's climate was marked by glacial periods separated by shorter interglacial periods, when air temperatures approximated those of the present. At both high latitudes and high altitudes there are extensive geological traces of the most recent ice age the earth has experienced. On Crete, only the heights of Psiloriti (the Ida massif) were elevated enough to have experienced cold-climate weathering, preserved in features such as cirques and moraines (Fabre and Marie 1982). Increased rock weathering during the Quaternary, however, fostered the erosion and deposition of large quantities of weathered rock in the Mesara plain as well as at higher altitudes in small basins of interior drainage such as the Omalo plain, the Nida basin, and the Lasithi plain.

GROUNDWATER AND SOILS ON CRETE

Pre-Neogene "hard" limestone rocks (as distinguished from the generally softer Neogene ones) are highly fractured and, because they form the highest elevations on Crete, capture a large portion of the island's annual precipitation. Instead of remaining on the surface, much of the rain- and meltwater flows into an underground system of fractured limestone rock, which it tends to dissolve away. A karst topography results, so that Crete, like the rest of Greece, has many caves (Petrocheilou 1984).

Surface water from winter storms often disappears into swallow holes, or poljes, of which the Lasithi plain contains several good examples, known as *katavothri* to the Cretans. Another characteristic of karst landforms is the tendency for groundwater to reappear as springs along the contact between the hard limestones and the underlying, less permeable, flysch and metamorphic rocks. Springs, some copious (Kourmoulis 1979), are common on Crete. The relationship between springs and archaeological sites, both habitation and ritual, is well known on Crete. The site at Syme is a fine example.

There is no recent detailed survey of soils on Crete, the only such work having been published half a century ago (Nevros and Zvorykin 1939). Some discussion of Cretan soils appears in Zohary and Orshan (1965). Investigation of soils on a much smaller scale and in association with archaeological surveys has been accomplished (e.g., Bintliff 1977, Parsons, forthcoming). Soil types on Crete are as varied as the geological parent material. While some have argued that only in the very recent past has soil cover, and thus agricultural potential, been

reduced through deforestation, a growing body of evidence shows that human activities in antiquity set off episodes of local slope erosion, soil erosion, and deposition of this eroded soil sediment as colluvium at the base of slopes and in valley bottoms. This occurred not only on Crete, as in the vicinity of Kommos (Gifford, forthcoming), at Gortyn, and at Zakro but on mainland Greece as well (van Andel et al. 1986). A consensus on the extent, severity, and causes of soil loss on Crete has yet to be reached.

GEOLOGICAL PROCESSES AFFECTING COASTAL ARCHAEOLOGICAL SITES

A clear relationship between coastal sites on Crete and present sea level often is not apparent, particularly in the case of Bronze Age sites, because that relationship has been altered during the past five thousand years by a combination of neotectonic activity and a worldwide change in sea level.

Several recent studies have focused on reconstructing the coastal paleogeography in the Aegean region (e.g., Kraft et al. 1985), often demonstrating that archaeological site location cannot now be understood unless the past relation of land to sea is known. Such studies depend on the coring of recent unconsolidated sediments at or below present sea level and the analysis of their mineralogical and microfossil content to determine the environment in which the sediments were deposited. This technique is not applicable to most of the Cretan coast because of the lack of stream drainage basins leading into coastal embayments (the Mesara shore is the one major exception). Instead, geoarchaeologists have made use of a different record of recent sea level change: the horizontal notches dissolved into coastal limestone outcrops by physico-chemical processes at the contemporary sea surface. These solution notches (Fig. I.19) have been correlated with major vertical earth movements during the last two thousand years (Flemming 1978; Pirazzoli 1986) to arrive at a neotectonic history of Crete that uses plate tectonic theory to explain the uplift of sites in the western part of the island, such as Phalasarna.

At older coastal sites in the central (e.g., Kommos) and eastern parts of the island (e.g., Mochlos) the net effect of neotectonism combined with eustatic sea level rise is less easily disentangled, but it is clear that the Minoan shoreline lies several meters below the present one, and we must look below the surface of water and sediment to see the coast as it appeared three to four thousand years ago.

Figure I.19   Limestone solution notches lifted above present sea level at Phalasarna

BIBLIOGRAPHY

Angelier, J., N. Lyberis, X. Le Pichon, E. Barrier, and P. Huchon. 1982. "The Tectonic Development of the Hellenic Arc and the Sea of Crete: A Synthesis," *Tectonophysics* 86:159–96.

Aubouin, J., J. Davidson, P. Leboulanger, S. Matesco, A. Zambetakis. 1976. "Esquisse structurale de l'arc égéen externe: Des Dinarides aux Taurides," *Bulletin de la Société Géologique de France* 18:327–36.

Baumann, A., G. Best, W. Gwosdz, and H. Wachendorf. 1976. "The Nappe Pile of Eastern Crete," *Tectonophysics* 30:T33–T40.

Bintliff, J. L. 1977. *Natural Environment and Human Settlement in Prehistoric Greece* 1, 2. British Archaeological Reports Supplementary Series 28. Oxford.

Bonneau, M., J. Angelier, and M. Epting. 1977. "Réunion extraordinaire de la Société Géologique de France en Crète," *Bulletin de la Société Géologique de France* 19:87–102.

Fabre, G., and R. Marie. 1982. "Découverte de relief glaciaire dans l'île de Crète (Grèce)," *Comptes Rendus, Académie des Sciences, Paris* 294:1135–37.

Flemming, N. C. 1978. "Holocene Eustatic Changes and Coastal Tectonics in the Northeast Mediterranean: Implications for Models of Crustal Consumption," *Philosophical Transactions of the Royal Society of London, Section A* 289:405–58.

Fortuin, A. R. 1978. "Late Cenozoic History of Eastern Crete and Implications for the Geology and Geodynamics of the Southern Aegean Area," *Geologie en Mijnbouw* 57:451–64.

Gifford, J. A. Forthcoming. "Physical Geology of the Western Mesara and Kommos." In *Kommos* 1, ed. J. W. Shaw. Princeton.

Hsu, K. J., L. Montadert, D. Bernouilli, M. B. Cita, A. Erickson, R. E. Garrison, R. B. Kidd, F. Melières, C. Muller, and R. Wright. 1978. "History of the Mediterranean Salinity Crisis," *Initial Reports of the Deep-Sea Drilling Project* 42:1053–78.

Kourmoulis, N. E. 1979. *Inventory of Karstic Springs of Greece, II: Crete* (in Greek, with English summary). Athens.

Kraft, J. C., I. Kayan, and S. Aschenbrenner. 1985. "Geological Studies of Coastal Change Applied to Archaeological Settings." In *Archaeological Geology*, ed. G. R. Rapp, Jr., and J. A. Gifford, 57–84. New Haven.

Kreutzberg, N., et al. 1977. *General Geological Map of Greece, Crete Island.* Institute of Geological and Mining Research, Athens.

Meulenkamp, J. E., and W. J. Zachariasse. 1973. "Messinian Deposits on Crete." In *Messinian Events in the Mediterranean*, ed. C. W. Drooger, 202–5. Amsterdam.

Meulenkamp, J. E., A. Jonkers, and P. Spaak. 1977. "Late Miocene to Early Pliocene Development of Crete," *Proceedings of the Sixth Colloquium on the Geology of the Aegean Region* 1:137–49. Athens.

Nevros, K., and I. Zvorykin. 1939. "Zur Kenntnis der Boden der Insel Kreta (Griechenland)," *Soil Research* 6:242–307.

Parsons, M. R. Forthcoming. "Soil and Land Use Studies at Kommos." In *Kommos* 1, ed. J. W. Shaw. Princeton.

Pirazzoli, P. A. 1986. "The Early Byzantine Tectonic Paroxysm," *Zeitschrift für Geomorphologie*, Suppl. Bd. 62:31–49.

Petrocheilou, A. 1984. *The Greek Caves.* Athens.

van Andel, T. H., C. N. Runnels, and K. O. Pope. 1986. "Five Thousand Years of Land Use and Abuse in the Southern Argolid, Greece," *Hesperia* 55:103–28.

Wachendorf, H., G. Best, and W. Gwosdz. 1975. "Geodynamische Interpretation Ostkretas," *Geologische Rundschau* 64:728–50.

Zohary, M., and G. Orshan. 1965. "An Outline of the Geobotany of Crete," *Israel Journal of Botany* Supplement 14:1–49.

Figure I.20 *Phrygana:* low, hard-leaved evergreen shrubs, many spiny and aromatic

THE CLIMATE AND VEGETATION OF CRETE

EDWARD FLACCUS

Crete shares a Mediterranean climate with the coastal fringe of the Mediterranean basin and only four other areas on earth, all coastal: southern California, Chile, southwestern Australia, and South Africa. All of these areas of Mediterranean climate lie between thirty-two and forty degrees latitude in their respective hemispheres (Aschmann 1973a). All have the same basic climatic constraints of hot, dry, essentially rainless summers and relatively moist, moderate winters, and all have characteristically evergreen sclerophyll vegetation. Some evidence suggests that in Greece and Crete the climate in Minoan times was essentially the same as it is today (Thirgood 1981). In addition to the question of climate change over time, there is the much surer, more easily measurable variation of climate over space. Slope aspect, altitude, and proximity to the sea all affect plant distribution; more specifically, the high mountains are exposed to both cold temperatures and considerable snow in the winter months. Though climate is a major shaper of vegetation life-forms and flora, geology and soils play an interrelated role. Crete is a mass of limestone rocks from which limited soils have developed. But there has been another determinant of vegetation here; some nine thousand years of human habitation have no doubt wrought great changes in the plant life of the island. Grazing, cultivation—especially of olives, grapes, and small grains and more recently a great range of fruits and vegetables—and the deforestation caused by the use of timber for buildings, ships, and fuel all must have changed vastly the botanical face of the land, particularly at lower altitudes.

Certainly the predominant life-form of vegetation on Crete today is the garrigue (called *phrygana* in Greece and Crete) covering the rocky slopes, characterized by low, hard-leaved evergreen shrubs, many of them spiny and many aromatic (Fig. I.20). No doubt such was the case in Minoan times; what has probably changed most with the deforestation, agriculture, and grazing of the coastal plains and lower slopes is that there are fewer stands of trees (cypress, evergreen oaks, and pines) and tall-shrub maquis (macchia), resulting in a real increase in *phrygana*. Over much of the island, as throughout the Mediterranean basin, many centuries of grazing of shepherded flocks

of sheep and goats have taken their toll. The goat in particular has earned its reputation as the enemy of tree and woody shrub growth, in some areas sculpting plant forms to dwarfed and spiny mounds. And as with any of the summer-dry Mediterranean climatic regions, the role of fires caused by humans has been important.

The long period of human use of Crete and its inhabitants' links with the larger world have resulted in the introduction of a large number of non-native species such as weedy companions of cultivation, many of which have become naturalized. Moreover, crop species have been introduced, a number from lands to the east (Aschmann 1973b). These plant immigrants are thought to make up as much as 30 percent of the seed plant species on Crete today (Polunin 1980). Additional botanical elements of interest and importance in Crete are (1) the species with Anatolian affinities; (2) the ancient endemic species (those found only on Crete)—estimated to comprise about 10 percent of Cretan seed-plant species (Polunin 1980); (3) the variety of orchids, which bloom in the spring; (4) the variety of herb species that escape the stress of summer drought by the means of storage organs such as bulbs (tulips and other Liliaceae and Amaryllidaceae); and (5) the many herbaceous annuals that escape the stress of drought by the survival of their seeds; the proportion of annual species among the floras of the two Northern Hemisphere areas of Mediterranean climate (the Mediterranean basin and California) has been estimated at about 50 percent (Raven 1973).

The ancient sites described in this atlas range from the large Minoan palaces at lower elevations, today usually surrounded by olive groves, vineyards, or field crops, to hill and peak settlements. The latter may be surrounded by more typical and less altered phrygana, or even, in better-watered and less-disturbed locations, by stands of Calabrian pines (Fig. I.21) and evergreen oaks. Stands of Kermes oak (*Quercus coccifera*) (Fig. I.22) and Holm oak (*Quercus ilex*) are probably relict; there is some evidence at Myrtos suggesting a more recent origin for the pine (*Pinus brutia/P. halapensis*) in that area (Rackham 1972). The westward climate in Crete is moister, the eastward drier, reflecting the same gradient that exists in the Mediterranean basin as a whole. At the highest elevations, as on the slopes

Figure I.21   Calabrian pines in the White Mountains

Figure I.22   Windblown Kermes oak above Syme

of Psiloriti (Mt. Ida) up to its summit, there are sparse Cretan ver-sions of alpine and subalpine communities. Below the peaks but still at high elevations poljes (limestone sinks) of varying sizes are com-mon on the three major mountain masses of Crete: the White Mountains to the west, the Psiloriti massif, and the Lasithi mountains to the east. Two large examples of sink formations, long much used by man, are the Nida plain on the Psiloriti massif and the much larger Lasithi plain, the former heavily grazed, the latter intensively cultivated.

Thus Crete has experienced at least nine millennia of human oc-cupation, which has profoundly affected the environment; it is likely to provide much additional information on the evolution of both plant species and ecosystems.

Even as brief a discussion of the vegetation of Crete as this should include an aesthetic appreciation of the spring show of wildflowers (Fig. I.23), many composites; the display of early summer flowering shrubs, including yellow-flowered legumes such as spiny broom; the pink masses of *Ebenus cretica* (a Cretan endemic) and the ubiquitous Labiatae (Fig. I.24), such as bush thyme, that contribute to the won-derful aromas of Cretan *phrygana* on hot summer days. The peaceful groves of very old olive trees (Fig. I.25) and the terraces where grapes and cereals have been grown for centuries are quiet, subtle witnesses to the antiquity of the land. The exciting variety and beauty of the vegetation combine with the rugged and often breath-taking topography to provide dramatic settings for the ancient sites described in this atlas.

BIBLIOGRAPHY

Aschmann, H. 1973a. "Distribution and Peculiarity of Mediterra-nean Ecosystems." In *Mediterranean Type Ecosystems: Origin and Structure*, ed. F. di Castri and H. A. Mooney, 13. New York, Heidel-berg, and Berlin.

———. 1973b. "Man's Impact on the Several Regions with Mediter-ranean Climates." In *Mediterranean Type Ecosystems: Origin and Structure*, ed. F. di Castri and H. A. Mooney, 364–66. New York, Heidelberg, and Berlin.

Barclay, C. 1986. *Crete: Checklist of the Vascular Plants, Englera 6.* Berlin.

Baumann, H. 1982. *Die griechische Pflanzenwelt in Mythos, Kunst, und Literatur.* Munich.

Greuter, W. 1972. "The Relic Element of the Flora of Crete and Its Evolutionary Significance." In *Taxonomy, Phytography, and Evolu-tion*, ed. D. H. Valentine, 161–77. London.

———. 1973. "Additions to the Flora of Crete 1938–1972," *Annual of the Goulandris Museum* 1 : 15–83.

———. 1974. "Floristic Report on the Cretan Area," *Memorias da Sociedade Broteriana* 24 : 131–71.

———. 1984. "Additions to the Flora of Crete, 1973–1983. Part I," *Willdenowia* 14 : 27–36, and "Part II," 14 : 269–97.

———. 1985. "Additions to the Flora of Crete, 1973–1983. Part III," *Willdenowia* 15 : 23–60.

Figure I.23   Spring wildflowers near Phaistos

Figure I.24   Yellow Phlomis in the Amari valley

Figure I.25   Poppies and olive grove

Mitrakos, K. 1980. "A Theory for Mediterranean Plant Life," *Acta Oecologica / Oecologia Plantarum* 1:245–52.

Polunin, O. 1980. *Flowers of Greece and the Balkans: A Field Guide.* Oxford.

Polunin, O., and A. Huxley. 1972. *The Flowers of the Mediterranean.* London.

Rackham, O. 1972. "The Vegetation of the Myrtos Region," Appendix 2 in P. M. Warren, *Myrtos: An Early Bronze Age Settlement in Crete*, 283–93. (British School at Athens Supplementary Paper 7) London.

Raven, P. 1973. "The Evolution of Mediterranean Floras." In *Mediterranean Type Ecosystems: Origin and Structure*, ed. F. di Castri and H. A. Mooney, 222. New York, Heidelberg, and Berlin.

Sfikas, G. 1987. *Wild Flowers of Crete.* Athens.

Thirgood, J. V. 1981. *Man and the Mediterranean Forest: A History of Resource Depletion*, 19–26. New York and London.

Turrill, W. B. 1929. *The Plant Life of the Balkan Peninsula: Phytogeographical Study.* Oxford.

Tutin, T. G., et al. 1964–1980. *Flora Europaea* 1–5. Cambridge.

Zohary, M., and G. Orshan. 1965. "An Outline of the Geobotany of Crete," *Israel Journal of Botany* Supplement 14:1–49.

Figure I.26 Psiloriti (Mt. Ida), from the Amari valley

ANCIENT AND MODERN CRETE

GERALD CADOGAN

The island of Crete is its own self-contained mainland. It is by far the largest Greek island, being about 250 km long, and its mountain ranges reach 2,456 m (Psiloriti, or Mt. Ida) and 2,453 m (the White Mountains). Its breadth varies from 12.5 km at the isthmus of Ierapetra to 58 km across the Psiloriti massif. Its population was a little over 500,000 in 1981, of whom 102,398 were in Herakleion.

Crete forms the southern edge of the Aegean Sea, lying west–east between the southeast tip of the Peloponnese and the island of Kythera (to the west) and the Dodecanesian islands of Kasos, Karpathos, and Rhodes and the southwest corner of Anatolia, now Turkey (to the east). To the north are the Cyclades and other Aegean islands. To the south is Libya and to the southeast lies Egypt.

The island is remarkable for an extraordinary diversity of scenery. Its high mountains are wild and bleak. Their limestone erodes easily into deep gorges, the most dramatic of which is the Samaria Gorge in the White Mountains. It is 17 km long and drops down to the sea from a height of 1,227 m at its head on the edge of the small plain of Omalo.

The sea seems close almost everywhere in the Cretan mountains, close enough so that the sheep that graze the upland pastures in summer and are carted to the coast in trucks for the winter were until recently herded down and back up again. At the foot of the mountains there are often rich valleys with copious water, ideal nowadays for growing oranges and lemons. Nearer the sea there is often rolling country, especially where the rock is the soft marl that the Cretans know as *kouskouras* (the common term on Crete for any light-colored, relatively soft limestone bedrock), which is excellent for vineyards—and easy to dig tombs in.

There are coastal plains, such as those around Mallia and at the foot of Souda Bay (an excellent anchorage because it is protected from the prevailing northwest winds), with Nerokourou placed where the plain starts to rise to the foothills. The largest plain is the Mesara in the center of the island on the south coast, at whose edges are many ancient settlements (including Ayia Triada, Phaistos, Platanos,

and Gortyn). In the mountain massifs there are small high plains, of which the best known are those of Lasithi, Nida in the Psiloriti range, and Omalo in the White Mountains. At 1,000 m or more high and usually ringed by peaks, they are a special feature of Crete. Snow lies on them in winter. As it melts, it pours down cavernous swallow holes to emerge far below at the foot of the mountains and provides water for the orange groves.

Seventeenth- and eighteenth-century travelers to Crete saw the island as fair, fruitful, and rich. Its uplands provide excellent grazing for sheep, as they have since the Bronze Age, if not earlier. There are also goats, which in the far east of Crete have nibbled so effectively that much of the land has become desert. Sheep and goats provide skins, horns, and wool as well as meat, milk, and cheese.

The staple crops of vines (for table grapes, currants, wine), olives (for oil and other uses), and cereals are nowadays joined by tomatoes and cucumbers and exotic fruits (including citrus fruit) and vegetables that flourish with irrigation, which has resulted in many places in a drastic recent lowering of the water table.

There is a great variety of wild plants and flowers, with many species restricted to Crete. In classical antiquity Crete was known as the home of the cypress tree, ideal for building because it grows long and straight. It has the extra advantage that once cut, it becomes ever harder and stronger. The fauna include the wild goat, or *agrimi*. It lives in the mountains (as well as on a reserve on the island of Dia, off Herakleion) and is rarely seen. To the Minoans it was a holy animal. *Agrimia* are pictured for instance on the Mountain Shrine rhyton from Zakro, some of them romping on the mountain rocks, others resting on the shrine building.

The mountain massifs divide Crete into four main regions, which correspond more or less to the present four nomes, or prefectures. These are the far west, with the White Mountains; the near west, with Psiloriti; the center, between Psiloriti and the Lasithi mountains; and the east, which may be divided into the Lasithi massif with its hinterland (sometimes seen as with the center, sometimes as with the far east) and the far east beyond the isthmus of Ierapetra. Before automobiles became common, land communication was by foot or on mule or donkey, with distance measured in hours rather than kilometers. People traveled also by sea along the island's coasts.

CHRONOLOGY

The chronology of Crete may be considered reasonably secure in historical times from about the 8th century B.C. onward. With a far greater latitude in the dates assigned to phases, the same holds for the long Neolithic period, whose chronology is based on the deep stratigraphic sequence of Knossos, dated by radiocarbon (Carbon-14).

The Neolithic dates in the table that follows are based on the calibrated radiocarbon dates of Knossos, except for the beginning of the Neolithic sequence, where two early dates cannot yet be fully calibrated. When they can be, we shall probably find that the beginning of Neolithic is to be taken back to well before 7000 B.C. or even before 8000 B.C.

Radiocarbon dates are given in section VII of the entries for sites that have produced them. The dates are listed by archaeological period, and by context or location, as explained in the relevant entry. Each date starts with its laboratory number, which is its unique reference. Many of the Cretan dates are from the British Museum (BM) or the University of Pennsylvania (P) laboratories; other laboratories cited are Cambridge (Q), Gif, Oxford (OxA), Pisa (Pi) and Stockholm (St). Next is the date in years B.P. (Before Present = Before A.D. 1950). Then comes the same date in years cal. B.C., which means that they have been calibrated (for all except the two early dates [BM-124 and BM-278] from Knossos that are outside or partly outside the range of the program) according to the 1σ and 2σ probability ranges of the University of Washington Quaternary Isotope Laboratory Radiocarbon Calibration Program 2.0 (1987). This program uses principally the calibration systems of Kromer et al. (1986), Linick et al. (1985, 1986), Pearson and Stuiver (1986), Pearson et al. (1986), Stuiver and Pearson (1986), and Stuiver et al. (1986). Dates with very large standard deviations (±200 years or more B.P.) have not been calibrated.

No comment is offered on what the dated sample was (for instance, was it short-lived or long-lived?) or on any other aspect of the date. For more information, consult the references to the radiocarbon dates grouped separately at the end of the site bibliographies (section VIII). (Also included in section VII are thermoluminescence (TL) dates from one site, Myrtos–Phournou Koryphi.)

For the Minoan Bronze Age, controversy is still strong, and no Minoan chronology is universally accepted. All chronologies, including the one in the table that follows, combine at present a relative chronology, based on the (much debated) styles and sequences of Minoan pottery, with an absolute chronology that is itself an uneasy combination of (1) correlations with the calendrical Pharaonic chronology of Egypt through imports and exports and (2) radiocarbon. Until very recently, radiocarbon dates have been used principally to determine the Early Minoan period, for which the elaborate framework of Minoan periods and Egyptian connections, established by Evans (1906) and in use ever since to date the Minoan sequence, is weaker than it is for the Middle Minoan and Late Minoan periods. There is as yet no complete radiocarbon-based chronology for the Minoan Bronze Age.

Evans's sequence divided the Bronze Age of Crete into a tripartite system of Early Minoan, Middle Minoan, and Late Minoan that to some extent reflects the Old, Middle, and New Kingdoms of Egypt. Early Minoan, Middle Minoan, and Late Minoan were further divided into a I, II, and III; and Evans himself subdivided many of these phases into an A and a B, producing, for example, Middle Minoan IA or Late Minoan IB. The final subdivisions, for Late Minoan only, came when Furumark (1941) added numbers to produce, for example, Late Minoan IIIA1.

Betancourt (1987) has recently proposed a major change in the system that Evans established, a "high" chronology for Late Minoan I–Late Minoan IIIB. On the strength, first, of the radiocarbon dates for the destruction of Akrotiri on Thera that tend strongly toward a date in the 17th century B.C. rather than in the 16th century or even the normative, and frequently found, 1500 B.C. and, second, on reconsideration of the contextual evidence of exports and imports (and influences), he would raise the beginning of Late Minoan I to about 1700 B.C. Warren and Hankey (1989) and several authors in *3 Thera* (1990) discuss the issue.

Betancourt's high chronology for Late Minoan I–Late Minoan IIIB (given at the end of the table) may prove to reflect better the real duration of the stages of Minoan development, but it has yet to be widely agreed. Although attitudes may change at any time, it seems sensible for now to use, with a few slight modifications and with skepticism about the precision of some of their dates, Warren and Hankey's judicious version (Warren and Hankey 1989:169 table 3.1) of the conventional chronology that Evans founded in 1906, together with their dates for Late Neolithic and Final Neolithic.

Parallel to Evans's Minoan system is the palatial system of chronology, which divides the Bronze Age into four main periods reflecting the main phases in the building history of the palaces: Prepalatial, Old Palace (Protopalatial), New Palace (Neopalatial), and Postpalatial. Although, as the table shows, the four main periods of the palatial system do not concur with the three main periods (Early

Minoan, Middle Minoan, and Late Minoan) of Evans, both systems are helpful; and in the atlas the palatial system is used where appropriate as well as the Minoan system and has been added to Warren and Hankey's table. (Included in the New Palace period, rather than in the Postpalatial as some scholars prefer, are the likely phases of Mycenaean rule at Knossos—Late Minoan II and IIIA1—before the destruction of the palace at a time when the Late Minoan IIIA2 style of pottery was superseding Late Minoan IIIA1. The problem of the date of the event is discussed briefly in the chapter on Knossos.)

The palatial system does not have the refinement of Evans's nine-part Minoan system but does allow more flexibility, especially in the Old Palace period where there has been much discussion of the stages in the development of the pottery styles and their relation to the phases of building and destruction. For instance, did the end of the Old Palace period come in Middle Minoan IIB or IIIA? And are there as many phases as Evans believed? Much of the new discussion is not yet published.

Regionalism presents another problem in chronology. That the development of pottery styles did not proceed at the same pace throughout the island affects the dating of the archaeology. Regionalism is marked in eastern Crete in the Old Palace period and at the end of the Prepalatial period (from Early Minoan III). The Early Minoan III pottery style of eastern Crete continued longer than that of central Crete, and, in turn, Middle Minoan IA may have begun later in eastern Crete than in central Crete. Similarly, in the Old Palace period the precise correspondence of the central Cretan and eastern Cretan phases is not yet certain.

The Early Iron Age dates are those of Coldstream (1977:385).

CRETAN CHRONOLOGY

Before 7000–c. 3650/3500 B.C.	*Neolithic (N)*
before 7000	Aceramic Neolithic
c. 7000–c. 4750	Early Neolithic (EN)
c. 4750–c. 4500	Middle Neolithic (MN)
c. 4500–c. 3750	Late Neolithic (LN)
c. 3750–c. 3650/3500	Final Neolithic (FN)
C. 3650/3500–c. 1900	*Prepalatial*
c. 3650/3500–c. 3000/2900	Early Minoan I (EM I)
c. 2900–c. 2300/2150	Early Minoan II (EM II)
c. 2300/2150–c. 2160/2025	Early Minoan III (EM III)
c. 2160/1979–20th century	Middle Minoan IA (MM IA)

C. 1900–c. 1650	*Old Palace (Protopalatial)*
19th century	Middle Minoan IB (MM IB)
19th century–1700/1650	Middle Minoan II (MM II) (and Middle Minoan IIIA [MM IIIA]?)
C. 1700/1650–c. 1370/60	*New Palace (Neopalatial)*
c. 1700/1650–c. 1600	Middle Minoan III (MM III)
c. 1600–c. 1480	Late Minoan IA (LM IA)
c. 1480–c. 1425	Late Minoan IB (LM IB)
c. 1425–c. 1390	Late Minoan II (LM II)
c. 1390–c. 1370/60	Late Minoan IIIA1 (LM IIIA1)
C. 1370/60–c. 970	*Postpalatial*
c. 1370/60–c. 1340/30	Late Minoan IIIA2 (LM IIIA2)
c. 1340/30–c. 1190	Late Minoan IIIB (LM IIIB)
c. 1190–c. 1070	Late Minoan IIIC (LM IIIC)
c. 1070–c. 970	Sub-Minoan (SM)
C. 970–c. 700	*Early Iron Age*
c. 970–c. 900	Early Protogeometric (EPG)
c. 900–c. 870	Middle Protogeometric (MPG)
c. 870–c. 840	Late Protogeometric (LPG)
c. 840–c. 810	Protogeometric B (PGB)
c. 810–c. 790	Early Geometric (EG)
c. 790–c. 745	Middle Geometric (MG)
c. 745–c. 700	Late Geometric (LG)
C. 700–c. 630	*Orientalizing (O); (Early Orientalizing (EO); Middle Orientalizing?; Late Orientalizing (LO)*
C. 630–c. 480	*Archaic (A)*
C. 480–c. 330	*Classical (C)*
C. 330–67	*Hellenistic (H)*
67 B.C.–A.D. 330	*Roman (R)*

CRETAN CHRONOLOGY (continued)

330–824	*Early Byzantine (EByz)—also known as Early Christian and, sometimes, Late Roman*
824–961	*Arab*
961–1204	*Late Byzantine (LByz)*
1204–1669	*Venetian (V)*
1669–1898	*Ottoman (Ott)*

Betancourt's tentative "high" chronology for Late Minoan I–Late Minoan IIIB (Betancourt 1987:47 table 1) is as follows:

c. 1700–1610 B.C.	Late Minoan IA
c. 1610–1550	Late Minoan IB
c. 1550–1490	Late Minoan II
c. 1490–1430/10	Late Minoan IIIA1
c. 1430/10–1365	Late Minoan IIIA2
c. 1365–1200	Late Minoan IIIB.

NEOLITHIC CRETE (BEFORE 7000–C. 3650/3500 B.C.)

The archaeology of Crete begins before 7000 B.C. The Neolithic settlers of Knossos are the first Cretans we know, but we do not know if they were indigenous or had arrived by sea. We can see that they had an already developed agriculture and used obsidian (volcanic glass) from Melos in the Cyclades for blades for cutting. Journeys by boat were necessary to bring the obsidian to Crete, but we do not know if the sailors were from Crete or the Cyclades. The voyages may have been infrequent.

There followed a long period of slow development until, probably, the later 4th millennium B.C. when the first pottery we can call Minoan (Early Minoan I) and the Minoan culture appeared. The earlier changes in Neolithic culture, such as the Early Neolithic I introduction of pottery (which the first Neolithic people did not use) and later of clay spinning and weaving equipment, are shown uniquely at Knossos. But as the period went on, people inhabited other sites, many of them caves, and continued to use them into Early Minoan times.

The transition to Early Minoan I is not at all clear. The principal evidence is that of pottery, which suggests that a transitional phase of Final Neolithic occurred between Late Neolithic and Early Minoan I; this phase has been recognized principally at Knossos and Phaistos.

MINOAN CRETE (C. 3650/3500–C. 970 B.C.)

With Early Minoan I, painted pottery appeared, staying thereafter in the Cretan repertoire. Excavated settlements with surviving house remains are few, more of the evidence coming from caves and from tombs. The first circular tholos tombs, built in Early Minoan I, were used for collective burial. The inhabitants of Crete continued to bury their dead in such tombs around the Mesara plain and the Asterousia mountains south of it until the Old Palace period: there are examples at Lebena, Odigitria, and Platanos. In eastern Crete a houselike tomb was more usual in the Prepalatial and Old Palace periods, and in some cases even in the New Palace period: there are examples at Mallia (Chrysolakkos), Mochlos, and Myrtos-Pyrgos. (But see also the circular structures, probably tombs, at Ayia Photia.) Archanes-Phourni, with both types of tomb, seems to mark the border between the two traditions.

Early Minoan II saw a considerable increase in population; the founding of many settlements, such as Vasiliki, Myrtos–Phournou Koryphi, and Myrtos-Pyrgos; and the opening of new cemeteries, such as the one at Archanes-Phourni. Crete was becoming richer and its technology more advanced. The Minoans began to make stone vases, to use seals (probably for labeling or identifying agricultural produce as well as for talismans), and to make tools and weapons regularly of copper. How much of a copper industry there had been in Early Minoan I is still uncertain. (The earliest copper object from Crete is a flat axe from Late Neolithic Knossos.) There is also evidence that in Early Minoan II contacts quickened with the Cyclades and mainland Greece. Even one or two imports from Egypt are among the finds.

Of the sites photographed, Myrtos–Phournou Koryphi and Vasiliki stand out for the picture they give of Early Minoan II settlements. Phournou Koryphi, chosen perhaps partly for its defensibility, belongs only to Early Minoan II. It was destroyed by fire and not resettled, whereas the nearby contemporary settlement of Myrtos-Pyrgos was resettled, probably after a period of desertion. Though Phournou Koryphi was a small settlement, its inhabitants used stone vases, seals, and copper and had an abundance of pottery, of which the most striking example is a goddess-jug, a vase in the schematized shape of a woman holding a jug that is a miniature of the typical jugs of Early Minoan II at both Myrtos settlements.

Vasiliki, at the north end of the isthmus of Ierapetra, shows several phases in Early Minoan II and some impressive buildings, including a public courtyard and a house with red plaster. Here too there was a destruction by fire, but the settlement was quickly—or immediately—reinhabited; and there is a distinct Early Minoan III building phase (whereas at Gournia the evidence of use in Early Minoan III is confined to pottery found in a dump).

Knossos has plentiful evidence of use in Early Minoan II and into Early Minoan III. The West Court House, a large building (not visible in the photographs) partly excavated beneath the later West Court and destroyed by fire in Early Minoan IIA, may have been a ruler's house or a community center, and thus a precursor of the Old Palace. Early Minoan III may have seen another such predecessor, a "proto-palace" that has been identified in remains in the northwest quarter of the palace.

Early Minoan III led to Middle Minoan IA, when polychrome pottery (pottery with decoration in red as well as white paint on a dark ground) appeared, a change that came quickly in the center of the island. During Early Minoan III the pottery traditions of the center and of eastern Crete started to diverge, eastern Crete developing its own white-on-dark style. The styles grew yet further apart in the Old Palace period. Such cultural differences may well suggest the beginnings of separate states in Crete that are a strong probability with the appearance of the Old Palaces of Knossos, Phaistos, Mallia, and probably Zakro. None of these places can be shown to have been the capital of a Pan-Cretan state. Each probably had its own separate territory.

Another important development in Early Minoan III was the appearance of mountain shrines, often known as peak sanctuaries. Whether holy caves or holy buildings or a combination of the two, they must have been centers for people from several different communities. Thus their appearance marks a stage in the collective growth of Crete that is likely to be linked to the construction soon afterward of the major community centers that, following Evans, we call palaces. Mountain shrines continued in use through the Old Palace period and, to a reduced extent, into the New Palace period; the shrine at Syme, high on the south flank of the Lasithi mountains and next to an abundant spring gushing out of the mountainside, was not even founded until late in the Old Palace period. Often the shrines were closely linked to the palaces and other centers. Knossos is dominated to the south by Mt. Juktas, which has a summit shrine (which we were unable to photograph) and, down the mountain, the temple of Archanes-Anemospilia, which was probably visible from the Palace of Knossos. The Central Court of Phaistos is aligned north with a saddle in the Psiloriti range in which the Kamares cave

is a conspicuous black spot. The cave is equally visible from Ayia Triada. Above Palaikastro is the sanctuary of Petsophas.

The arrival of the palaces marks a turning point in Cretan history. There is considerable debate as to how, and when, and in what stages they came about. The chronology depends on revisions, not yet completed, of the pottery and building sequences. Until these revisions have been published and assimilated, it is reasonable to follow Evans, who saw the palaces (the Old Palaces) as starting with the appearance of the first wheel-made pottery, which he classed as Middle Minoan IB, about 1900 B.C.

How the palaces came into being is a fascinating problem. There are two main points of view. Some archaeologists accept a "steady state" interpretation. They point to the gradual development of technology through the Prepalatial period; the growth of population; the use of increasingly sophisticated seals; the appearance of the mountain shrines, the likely forerunners of the palaces in Early Minoan III at Knossos and Mallia (and also the Early Minoan II grand buildings at Knossos and Vasiliki); and the (slight) increase in foreign contacts, and they suggest from this evidence a gradual transition from a nonpalace society to a society with palaces. The other side accepts all these factors as relevant and then suggests that the actual change was a quick event or series of events.

What is certain is that the change revolutionized Crete. The appearance of the Old Palaces of Zakro, Mallia, Knossos, and Phaistos suggests the arrival of states centered on those palaces (and perhaps on others yet to be found, for instance in western Crete) that would have been analogous to the Classical cities (city-states) of Crete, though with much larger territories. The idea of four or five different states is supported by a growing body of evidence for regional differences in culture, which may reflect political boundaries. The best evidence is pottery. That of Monastiraki is remarkably close to that of Phaistos, which may suggest that Monastiraki was part of a Phaistos state. That of Myrtos-Pyrgos (and probably of Gournia and Vasiliki also) so closely resembles that of Mallia as to suggest a "Lasithi" state comprising the high plain of Lasithi and at least three sides (north, east, and south) of the Lasithi mountains and focused on Mallia.

The best preserved among the Old Palaces is the one at Phaistos, where the New Palace was set several meters back on the west side, leaving much of the Old Palace undisturbed to await archaeologists. At the other palaces little has survived. That makes it difficult to work out the functions of the Old Palaces, except by working backward from the New Palaces, which is probably a justifiable procedure. If correct, it means that we should envisage similar functions for the palaces in both periods, as centers of the society, the economy, administration, trade, and arts and crafts, with a huge capacity for storing and distributing agricultural wealth.

What is not clear, however, is the extent to which religion centered on the palaces was the binding force of society that it seems to have been in New Palace times. There is also important evidence from Mallia to show that there, at least, the parallel with the New Palaces is not complete. The finds and the quality of an Old Palace period group of buildings at Mallia (Quartier Mu, not photographed separately because it was roofed), some distance from the palace, suggest that these structures served the functions one would expect of the Old Palace, even though Quartier Mu is not arranged around a central court. What then was happening in the Old Palace (beneath the presently visible New Palace) with its Central Court? The matter becomes yet more complicated with efforts to explain the function of a public square (the Agora) that is close to the palace. Fortunately, enough of Middle Minoan Mallia has been excavated so that we can discuss these problems. Little of the Old Palace period towns of Knossos and Phaistos has been excavated. With further digging, we may yet find that Mallia is part of the normal pattern.

The evidence from almost all the Minoan sites, palatial or provincial, suggests that the Old Palace period was a prosperous time, fostered by the boom effect of the arrival of the palaces. In the provinces the very large area at Monastiraki for storing produce and the impressive buildings at Myrtos-Pyrgos (a tower and two plastered cisterns) are good evidence of the wealth of the period. The cisterns at Pyrgos may have been built in preparation for siege, as was the case centuries later at Lato and Dreros, each of which has a large cistern in the center of the city.

The Old Palace period ended in destructions by fire, which may have been caused by human agency or by earthquake (as discussed in section III of Phaistos) or by both.

The New Palace period lasted from Middle Minoan III until Late Minoan IB and on till late Minoan IIIA1. In Late Minoan IB most of the Cretan centers were destroyed by fire. At Mochlos there were human bodies in the debris; at Knossos there is evidence of what seems to have been propitiatory cannibalism. Buildings in the town of Knossos were destroyed, but the New Palace survived and continued its life for two to three generations more until it too was destroyed (by fire) around 1370 B.C., when the Late Minoan IIIA2 style of pottery was superseding the Late Minoan IIIA1 style, according to Popham's study (1970) of the Knossos pottery (see the bibliography for Knossos and the brief discussion, p. 130).

Although many of the old ways of life seem to have continued into Late Minoan II–IIIA1, there were also some startling changes. A new martial spirit is noticeable in the burial of warriors with their weap-

ons, in chariot scenes that appeared among the Knossos palace frescoes, and in the lists of chariots and their parts in the Linear B tablets of Knossos. And burials, of which we know hardly anything for Late Minoan I, reappear in the archaeological record, some of them richly equipped with offerings such as bronze vessels (at Knossos, Archanes-Phourni, and Phaistos). Some of these were in chamber tombs of mainland Greek (Mycenaean) type. They have long, narrow entrance passages (dromoi) cut into the rock leading to rectangular chambers. (This type remained popular into Late Minoan IIIB, as can be seen in the large cemetery at Armeni.)

Cultural changes as well as the biggest change of all—the appearance of the Linear B script at Knossos and its use for Greek administrative documents written on clay tablets—suggest that mainland Greeks had come to Knossos. The Linear B tablets point to an island-wide control of Crete from Knossos, administered through a seemingly meticulous bureaucracy, until the time of Knossos's destruction.

The bureaucracy may have been demanding and detailed in Middle Minoan III and Late Minoan I, but if so, we do not have archives as large as that of Linear B at Knossos to tell us—or the records were kept on a perishable material. The Hieroglyphic script used in the Old Palace period for lists and inventories was joined by the Linear A script before the end of that period. Linear A continued as the script of Crete until the Late Minoan IB destructions or the subsequent appearance of Linear B. We do not know Linear A's language(s). Its tablets—far fewer than the number of Linear B tablets—are widely distributed rather than being concentrated at Knossos. There are large enough groups to be called archives at Knossos, Ayia Triada, Zakro, and Chania, and several of the provincial centers have one or two tablets apiece. The wide distribution of Linear A, and the widespread evidence for the use of seals, suggest that the island-wide administration of Mycenaean Linear B times had its counterpart in Minoan Linear A times. The homogeneity of culture in Late Minoan I, particularly evident in the pottery and architecture, offers good reason to think that with the New Palace period Knossos had become the capital of Crete. The diverse culture of the Old Palace period argues against any earlier date for such a development. And although the Linear B tablets belong to a time when there were probably foreign masters at Knossos, the picture of the economy they give probably holds for Late Minoan I even if the social system had changed.

Another important change to keep in mind is a negative conclusion of archaeology. After the Late Minoan IB destructions, there must have been enormous dislocation in Crete. Many settlements were abandoned. A few continued, and several were resettled by the time of the Linear B tablets and the destruction of Knossos. But an enormous number of settlements must have been deserted. We do not know what happened. Perhaps people took to the hills after the Late Minoan IB destructions, as they have done often during times of trouble in Crete.

Before the disasters of Late Minoan IB (which may not have occurred at exactly the same time), Crete was more settled and more densely populated and made more use of the island's lowlands than at any other time in its history except under the Romans and in the 20th century A.D. The obvious conclusion is that the security of peace (even if it was an imposed peace rather than one that manifested the eirenic character of the Cretans of Late Minoan I) allowed the full use of the best parts of the country.

The building boom in Late Minoan IA gives strong support to the idea of peace and security. The Old Palaces were rebuilt as the New Palaces; buildings of palatial quality appeared at Archanes-Tourkoyeitonia, Ayia Triada, and Kommos; grand town houses were built, or begun, at Knossos and Mallia; Gournia has a grand house at its center, which must have been the ruling house of the town and may have controlled the Ierapetra isthmus; there are impressive buildings in the towns of Palaikastro and Zakro; grand country houses (often called villas, and used like Roman villas or English country houses) were spread throughout Crete, with important examples at Makryyialos, Myrtos-Pyrgos, Nerokourou, Tylissos (where there were two adjacent grand houses, with a third that may have been a warehouse), and Vathypetro and many humbler country houses, as at Achladia; and everywhere there is evidence of settlement, both isolated farmsteads and villages and towns such as Vasiliki and Mochlos. This great burst of building suggests a sudden growth of population that may even have led to Cretans' being sent to the islands of the southern Aegean and to the west coast of Anatolia: many settlements in both areas show a Minoanized culture and a similar burst of building activity, often in a clearly Minoan-influenced style.

In Crete we may imagine that a small band of master masons took metropolitan notions into the country and applied them to the grander country houses, whose occupants must have functioned in some way as agents of the palaces. It was a ranked society, though to judge from our difficulty in defining what is a palace and what is a country house, the patterns must have been somewhat fluid. Envisage the palaces (and their surrounding towns) in command of Crete. Chief among them was Knossos. Then the pattern becomes more difficult. Very close to, if not the equals of, the palaces must be the imposing structures at Archanes and Kommos, while Ayia Triada was becoming ever more important. (By Postpalatial times Ayia

Triada had superseded Phaistos.) Next level down are the large and impressive towns such as Gournia and Palaikastro and the grander country houses: in different ways these must have been chief places at the district level in the system of governing. And below them come the multitude of other settlements.

What then were the palaces? Probably they functioned something like medieval monasteries, overseeing an often vast agricultural economy, carefully administered, whose surplus could be used to pay for arts and crafts. This secular role was part of their far more important sacred role, the worship of their deity or deities. In the New Palaces of Crete the evidence is overwhelming for a complete intermingling of the sacred and profane, so that for the Late Bronze Age Cretan there could have been little or no difference between them. The shrines and their treasuries containing works of art are regularly found next to the archives (or counting houses) and the storerooms where agricultural produce was brought to be kept and dispersed as payment or rations to artists and accountants and to the rulers who are likely to have been also the chief priests or priestesses (it is not impossible that Minoan Crete was run by women) and their courts. The art of the frescoes shows principally rituals, and in the so-called Camp Stool Fresco from Knossos, which depicts women sitting on stools and toasting each other, the principal figure (known as La Parisienne since the days of Evans) is painted twice the size of the others—a clear sign of importance and probably of divinity, to judge from Egyptian art, where the divine pharaoh is regularly shown in this way. The Cretan royal priests and priestesses, in charge of a complicated system of life, may well have been seen as gods on earth. If so, that belief helped to hold society together.

They may have made ceremonial appearances at upper windows on the west side of the palaces, where there seem to have been staterooms and shrines over the storerooms, shrines and counting houses below, to be saluted by a faithful populace gathered in the west courts (a feature of Knossos, Mallia, Phaistos, and, on a very small scale, Gournia).

The internal central court, usually aligned north–south (the one at Zakro is slightly off the axis), is a common factor of the four palaces that does not occur in the buildings of palatial standard, although Ayia Triada is like half a palace, built on only two sides of the court. On the north side of the central court Knossos, Mallia, and Zakro have halls with pillars, which, it has been suggested, supported dining halls on the upper floor. There may have been something similar at Phaistos, where the rooms on the north, with the best view toward the Kamares cave, are often seen as the residential or domestic quarter. At Mallia these are to the northwest, and at Knossos and Zakro on the east. Mallia has on the east a well-built series of storerooms designed for keeping olive oil (and collecting the spillage). To the south Zakro and Mallia have what are probably workrooms. The south buildings of Phaistos have fallen off the cliff. At Knossos there was a ceremonial entrance into the Central Court, reached by a corridor coming from the west entrance to the palace off the West Court. This passage was adorned with a fresco of people in procession, carrying gifts or offerings, who thus figuratively escorted real people entering the palace with gifts or offerings or coming for an audience.

Around 1425 B.C. (on the conventional chronology) most centers in Crete were destroyed and abandoned for reasons that remain unknown. Because Mycenaean Greeks seem to have taken over Crete after this date, they may well have been the agents of the disasters. Or the Mycenaeans could have arrived in the wake of a natural disaster. What seems unlikely is the view once popular (though with few archaeologists) that the volcanic eruption of Thera (Santorini) in the southern Aegean caused the disasters. Evidence for the tidal waves or airborne incendiarism that would have resulted—or even for the right date—is now generally thought inadequate.

The destruction of Knossos some fifty-five years later led to, or was accompanied by, interesting changes in the rest of Crete. It seems likely that Chania (which we could not photograph) became the capital, of western Crete at least and perhaps of the whole island, having close links with mainland Greece (to which it exported large jars, with Linear B inscriptions, that probably contained olive oil) as well as with Cyprus. Linear B literacy continued at Chania after the fall of Knossos.

Ayia Triada similarly flourished, with a building program that included the construction of a megaron (a hall of the mainland Greek type) over the ruins of the Royal Villa and an impressive stoa (or row of shops or storerooms) in the town. Nearby at Kommos, another place with links to Cyprus, a large building by the sea that carried on the tradition of the earlier palatial building may have been involved in Kommos's foreign trade.

Many of the other New Palace period settlements revived in Late Minoan IIIA2–IIIB, the first two centuries of the Postpalatial period. Gournia has a house of megaron type. At Knossos there is ample evidence of continued occupation, although the palace had become a ruin where people lived a reduced life among the debris. Chania and Ayia Triada flourished, as did Chondros, which seems to have been a new settlement. (The evidence for earlier occupation is very slight.) The Armeni cemetery came into use, showing links in its lively painted larnakes, or clay coffins, with both eastern Crete and Chania. Such evidence suggests that the island-wide culture of the New Palace period had not altogether evaporated.

The evidence of correlations with mainland Greece suggests that the Late Minoan IIIB phase ended around 1190 B.C. It is certain that there were troubles on the mainland, but what form they took in Crete is uncertain. Refugees from the mainland are a likely possibility.

In Crete the Late Minoan IIIC phase, running into an insufficiently defined Sub-Minoan phase equivalent to a late Late Minoan IIIC, marks the end of the Bronze Age and the beginning of the long transition to the Classical period. Although some long-used sites, such as Knossos and Ayia Triada, were still occupied, the most interesting development is the building of new settlements on very high, bleak, and inaccessible peaks, both in this phase and in the subsequent Protogeometric phases. These refuge sites (of which Karphi, Kavousi, and Vrokastro are good examples) are indisputable evidence of troubled times, which continued in Crete during much of the 1st millennium. They are all in spectacular situations and have breathtaking views, and nobody would choose to live in them unless forced to by circumstances (though Karphi and Vrokastro had probably been shrines in Middle Minoan times, or possibly there was a settlement at Vrokastro). The hill of Kastri above Palaikastro is another refuge site that seems to have been inhabited at only three periods, in Early Minoan I (–II), Early Minoan III, and Late Minoan IIIC, all of which must have been times of danger.

EARLY IRON AGE–HELLENISTIC CRETE (c. 970–67 B.C.)

The Early Iron Age saw the emergence of the polis, the city-state, from the dislocations and desertions of the end of the Late Bronze Age. Crete had turned, or was reverting, to a pattern of independent states often at war or making or breaking alliances with each other. The cultural and political homogeneity of Late Minoan I was long dead, and the divisiveness inherent in the geography of the island reasserted itself. The cities of Protogeometric, Geometric, Archaic, Classical, and Hellenistic Crete tend to have formidable acropoleis, whose defensive purpose cannot be doubted. Phalasarna and Polyrrhenia in western Crete, Gortyn and Phaistos in the center, Dreros and Lato to the east, and Praisos in the far east are excellent examples of places easy to defend. All have splendid views and are well worth a visit.

Knossos is an exception. The hill to the west of the Minoan palace known as the Acropolis is not notably impressive, and we do not know that it was used as an acropolis. What is clear is that the Iron Age inhabitants and their successors chose to live at a venerable location, on the remains of the Minoan town to the west, northwest, and north of the palace; their main cemetery was at some distance to the north from Sub-Minoan times until the late 7th century (and was used again in Hellenistic times). On the palace site itself there seems to have been a temple of Rhea. Southwest of the palace at Phaistos was another such temple, which may go back to Geometric times.

Holy places on the ruins of the Minoan palaces suggest that some of the old centers still retained their power, if by now it was one of magic and mystery. Other places show a more direct continuity from the Bronze Age: the town of Knossos has been mentioned; the refuge settlements of Kavousi, Vrokastro, and perhaps Karphi carried on from Late Minoan IIIC/Sub-Minoan times into the Iron Age; so did Phaistos and Gortyn; and there was continuity of cult in the long-lived sanctuary at Syme and possibly in the new sanctuary at Kommos (where the shrine buildings begun in Protogeometric times lasted through Roman), as well as in such places as the sacred cave at Psychro in the Lasithi mountains and the Idaean Cave on Psiloriti.

In the 8th century we can recognize a fully functional polis at Dreros. In the saddle between two hills an agora was made, and above it a temple was built for Apollo Delphinios. (The large cistern is Hellenistic.) Dreros continued to prosper into the 6th century.

At other cities there are few visible remains of construction from Geometric, Archaic, and Classical times. The most impressive is the Classical enclosed harbor at Phalasarna on the wild west coast. But there is much art of importance in the Herakleion Museum from places such as Eleutherna, Gortyn, Knossos, Palaikastro, Praisos, and Syme as well as Dreros. And at Gortyn, set on the walls of the Odeion (middle of the 1st century B.C.; rebuilt under Trajan), is the great inscription of the city's law code, which had been cut in the first half of the 5th century. That inscription and a chance find of part of another legal inscription at Phaistos are tangible evidence of the Cretans' skill, renowned in antiquity, as lawmakers.

In the 5th century Crete seems to have been something of a backwater, on the whole undisturbed by the stirring events in mainland Greece and the rest of the Aegean. It was known for old-fashioned political and educational systems, and also for piracy.

In Hellenistic times the island assumed a new importance, helped by its useful position controlling sea routes out of the Aegean. The cities of Crete made war on each other, with Gortyn, Knossos, Kydonia (Chania) and Lyttos all vying for power. Gortyn eventually destroyed its local rival Phaistos, and in eastern Crete Praisos fell to Hierapytna (Ierapetra). Some cities looked abroad for help: Olous to Rhodes, for instance, and Gortyn to Ptolemy IV Philopator; and in 183 B.C. Eumenes II of Pergamon made a separate treaty with each of the thirteen members of the Cretan Koinon, a confederation of cities that helped at times to deter war in the island.

Considerable remains of Hellenistic Crete survive. Much of Lato is of this period; so are the cistern of Dreros and buildings at Gortyn, Phaistos (where the Hellenistic city was almost as large as the Minoan), and Polyrrhenia. At Knossos recent rescue excavations have increased our knowledge greatly. The records of Cretan mercenaries being sent abroad may suggest an increase of population during the Hellenistic phase, as does the increased building activity.

Rome began to be involved in Cretan affairs after its conquest of mainland Greece; in 71 B.C. a Roman expedition was sent to conquer what was the last stronghold of free Hellenism (and piracy). That expedition failed. In 68–66 another expedition came, led by Quintus Caecilius Metellus, who subdued the island so ruthlessly that he earned the name of Creticus.

ROMAN–VENETIAN CRETE (67 B.C.–A.D. 1669)

Roman rule brought prosperity back to Crete. Augustus united the island with Cyrene in North Africa to make a joint province whose capital was offshore at Gortyn, a choice of location that demonstrates how the Romans had brought peace and had cleared the sea of pirates.

There are many Roman remains in Crete, which seems to have been densely inhabited. Isolated farms reappeared, probably for the first time since Late Minoan I; and people lived on the lowlands that had been dangerous for so many centuries. Crete sent grain to Rome; and St. Paul sent Titus to convert Crete to Christianity.

With Constantine's building of Constantinople at Byzantium and his division of the empire, Crete came under the Byzantine or Eastern Empire. The principal building form of this Early Byzantine phase is the basilica; the best example in Crete is that of Ayios Titos (to use his Greek name) at Gortyn (its first phase was 6th century or earlier): near it were at least five more basilicas and smaller churches. Many other ancient sites that we photographed also have basilicas. Another notable construction at Gortyn is the great aqueduct of the late 4th century, which replaced the earlier underground pipes.

During these centuries Gortyn suffered from repeated severe earthquakes. Although it was rebuilt on the debris of the most recent earthquakes, the destructions led to the breakdown of its urban infrastructure. An especially bad earthquake in 670 was followed in 673 by an invasion of Arabs, who turned Crete into a base for launching attacks against Constantinople every summer until 677, when their fleet was destroyed under the walls of that city.

The Arab threat did not disappear. In 824 Arabs captured Crete, holding it until 961, when Byzantium regained it under the generalship of Nikephoros Phokas, after he had captured the new Arab city of El Chandak, "ditch; moat," which later became Candia (now Herakleion). At Knossos an Arab building has been found by the Kairatos river.

The Late Byzantine phase lasted until 1204, when after the infamous sack of Constantinople by the Fourth Crusade, the Venetians obtained Crete. They held it until in 1645 the Ottoman Turks began to attack, soon taking Chania and Rethymno. Herakleion held out through an epic siege of over twenty years until it capitulated in 1669. Crete became part of the Ottoman Empire.

A few Late Byzantine and Venetian sites are among the entries, such as Ayia Triada and Eleutherna, but most are outside the scope of this book.

OTTOMAN AND MODERN CRETE (1669–1989)

Ottoman Crete lasted from 1669 to 1898. There were frequent rebellions, fostered in 1821 by the start of the Greek War of Independence. In 1898 an independent Crete was established under the supervision of Britain, France, Italy, and Russia. One immediate effect was the beginning of intense archaeological activity.

In 1913 Crete was united with Greece, as it is today. In 1941 the Germans invaded Crete by air (their first and last such attack in World War II). Now the island prospers from greatly improved agriculture and tourism. In recent years there has been a massive amount of building, often ugly, and the lowlands have been more densely settled than at any time since the Roman Empire and Late Minoan I.

The Cretans are an independent people. Their archaeology and written history show that they have always been so.

SELECT BIBLIOGRAPHY

Crete

Admiralty, Naval Intelligence Division. 1945. "Chapter VIII. Crete (Kríti)," in *Greece* III. *Regional Geography*, 203–315. London.

Allbaugh, L. G. 1953. *Crete: A Case Study of an Underdeveloped Area.* Princeton.

Buondelmonti, C. 1981. *Descriptio insule Crete et liber insularum, chap. XI. Creta,* ed. M.-V. van Spitael. Herakleion.

Burgel, G. 1965. *Pobia: Etude géographique d'un village crétois.* Athens.

Cameron, P. 1988. *Crete,* Blue Guides, 5th ed. London and New York.

Cornelius, F. 1755. *Creta sacra* 1–2. Venice; reprinted Modena 1971.

1 Cretological. 1961–62. 1–3.

2 Cretological. 1968. 1–3.

3 Cretological. 1973–75. 1–3.

4 Cretological. 1980–81. 1–3.

5 Cretological. 1985. 1–3.

6 Cretological. 1990–91. 1–3.

Hazzidakis, I. 1881. *Periigisis eis Kritin.* Ermoupolis, Syros; reprinted Athens 1969.

Lear, E. 1984. *The Cretan Journal,* ed. R. Fowler. Athens and Dedham, Essex.

Pashley, R. 1837. *Travels in Crete* 1–2. London; reprinted Amsterdam 1970.

Prevelakis, P. 1938. *To chroniko mias politeias.* Athens.

Raulin, V. 1869. *Description physique de l'île de Crète.* Paris.

Spanakis, S. G. 1986. *I Kriti,* 1–2, 3rd. ed. Herakleion.

———. 1990. *To Herakleio sto perasma ton aionon.* Herakleion.

Spratt, T. A. B. 1865. *Travels and Researches in Crete,* 1–2. London.

Trevor-Battye, A. 1913. *Camping in Crete.* London.

Vallianos, C., and S. Kokkori. 1987. *Kritiki paradosiaki architectoniki: Ikismi kai mnimeia tis dytikis Mesaras (Nomos Irakleiou).* Vori, Crete.

Watrous, L. V. 1982. *Lasithi: A History of Settlement on a Highland Plain in Crete. Hesperia* Supplement 18. Princeton.

Chronology

Betancourt, P. P. 1987. "Dating the Aegean Late Bronze Age with Radiocarbon," *Archaeometry* 29:45–49.

Coldstream, J. N. 1977. *Geometric Greece.* London and New York.

Evans, A. J. 1906. *Essai de classification des époques de la civilisation minoenne.* London.

Furumark, A. 1941. *The Mycenaean Pottery: Analysis and Classification; The Chronology of Mycenaean Pottery,* reprinted 1972. Stockholm.

Kromer, B., M. Rhein, M. Bruns, H. Schoch-Fisher, K. O. Münnich, M. Stuiver, and B. Becker. 1986. "Radiocarbon Calibration Data for the 6th to 8th Millennia B.C.," *Radiocarbon* 28:954–60.

Linick, T. W., H. E. Suess, and B. Becker. 1985. "La Jolla Measurements of Radiocarbon in South German Oak Tree-Ring Chronologies," *Radiocarbon* 27:20–32.

Linick, T. W., A. Long, P. E. Damon, and C. W. Ferguson. 1986. "High-Precision Radiocarbon Dating of Bristlecone Pine from 6654 to 5350 B.C.," *Radiocarbon* 28:943–53.

Pearson, G. W., J. R. Pilcher, M. G. L. Baillie, D. M. Corbett, and F. Qua. 1986. "High-Precision ¹⁴C Measurements of Irish Oaks to Show the Natural ¹⁴C Variations from A.D. 1840–5210 B.C.," *Radiocarbon* 28:911–34.

Pearson, G. W., and M. Stuiver. 1986. "High-Precision Calibration of the Radiocarbon Time Scale, 500–2500 B.C.," *Radiocarbon* 28:839–62.

Stuiver, M., B. Kromer, B. Becker, and C. W. Ferguson. 1986. "Radiocarbon Age Calibration back to 13,300 Years B.P. and ¹⁴C Age Matching of the German Oak and U.S. Bristlecone Pine Chronologies," *Radiocarbon* 28:969–79.

Stuiver, M., and G. W. Pearson. 1986. "High-Precision Calibration of the Radiocarbon Time Scale, A.D. 1950–500 B.C.," *Radiocarbon* 28:805–38.

3 Thera. 1990. 3.

Warren, P. M., and V. Hankey. 1989. *Aegean Bronze Age Chronology.* Bristol.

Neolithic–Roman Archaeology and History

A Land Called Crete. 1968.

Alexiou, S. 1969. *Minoan Civilisation.* Herakleion.

Ancient Crete. 1985.

Antichità cretesi. 1973–74. 1–2.

Aux origines de l'hellénisme. 1984.

Betancourt, P. P. 1985. *The History of Minoan Pottery.* Princeton.

Blome, P. 1982. *Die figürliche Bildwelt Kretas in der geometrischen und früharchaischen Periode.* Mainz.

Boardman, J. 1961. *The Cretan Collection in Oxford: The Dictaean Cave and Iron Age Crete.* Oxford.

Branigan, K. 1970. *The Foundations of Palatial Crete: A Survey of Crete in the Bronze Age.* London.

———. 1970. *The Tombs of Mesara.* London.

———. 1974. *Aegean Metalwork of the Early and Middle Bronze Age.* Oxford.

Cadogan, G. 1976. *Palaces of Minoan Crete.* London; rev. ed. 1980. London and New York.

Canciani, F. 1970. *Bronzi orientali e orientalizzanti a Creta nell'VIII e VII sec. a.C.* Rome.

Cherry, J. F., D. J. L. Bennet, and A. L. Wilson. Forthcoming. *A Gazetteer of Aegean Civilisation in the Neolithic and Bronze Age,* Vol. II: *Crete, SIMA* (Gothenburg).

CMS 1–. 1964–.

Creta antica. 1984.

Darcque, P., and J.-C. Poursat, eds. 1985. *L'iconographie minoenne,* Actes de la Table Ronde d'Athènes (21–22 April 1983), *BCH* Supplement 11 (Athens).

Darque, P., and R. Treuil, eds. 1990. *L'habitat égéen préhistorique,* Actes de la Table Ronde d'Athènes (23–25 June 1987), *BCH* Supplement 19 (Athens).

Davaras, C. 1976. *Guide to Cretan Antiquities.* Park Ridge, N.J.

Evans, A. J. 1921–36. *The Palace of Minos at Knossos* 1–4 and index vol. London.

Faure, P. 1964. *Fonctions des cavernes crétoises.* Paris.

———. 1973. *La vie quotidienne en Crète en temps de Minos, 1500 av. J.-C.* Paris.

Foster, K. P. 1979. *Aegean Faience of the Bronze Age.* New Haven.

Gesell, G. C. 1985. *Town, Palace, and House Cult in Minoan Crete, SIMA* 67 (Gothenburg).

Graham, J. W. 1962. *The Palaces of Crete,* rev. ed. 1986. Princeton.

Hiller, S. 1977. *Das minoische Kreta nach den Ausgrabungen des letzten Jahrzehnts.* Vienna.

Hood, M. S. F. 1971. *The Minoans.* London and New York.

———. 1978. *The Arts in Prehistoric Greece.* Harmondsworth and New York.

Hutchinson, R. W. 1962. *Prehistoric Crete.* Harmondsworth.

IC. 1935–50. 1–4.

Immerwahr, S. A. 1990. *Aegean Painting in the Bronze Age.* University Park, Pa.

Jenkins, R. J. H. 1936. *Dedalica.* Cambridge.

Kanta, A. 1980. *The Late Minoan III Period in Crete: A Survey of Sites, Pottery, and Their Distribution, SIMA* 58 (Gothenburg).

Kunze, E. 1931. *Kretische Bronzereliefs.* Stuttgart.

Le Rider, G. 1966. *Monnaies crétoises du Ve au Ier siècle av. J.C., EtCr* 15 (Paris).

Marinatos, N. 1986. *Minoan Sacrificial Ritual: Cult Practice and Symbolism.* Stockholm.

Matthäus, H. 1980. *Die Bronzegefässe der kretisch-mykenischen Kultur, Prähistorische Bronzefunde* 2.1 (Munich).

Matz, F. 1928. *Frühkretische Siegel*. Berlin.

———, ed. 1951. *Forschungen auf Kreta 1942*. Berlin.

———. 1958. *Göttererscheinung und Kultbild im minoischen Kreta*. Wiesbaden.

Minoan Society. 1983.

Moody, J. A. 1987. *The Environmental and Cultural Prehistory of the Khania Region of West Crete: Neolithic through Late Minoan III*, Ph.D. diss., University of Minnesota.

Niemeier, W.-D. 1985. *Die Palaststilkeramik von Knossos: Stil, Chronologie und historischer Kontext*. Berlin.

Nilsson, M. P. 1950. *The Minoan-Mycenaean Religion*, 2nd ed. Lund.

Pelon, O. 1976. *Tholoi, tumuli et cercles funéraires*. Athens.

Pendlebury, J. D. S. 1939. *The Archaeology of Crete: An Introduction*. London.

Platon, N. 1966. *Crete*. London.

Preziosi, D. 1983. *Minoan Architectural Design*. Berlin.

Problems in Greek Prehistory. 1988.

Renfrew, A. C. 1972. *The Emergence of Civilisation: The Cyclades and the Aegean in the Third Millennium B.C.* London.

Rutkowski, B. 1986. *The Cult Places of the Aegean*. New Haven.

Sakellarakis, Y. 1973. "Neolithic Crete," in D. R. Theocharis et al. *Neolithic Greece*, 131–46, Athens.

Sanctuaries and Cults in the Aegean Bronze Age. 1981.

Sanders, I. F. 1982. *Roman Crete*. Warminster.

Shaw, J. W. 1971. *Minoan Architecture: Materials and Techniques*, *ASAtene* 49.

Svoronos. 1890.

The Minoan Thalassocracy. 1984.

Tiré, C., and H. Van Effenterre. 1966. *Guide des fouilles françaises en Crète*, 3rd ed. 1983. Paris.

Treuil, R., P. Darcque, J.-C. Poursat, and G. Touchais, et al. 1989. *Les civilisations égéennes du Néolithique et de l'Age du Bronze*. Paris.

Van Effenterre, H. 1949. *La Crète et le monde grec de Platon à Polybe*, 2nd ed. 1968. Paris.

Ventris, M. and J. Chadwick. 1956. *Documents in Mycenaean Greek*, 2nd ed. 1973. Cambridge.

Verlinden, C. 1984. *Les statuettes anthropomorphes crétoises en bronze et en plomb, du IIIe millénaire au VIIIe siècle av. J.-C.* Providence, R.I., and Louvain.

Warren, P. M. 1969. *Minoan Stone Vases*. Cambridge.

———. 1988. *Minoan Religion as Ritual Action, SIMA PB* 72 (Gothenburg).

Warren, P. M., and V. Hankey. 1989. *Aegean Bronze Age Chronology*. Bristol.

Willetts, R. F. 1955. *Aristocratic Society in Ancient Crete*. London.

———. 1962. *Cretan Cults and Festivals*. London.

———. 1965. *Ancient Crete: A Social History*, 2nd ed. 1974. London and Toronto.

———. 1977. *The Civilization of Ancient Crete*. London and Berkeley.

Xanthoudides, S. 1924. *The Vaulted Tombs of Mesará*. London.

Yule, P. *Early Cretan Seals: A Study of Chronology*. Mainz.

Zervos, C. 1956. *L'art de la Crète néolithique et minoenne*. Paris.

Zois, A. A. 1973. *Kriti, Epochi tou lithou*, Ancient Greek Cities 18. Athens.

Byzantine–Modern Archaeology and History

Alexiou, S. 1969. *Kritiki anthologia (15'–17' aionas)*, 2nd ed. Herakleion.

Beevor, A. 1991. *Crete: The Battle and the Resistance* (London).

Christides, V. 1984. *The Conquest of Crete by the Arabs (ca. 824): A Turning Point in the Struggle between Byzantium and Islam*. Athens.

Curuni, S. A., and L. Donati. 1987. *Creta bizantina*. Rome.

———. 1988. *Creta veneziana: L'Istituto Veneto e la Missione Cretese di Giuseppe Gerola. Collezione fotografica 1900–1902*. Venice.

Di Vita, A., N. Yannadakis, V. La Rosa, and M. A. Rizzo. 1984. *Timi stin Kriti 1884–1984*, with parallel translation as *Homage to Crete 1884–1984* and *Omaggio a Creta 1884–1984*. Herakleion.

Embiricos, A. 1960. *La renaissance crétoise: XVIe et XVIIe siècles*. Paris.

———. 1967. *L'école crétoise: Dernière phase de la peinture byzantine*. Paris.

Gallas, K., K. Wessel, and M. Borbudakis. 1983. *Byzantinisches Kreta*. Munich.

Gerola, G. 1905–32. *I monumenti veneti dell'isola di Creta* 1–4. Venice.

Hadjipateras, C. N., and M. S. Fafalios. 1989. *Crete 1941 Eyewitnessed*. Athens.

Kalokyris, K. D. 1954. *La peinture murale byzantine dans l'île de Crète*. Herakleion.

————. 1973. *The Byzantine Wall Paintings of Crete.* New York.

Marcoglou, E. E. 1971. *The American Interest in the Cretan Revolution. 1866–1869.* Athens.

Psilakis, N. 1986. *Ta monastiria tis Kritis.* Athens.

Psychoundakis, G. 1955. *The Cretan Runner.* London.

Spanakis, S. G. 1940–. *Mnimeia tis kritikis istorias 1–.* Herakleion.

Stewart, I. McD. G. 1966. *The Struggle for Crete, 20 May–1 June 1941: A Story of Lost Opportunity.* Oxford.

PART II

THE SITES

Site entries are divided as follows:

PHOTOGRAPHS

Individual aerial photographs provide information to be found in pattern and relationship not visible to the ground observer. They record all that can be seen and recognized from a given altitude. Grouped together, these photographs of Crete, complimented by text and plans, offer a primary source for further close study and comparison.

PLANS

The drawn plans supplement the photographs through interpretative simplification and point out items mentioned in the text. In these plans, as far as possible, the principal phase of the site has been rendered solid black. At multi-period Minoan sites, this is often, but not always, the New Palace period.

The involvement of many people in the atlas project and the long period during which data were collected and collated made it impossible to establish exact correspondences between the dates of photographs, drawings, and text entries. The photographs were made first and are dated; the excavators or investigators were given copies and asked to provide current (or the best available) drawings or to furnish materials so that we could arrange to have plans drawn; the site texts usually came to us last and occasionally include information more recent than that reflected in the drawings.

TEXT

I. Importance

Why the site matters and what is special about it.

II. Use

An abbreviated account of the site's periods of use. The atlas tries to follow a sensible path through the thickets of their dates, whether on the Minoan or the palatial systems for the Bronze Age sites, but the reader should remember that chronology is not universally agreed. For more on chronology, see pp. 32–34 above.

III. Situation

An account of the location of the site and the country around it. For information in English on how to reach the sites, the best source is P. Cameron, *Crete* (Blue Guides), 5th ed., London and New York, 1988.

IV. Geomorphology

An account of the site's geomorphology, written by John A. Gifford for all sites save Pseira, which is by William R. Farrand.

V. Excavation History

A list of the systematic excavations at the site, giving the name of the director and the sponsoring body.

The information about sponsors may help those wanting permission to study a site or finds from it, particularly if the site is not yet fully published and in the public domain or if the excavation director is no longer alive. (Regardless of what other permissions may be needed, the permission of the Archaeological Service is required.)

VI. Buildings

The man-made features of the site, divided by periods.

VII. Radiocarbon Dates

A list of the dates from the site, divided by period and location or context. For an explanation of the information, see p. 32 above. Also included are thermoluminescence dates at one site, Myrtos–Phournou Koryphi.

VIII. Bibliography

A selective listing of the principal references to the site, divided into sections by periods and locations or contexts, if appropriate. Frescoes, geomorphology, radiocarbon dates, and scripts and seals are grouped separately. Many of the references cross the at times rather artificial boundaries between the sections. References to *CMS* are given for seals and sealings with a secure provenance: those in private collections are omitted.

Excavation references include final reports, if these are available, or preliminary reports. For continuing excavations under the auspices of the Archaeological Society, references to *Ergon* (the society's annual report) are not included, as there will be in due course fuller accounts in *PAE*. Forthcoming issues of *ArchDelt*, *Ergon*, and *PAE* as well as *AR* and *BCH* will contain information on all continuing excavations.

Works listed in the select bibliography for Ancient and Modern Crete (pp. 40–43) generally contain useful bibliographies that include sites we were unable to photograph and include in the Atlas. For the history and archaeology of classical sites, Greek and Roman, the entries in *IC* have notably full and helpful references to ancient and modern sources.

IX. Finds

The principal museums whose collections include finds from the site.

X. Date of Photography

Given for the aerial photographs.

NIKOLAOS PLATON

35°10′ N, 26°03′ E

I. IMPORTANCE

The Minoan settlement at Achladia is on the edge of the flat country in eastern Crete that stretches from around the town of Siteia to the steep hill on which are the oval buildings of Chamaizi. The large House A at Achladia is a good example of how metropolitan architectural practices were followed in quite small settlements on the island in the New Palace period.

Earthquakes, tree roots, and long cultivation have caused considerable damage to the buildings.

II. USE

MM III–LM I settlement; LM III tholos tomb and kiln nearby.

III. SITUATION

At Riza, "root" or "foothill," 3 km northeast of village of Achladia and south of Siteia; nearby, LM IIIB tholos tomb at Platyskinos and LM III potter's kiln.

IV. GEOMORPHOLOGY

The site is on a north–south trending hill that offers a commanding view of the valley draining into the Bay of Siteia and the shoreline formed by the northeastern spur of the Ornon mountains.

According to Gradstein (1973), the Neogene formations in this region represent lime-rich sediments deposited in environments ranging from large rivers (Kastri formation) to deltas with giant fore-set beds (Toplou formation) to open marine conditions (Achladia formation). The last formation is defined on the basis of a geological type section located not far from the Minoan site. Characteristic rock types are calcareous marlstones and fine sandstones, very similar to units of comparable age south of Herakleion.

There is evidence of small-scale quarrying of the tabular sandstone strata below the hillcrest. The siting is similar to that of Kommos on the south coast, at least in local topography and underlying bedrock.

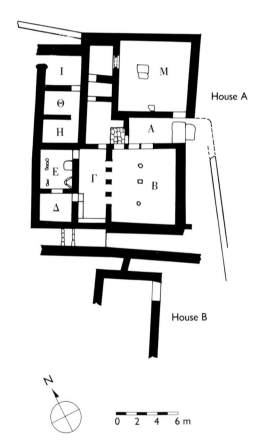

House A

House B

N

0 2 4 6 m

Figure 1.1   Achladia, House A and partly excavated House B to the south

Figure 1.2   House A

V. EXCAVATION HISTORY

N. Platon, 1939, for the Archaeological Service, and 1952 and 1959, for the Archaeological Society.

VI. BUILDINGS

House A, a rectangular house (about 270 sq m) in a small settlement stretching south and west along the low hill of Riza. South part best preserved. Exterior enclosure walls added in second phase, perhaps to pen animals.

Main entrance in middle of east side and second entrance at the northwest corner. External walls of large stones; leveled rock for floors (some strewn with pebbles). Twelve rooms. Main room B connects to room Γ by a pier-and-door partition. Benches in room Γ and a box made from stone slabs (containing a rhyton in the shape of an *agrimi*, "wild goat"). Room Δ a storeroom and room E a kitchen, with much household equipment, including grinders and querns, and a cupboard of stone slabs and a stone shelf in its east wall. Three rooms on the west wall (H, Θ, I) perhaps storerooms. Large room M at the northeast corner had six or seven pithoi and many other vases. Slab in center held roof post. No evidence of an upper floor. Destruction by violent earthquake.

House B, south of House A, partly excavated. Traces of other contemporary buildings and of earlier buildings.

VIII. BIBLIOGRAPHY

General

1940   Walter, O. "Archäologische Funde," *AA* 304–5.

1952   Platon, N. "Anaskaphai periochis Siteias," *PAE* 643–48.

1959   ———. "Anaskaphi Achladion Siteias," *PAE* 210–17.

1976   Pelon, O. *Tholoi, tumuli et cercles funéraires* (Athens 1976) 260–61.

1983   Preziosi, D. *Minoan Architectural Design* (Berlin) figs. 1.32 and 4.3.

1984   Michailidou, A. "Endeixeis yia tin organosi kai leitourgia trion neoanaktorikon spition. Ena methodologiko peirama," *Anthropologika* 5:37–50.

Geomorphology

1973   Gradstein, F. M. "The Neogene and Quaternary Deposits in the Sitia District of Eastern Crete," *Annales géologiques des pays helléniques* 24:527–72.

IX. FINDS

Herakleion Museum; Siteia Museum.

X. DATE OF PHOTOGRAPHY

June 22, 1983.

YANNIS SAKELLARAKIS AND EFI SAKELLARAKI

35°15′ N, 25°09′ E

I. IMPORTANCE

The important temple at Anemospilia, of tripartite plan and set in an enclosure, was found untouched since the Middle Minoan period, when it was destroyed by an earthquake. All objects were in position, as were the skeletons of people who had been performing rituals.

A skeleton was found in the middle of the corridor at the front of the temple. On the bench along the south wall of the central room were clay feet from a wooden statue, or *xoanon*. The east room would have been used for sacrifices that did not involve blood; it has a stepped altar along its south wall. The west room was intended for sacrifices with blood; it has a simple altar, on which was found the skeleton of a young man with a knife on his chest. There were two other skeletons (of a man and a woman) in the room.

II. USE

MM IIB–IIIA temple.

III. SITUATION

On a small piece of flat ground at the front of Mt. Juktas, immediately between the mountain massif and the arable uplands. The view from the site stretches from the Lasithi mountains on the east, past Knossos and the north coast, and on to Psiloriti to the west. The site itself occupies a natural meeting point of old paths and modern roads and lies immediately east of the Minoan road ascending to the mountain shrine on Mt. Juktas (not visible from Anemospilia), 3.2 km northwest of Archanes-Tourkoyeitonia and 440 m high.

IV. GEOMORPHOLOGY

The geology of the Archanes area is distinctive: a landscape of low rolling hills made of the Neogene marine marls that predominate south of Herakleion, but here dominated by Mt. Juktas, an elongate, fault-bounded ridge of dark bluish gray dense limestones and quartz phyllites belonging to the Gavrovo-Tripolitza (Tripolis) series. The 811-m-high ridge is a klippe, an erosional remnant of the thrust sheet that is surrounded by the younger Neogene marine strata. Although it dominates the local topography, it is only a small fragment of the earliest tectonic unit found above the basement rock (Platten-kalk series) of the island.

The site of Anemospilia itself represents a leveling of about 200 sq m of the limestone bedrock to provide a horizontal floor surface for the temple. In spite of this, the steeply dipping limestone strata impart a rough, uneven appearance to the ground. Because it is highly fractured, the limestone bedrock at Anemospilia is not suitable for quarrying and dressing as building stone. Thus the large ashlar blocks flanking the entrances to the three rooms were quarried from nearby outcrops of Neogene limestone, a much softer, lighter colored, and more homogeneous stone. In the entrance to the central room, the threshold slab of Neogene limestone is partially set into the Tripolitza limestone bedrock. Small irregular boulders of Tripolitza limestone were used to build the partition walls of the room, which were probably covered with a heavy coat of lime plaster.

V. EXCAVATION HISTORY

Y. Sakellarakis and E. Sakellaraki, 1979, for the Archaeological Society.

VI. BUILDINGS

MM IIB–IIIA Temple (221 sq m) in enclosure (approx. 1,085 sq m). Rectangular tripartite building arranged on a north–south axis, with anterooms to the north: of palatial standard, with doorways of dressed limestone with masons' marks, plaster, fresco (traces), and limestone horns of consecration.

Bench along north wall of anteroom and stone ritual equipment either side of door to central room. Central room has uncut rock to the west and a bench along south (back) wall. In east room a stepped altar along south (back) wall. In west room a low altar. The west

Figure 2.1 Temple

Figure 2.2   Temple and surroundings

Figure 2.4   Temple from the north

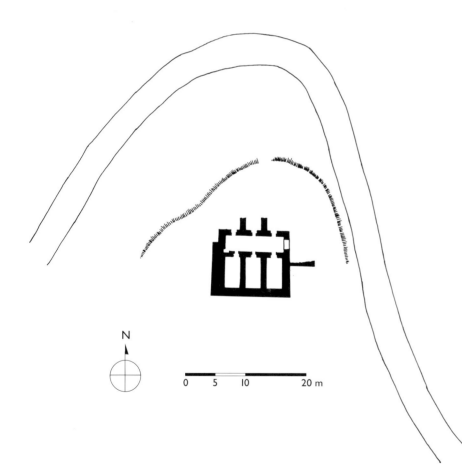

N

0   5   10   20 m

Figure 2.3   Archanes-Anemospilia
temple and enclosure wall

doorpost of west room is pillar shaped. The recess beside it in the anteroom opens onto a small stairway leading up toward the wide west wall.

In the east part an east–west wall. The enclosure wall survives in its north, northeast, and northwest parts and to the southwest.

VIII. BIBLIOGRAPHY

1979   Sakellarakis, Y., and E. Sakellaraki. "Anaskaphi Archanon," *PAE* 347–92.

1981   ———. "Drama of Death in a Minoan Temple," *National Geographic Magazine* 159 (February): 205–23.

IX. FINDS

Herakleion Museum.

X. DATE OF PHOTOGRAPHY

June 8, 1982.

YANNIS SAKELLARAKIS AND EFI SAKELLARAKI

35°15′ N, 25°10′ E

I. IMPORTANCE

At Phourni, outside the village of Epano Archanes, is a Minoan cemetery that was so large, spread out, and long used and has such a range of tombs that it is the most important prehistoric cemetery of the Aegean. To date twenty-four funerary buildings have been identified as the principal buildings at Phourni. Of many different types, they form virtually a dictionary of early Cretan burial habits.

There is also one secular building (Building 4). The evidence for the continuous growth of the burial area is important. Rooms were added successively to buildings, and some buildings had an exceptionally long use, such as Tholos Tomb B (Building 2), with its many successive additions and alterations. It marks the northern boundary of the type of tholos tomb so popular in Prepalatial times in the Mesara plain of south central Crete.

The cemetery has yielded a great variety and wealth of grave goods: jewelry, signet rings, seals, weapons, pottery, and, among imports, Early Cycladic marble figurines and goods from Egypt. The cemetery began in Early Minoan II and spread gradually from south (near the modern village and the site of Archanes-Tourkoyeitonia) to north. Middle Minoan IA was the principal time of use of the south and central parts.

The north part has a grave circle (Building 11) that would seem more at home on the Greek mainland. It contains seven shaft graves with stone markers (stelai). Nearby is Tholos Tomb A (Building 1), which had a Late Minoan IIIA intact royal burial, complete with bronze vessels, jewelry, and a footstool with ivory inlays, probably to

be dated to the time the palace at Knossos was destroyed or a little earlier. Other rich burials with hoards of bronze vessels have been found at Knossos and Phaistos. Tholos Tomb A is also remarkable for a horse sacrifice (the body of the animal dismembered) to the right of the door to the tomb's side chamber and a bull sacrifice, the bull's head having been found in the blocking wall of the side chamber.

The many burials at Phourni point to the importance and long life of the settlement at Archanes-Tourkoyeitonia, where extensive earlier settlement levels have yet to be uncovered. It is clear too that Archanes always had an important link with Knossos (best seen perhaps in Tholos Tomb A). Although many connections still must be elucidated, we may imagine that Archanes and Knossos complemented each other (with first one and then the other more important) in a changing relationship similar to that between Ayia Triada and Phaistos.

II. USE

EM II–SM cemetery; C, R, V, and later sherds and chance finds.

III. SITUATION

On the east side, the one most accessible from Epano Archanes village, of the south part of Phourni hill, which rises gently from the plain. The west side is sheer, rising steeply from the deep gorge of

Figure 3.1   Archanes-Phourni cemetery

Figure 3.2   Phourni hill and cemetery

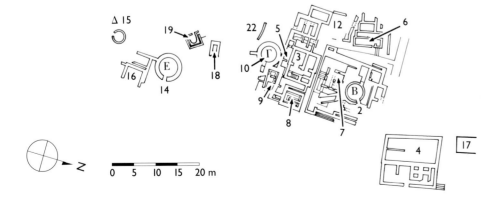

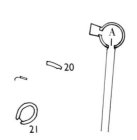

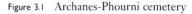

the river that begins at Archanes and flows into the sea at Karteros, north of Knossos. About 1.2 km from Archanes-Tourkoyeitonia, which lies under the modern village, east of Archanes-Anemospilia, and northeast of Mt. Juktas.

The main approach to the cemetery was from the south. It is likely that the present path up the hill contains remains of Minoan paving. There was also an approach from the east.

Area: about 6,600 sq m. Many of the buildings open to the east and are aligned north–south. On the west (upslope) side the buildings stop where the rock breaks the surface of the ground.

IV. GEOMORPHOLOGY

Phourni is a south-sloping ridge of Neogene bedrock where there is a massive clayey marlstone dipping to the southeast. The wall blocks are of this Neogene rock type and came from quarries upslope to the west (there are also traces of quarrying west of Tholos Tomb Γ [Building 10]). Most buildings are founded on bedrock, and some tholos tomb floors are cut into the bedrock. The dromoi appear not to be quarried into bedrock.

Upslope to the west the structures are built on and around large slabs of bedrock naturally detached and weathered in situ. Terra rossa soil sediment fills the crevices between these slabs. Faults are common in the area; modern access to the site is along a small fault zone that also serves as a drainage channel. A fault line is exposed in the floor of some buildings in the south central part of the site.

A local source of fresh water exists in the small, deep valley eroded into Neogene bedrock that curves around the west side of the Phourni ridge.

V. EXCAVATION HISTORY

Y. Sakellarakis and E. Sakellaraki, 1964–, for the Archaeological Society.

VI. BUILDINGS

EM II Tholos Tomb E (Building 14) (south part of cemetery), lower burial layer.

EM III Tholos Tomb Γ (Building 10) (south part); central part of cemetery and rocky area where bones and offerings were thrown southwest of Tholos Tomb Γ and west of Buildings 18 and 19.

MM IA Tholos Tombs B (Building 2) and E (Building 14) in use and nine other buildings (5–9, 12, 16, 18, 19) used as ossuaries or for primary burials. Building 5: nine rooms, in one of which lintel of south door

Figure 3.3 Cemetery, southern part

is preserved. Destroyed in northeast part by founding of Building 3. Tholos Tomb E (Building 14): upper burial layer. Building 6: six rooms. Building 7: five rooms. Building 8: two rooms. Building 9: three rooms. Building 12: collapsed. Building 16: three rooms. Building 18 (south of Tholos Tomb Γ [Building 10]): ten rooms. Building 19: apsidal.

MM IB Building 5 continued in use, with room 4 added to west side of its middle section and other additions to room 7. Building 17 continued in use.

MM IIIB–LM I Building 20 (north part of cemetery). An oval building, 4.4 m long, in a stone pile of 35 sq m enclosed by circular wall.

LM I Central part in use. Continued use of Tholos Tomb B (Building 2). Buildings 3, 4, 17 built. Tholos Tomb B: south half of complex used; stairs to upper floor over pillar room.

Building 4 (the secular building) divides into two halves: western half is terrace; eastern half has two floors, with entrance from east, small rooms to north and possible stairs to upper floor, and two large rooms (wine press and storeroom) to south.

LM II Building 3 continued in use.

LM IIIA Mainly north and extreme south parts in use. Tholos Tombs A (Building 1) (LM IIIA2) and Δ (Building 15), burial enclosure (Building 11) and drop-shaped Building 21 built. Tholos Tomb B (Building 2) and Building 3 continued in use. Tholos Tomb A: long

Figure 3.4   Cemetery, central part

Figure 3.5   Cemetery, northern part

dromos; side chamber cut in rock. Tholos Tomb E: small tomb in extreme southwest part of cemetery. Tholos Tomb B: original entrance blocked; floor raised and new entrance opened to east; west chamber used for burials. Building 11: burial enclosure at north end of cemetery, its west section preserved, containing seven burial cists; gravestones. LM IIIA1 chamber tomb on eastern edge of Phourni hill.

LM IIIB   Main use of Building 21, covered horseshoe-shaped underground building, with stairs in from east.

SM   Burials in fallen debris inside Tholos Tomb Δ (Building 15).

C, R, V,   Chance finds.
and later

Figure 3.6   Quarrying on Phourni hill,   Figure 3.7   Tholos Tomb A
to the west of cemetery

VIII. BIBLIOGRAPHY

General

1965   Sakellarakis, Y. "Archaiotites kai mnimeia kentrikis kai anatolikis Kritis," *ArchDelt* 20, pt. 2:557.

————. "Archanes 1965: Report on the Excavations," *Kadmos* 4:177–80.

————. "Ysterominoiko kenotaphio stis Archanes," *ArchDelt*
20, pt. 1:110–18.

1966   ————. "Anaskaphi Archanon," *PAE* 174–84.

————. "Archaiotites kai mnimeia kentrikis kai anatolikis
Kritis," *ArchDelt* 21, pt. 2:411–13.

————. "First Untouched Royal Burial Found in Crete,"
ILN March 26:32–33.

1967   ————. "Anaskaphi Archanon," *PAE* 151–61.

————. "Minoan Cemeteries at Archanes," *Archaeology* 20:
276–81.

1968   ————. "Elephantosta ek ton Archanon," in *1 Mycenological*
245–61.

————. "Paratiriseis epi tis simeiotheisis eis Archanas YM III
thysias tavrou," in *2 Cretological* 2:238–46.

1970   ————. "Das Kuppelgrab von Archanes und das kretisch-
mykenische Tieropferritual," *PZ* 45:135–218.

1971   ————. "Anaskaphi Archanon," *PAE* 276–83.

1972   ————. "Anaskaphi Archanon," *PAE* 310–53, 360–62.
Sakellarakis, Y., and E. Sakellaraki. "Apothetis kerameikis tis

teleftaias phaseos ton proanaktorikon chronon eis Archanas,"
ArchEph Chronika 1–11.

1973   Sakellarakis, Y. "Anaskaphi Archanon," *PAE* 167–87.

1974   ————. "Anaskaphi Archanon," *PAE* 207–12.

1975   ————. "Anaskaphi Archanon," *PAE* 255–321.

1976   Pelon, O. *Tholoi, tumuli et cercles funéraires* (Athens) 14–16,
262–63.

Sakellarakis, Y. "Die Kykladen und Kreta," in *Kunst und Kultur der Kykladeninseln im 3. Jahrtausend v. Chr.*, ed. J. Thimme
(Karlsruhe) 149–55.

Sakellarakis, Y., and E. Sakellaraki. "Anaskaphi Archanon,"
PAE 342–99.

1977   Sakellarakis, Y. "Ta kykladika sticheia ton Archanon," *AAA*
10:93–115.

————. "The Cyclades and Crete," in *Art and Culture of the
Cyclades*, ed. J. Thimme (Chicago) 150–53.

Sakellarakis, Y., and E. Sakellaraki. "Anaskaphi Archanon,"
PAE 459–82.

1979   ————. "Anaskaphi Archanon," *PAE* 392.

1980   Hiller, S. "Das Vorpalastzeit aus datierten geschlossenen
Funden," *JRGZM* 27:1–12.

Kanta, A. *The Late Minoan III Period in Crete: A Survey of Sites,
Pottery, and Their Distribution*, SIMA 58 (Gothenburg) 50–53.

Sakellarakis, Y., and E. Sakellaraki. "Anaskaphi Archanon,"
PAE 388–401.

1981   ————. "Anaskaphi Archanon," *PAE* 427–48.

1982   ————. "Anaskaphi Archanon," *PAE* 468–502.

1986   Sakellarakis, Y. "Protogeometriki–geometriki kerameiki apo
tis Archanes," *KrChron* 26:7–50.

Seals

1966   Sakellarakis, Y. "Die neuen Hieroglyphensiegel von Phourni
(Archanes). I," *Kadmos* 5:109–14.

1969   *CMS* 2.1:442–68 nos. 379–95 (Y. Sakellarakis).

1981   Sakellarakis, Y. "Chronologimena synola proanaktorikon minoikon sphragidon apo tis Archanes," in *4 Cretological* 1, pt. 2:
510–31.

IX. FINDS

Herakleion Museum.

X. DATE OF PHOTOGRAPHY

June 12, 1982.

4 ARCHANES-TOURKOYEITONIA

YANNIS SAKELLARAKIS AND EFI SAKELLARAKI

35°14′ N, 25°10′ E

I. IMPORTANCE

The rich modern village of Epano Archanes, in a fertile, well-watered valley beneath Mt. Juktas, covers an important and rich Minoan settlement. At Tourkoyeitonia, "Turkish neighborhood," in the middle of the village a New Palace period palatial building is being excavated that is clearly of the same quality and scale as buildings at Knossos, Mallia, Phaistos, or Zakro, and is reasonably called palatial, though of a different plan. It is likely that remains found in earlier excavations elsewhere in the village are part of this building, for they are of the same high quality and have the same orientation as the palatial building. The most interesting of these is the Late Minoan IA circular spring chamber excavated by Evans in 1922, which is a close contemporary parallel to the cistern in the palace at Zakro.

The palatial building is very well built, with a variety of materials (marbles, schist, gypsum, and ashlar) that may best be compared to those used at Phaistos. Fragments survive to show there were frescoes and relief frescoes. Among the finds are many stone vases, including porphyry lamps; Late Minoan IB Marine Style pottery; and five chryselephantine figurines, one of which has a shaved head (compare the newly found figure from Palaikastro).

The sacred character of the building stands out. Two shrines have been found, and there are concave, stepped, and trapezoidal altars, tripod hearths, horns of consecration, and tables of offering. The building itself is immediately east of, and lies on the route to, the mountain shrine on Mt. Juktas and to Archanes-Anemospilia.

The links of Archanes with Knossos, likely to have been long-standing, are discussed under Archanes-Phourni. It is also likely that Tourkoyeitonia will prove to have a history (of which the early parts are yet to be discovered) to match that of Phourni.

II. USE

MM IIB–LM I, LM IIIA–IIIB settlement, with MM IIIB–LM I palatial building; LM IIIC pottery; G levels; C, H, Byz, Arab, and later finds.

III. SITUATION

In the middle of the village of Epano Archanes, at the foot of a hill that rises 300 m east of a small river that reaches the sea at Karteros, near Amnisos (east of Herakleion). Immediately opposite Mt. Juktas to the west and, in particular, its peak sanctuary (at Psili Korphi), 1.2 km from Archanes-Phourni (to the northwest), 3.2 km from Archanes-Anemospilia (further around to the west), 5 km north of Vathypetro, and 10 km south of Knossos. In one of the richest regions of Crete, planted mainly with vines. Many springs and wells. Evidence for waterworks in MM III–LM I.

IV. GEOMORPHOLOGY

Tourkoyeitonia shows an interesting mixture of building stones. Blocks in the western half of the main excavated area are predominantly from Neogene bedrock, whereas those in the eastern half, about 30 m away, are frequently made of the dense bluish gray limestone (*sideropetra*) from Mt. Juktas. Some cobble-sized gray platy fragments of phyllite, also from Mt. Juktas, are visible in the excavation area.

Because of the modern buildings, it is difficult to determine the original relationship of the Minoan building to the landscape. This building was constructed on a low-angled slope leading down to the valley draining Mt. Juktas. About a meter of pebbly slopewash had accumulated over the tops of the wall stumps before excavations began.

V. EXCAVATION HISTORY

Y. Sakellarakis and E. Sakellaraki, 1964–, for the Archaeological Society.

VI. BUILDINGS

MM IIB–IIIA   Levels preserved in various places, e.g., by west doorpost of room of concave altars and in lower levels in areas 17 and 18.

Tourkoyeitonia

0 5 10   50 m

N

Figure 4.1 Tourkoyeitonia excavation
Figure 4.2 Archanes-Tourkoyeitonia
           and other remains in Epano
           Archanes village

MM IIIB–LM I Large palatial building in excellent preservation, excavated mostly at Tourkoyeitonia and partly at Ayios Nikolaos (to the northeast), where a theatral area was discovered. Other parts of the building have been excavated to the north (the circular spring chamber, internal d about 5 m, with a built conduit) and south (in the building plot of G. Kalpadaki) of the main excavation but do not show in the photographs because they have been covered over. Neither, naturally, do important walls in the center of the site that are preserved in the foundations of modern village houses. It is most likely that all the building remains belong to the same building; they are built in the same way and are all on the same alignment as the palatial building. The spring chamber is about 40 m northwest of the palatial building.

Palatial building: ashlar masonry (with masons' marks), plentiful use of gypsum, floors with patterned bands of red plaster, and many traces of frescoes. Some parts of the building clearly had three storeys. The only open space is on the south, with two entrances: one has two columns and four concave altars in situ and leads to various corridors; the other is wide and leads to a grand room with a marble floor and benches along three walls. Another interior entrance in the north part of the excavated area leads to an open yard flanked by columns on two sides and broad stairs to the upper floor (which had two LM IA shrines, above rooms 10 and 17).

LM IB Levels in areas 17 and 18 and continuing use of LM IA shrine above room 17. Destruction by fire.

LM IIIA–IIIB Levels and building remains in southwest part of excavated area.

LM IIIC Some pottery.

G Levels in south part of excavated area.

C, H, Byz, Arab, and later Various finds.

VIII. BIBLIOGRAPHY

1909   Xanthoudides, S. "Ek Kritis," *ArchEph* 180–96.

1921   Evans, A. J. *The Palace of Minos at Knossos* 1:623–36.

1928   ———. *The Palace of Minos at Knossos* 2:64–67.

1956   Marinatos, S. "Ergasiai en Vathypetro, Archanais kai Idaio Antro," *PAE* 223–24.

1957   Platon, N. "Dokimastikai anaskaphai eis ikopedon Ioannou Mavroyannaki synikias Troullou Archanon," *PAE* 133–35.

Figure 4.3   Tourkoyeitonia excavation
in Epano Archanes village
(in square)

Figure 4.4   Epano Archanes

1965   Sakellarakis, Y. "Archaitotites kai mnimeia kentrikis kai anatolikis Kritis 1964," *ArchDelt* 20, pt. 2:558–61.

1967   ———. "Mason's Marks from Arkhanes," in *Europa. Studien zur Geschichte und Epigraphik der frühen Ägäis. Festschrift für Ernst Grumach*, ed. W. C. Brice (Berlin) 277–80.

1970   Lebessi, A. "Anaskaphikai erevnai eis anatolikin Kritin," *PAE* 256–70.

1976   ———. "O ikiskos ton Archanon," *ArchEph* 12–43.

        Sakellarakis, Y., and E. Sakellaraki. "Anaskaphi Archanon," *PAE* 397–98.

1977   Hiller, S. *Das minoische Kreta nach den Ausgrabungen des letzten Jahrzehnts* (Vienna) 157–60.

        Sakellarakis, Y., and E. Sakellaraki. "Anaskaphi Archanon," *PAE* 482.

1978   ———. "Anaskaphi Archanon," *PAE* 315–19.

1979   ———. "Anaskaphi Archanon," *PAE* 331–47.

1980   Kanta, A. *The Late Minoan III Period in Crete: A Survey of Sites, Pottery, and Their Distribution*, SIMA 58 (Gothenburg) 30–31, 34.

        Sakellarakis, Y., and E. Sakellaraki. "Anaskaphi Archanon," *PAE* 216–23.

1981   ———. "Anaskaphi Archanon," *PAE* 410–27.

1982   ———. "Anaskaphi Archanon," *PAE* 502–28.

1983   ———. "Anaskaphi Archanon," *PAE* 367–414.

1986   Sakellarakis, Y. "Protogeometriki-geometriki kerameiki apo tis Archanes," *KrChron* 26:7–50.

1987   ———. "Archaiologiki erevna yia mian archaiokapilia to 1949 stin Kriti," in *Philia epi eis Yeoryion Mylonan* (Athens) 2:37–70.

1988–89 Sakellaraki, E. "I kerameiki thalassiou rythmou apo tis Archanes kai i pithani uparxi topikou ergastiriou," *KrChron* 28–29:28–52.

1990   ———. "Archanès à l'époque mycénienne," *BCH* 114:67–102.

IX. FINDS

Herakleion Museum.

X. DATE OF PHOTOGRAPHY

June 9, 1982.

YANNIS TZEDAKIS

35°18′ N, 24°28′ E

I. IMPORTANCE

The continuing excavation of the large Late Minoan IIIA and IIIB cemetery at Armeni in the foothills south-southwest of Rethymno has added greatly to knowledge of western Crete and of the Postpalatial period. To date, 211 chamber tombs (their chambers cut in fairly hard rock and approached by sunken passages, or dromoi) and one tholos tomb have been explored over an area of 4 ha.

Some of the tombs have steps, or an internal column or pillar and benches. In places the ground had been leveled before work on digging the tombs began, and a Minoan road with branch roads leads through the cemetery. The tombs divide into groups of different sizes. Some small tombs found among the groups of large tombs reflect changes to the original plan of the cemetery.

The finds include a varied range of pottery; bronze vessels, tools, and jewelry; beads and jewelry in semiprecious stones; sealstones; and stone vases. Among the chief finds are the clay larnakes, or coffins, painted with double axes, sacred horns of consecration, and scenes of ritual hunting and of bulls. Executed in a lively style, the painting gives a new view of the artistic prowess of Postpalatial Crete.

Over five hundred skeletons form a valuable document for understanding the state of health and the physical appearance of Postpalatial-period Minoans. The dental evidence suggests that they consumed a high-carbohydrate diet but ate little meat.

There is no trace either near the cemetery or in the surrounding country of any earlier or later occupation. Traces of the workshops and kilns for making the larnakes have been found near the cemetery.

II. USE

LM IIIA–IIIB cemetery.

III. SITUATION

Armeni is about 8 km almost due south of Rethymno in low hills on one of the principal routes to the south coast.

IV. GEOMORPHOLOGY

The bedrock at Armeni is a fluvioterrestrial conglomerate of Miocene age, containing a large percentage of phyllite rock fragments weathered from the outcrops of the Phyllite-Quartzite series surrounding the site. It is an unusual rock type in which to cut tombs.

V. EXCAVATION HISTORY

Y. Tzedakis, 1969–, for the Archaeological Service.

VI. BUILDINGS

Groups of large or small tombs. Small tombs also inserted among groups of large tombs.

Plan of tombs: rock-cut chamber; ramps or steps starting at ground level lead to a narrow passage (or doorway) at the entrance to the chamber. The passage is usually blocked by a slab, sometimes by a wall. The chamber is rectangular or semicircular. Two rectangular chambers have a pillar and benches in the middle or at the back. Each of these two tombs also had a grave marker (not found in position, however).

VIII. BIBLIOGRAPHY

General

1970   Tzedakis, Y. "Archaiotites kai mnimeia dytikis Kritis," *ArchDelt* 25, pt. 2:476–77.

1971   ———. "Archaiotites kai mnimeia dytikis Kritis," *ArchDelt* 26, pt. 2:513–16.

        ———. "Larnakes ysterominoikou nekrotapheiou Armenon," *AAA* 4:216–22.

1972   ———. "Archaiotites kai mnimeia dytikis Kritis," *ArchDelt* 27, pt. 2:639–44.

Figure 5.1   Armeni cemetery

Figure 5.2   A chamber tomb

Figure 5.3   Armeni Tomb 10

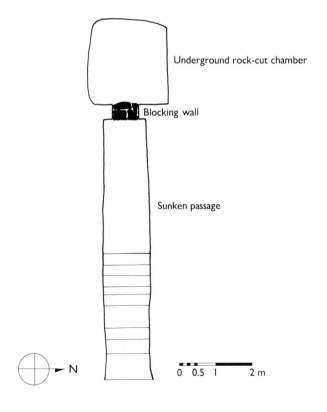

Underground rock-cut chamber

Blocking wall

Sunken passage

N

0 0.5 1   2 m

1973-74   ———. "Archaiotites kai mnimeia dytikis Kritis," *Arch-Delt* 29, pt. 2:917-21.

1976   ———. "Archaiotites kai mnimeia dytikis Kritis," *Arch-Delt* 31, pt. 2:368-72.

1977   Hiller, S. *Das minoische Kreta nach den Ausgrabungen des letzten Jahrzehnts* (Vienna) 201-3.

1978   Tzedakis, Y. "Ephoreia proistorikon kai klasikon archaiotiton Chanion," *ArchDelt* 33, pt. 2:378-80.

1980   Kanta, A. *The Late Minoan III Period in Crete: A Survey of Sites, Pottery, and Their Distribution, SIMA* 58 (Gothenburg) 213-14.

Tzedakis, Y. "KE' ephoreia proistorikon kai klasikon archaiotiton," *ArchDelt* 35, pt. 2:512-17.

1988   McGeorge, P. J. P. "Health and Diet in Minoan Times," in *New Aspects of Archaeological Science in Greece*. Proceedings of a meeting held at the British School at Athens, January 1987. British School at Athens, Occasional Papers of the Fitch Laboratory 3, ed. R. E. Jones and H. W. Catling (Athens) 47-54.

1990   Tzedakis, Y. "I archaiologiki erevna sti dytiki Kriti ta telefraia eikosi chronia," in *6 Cretological* 1, pt. 2: 439-450.

Seals

1975   *CMS* 5.1:197-224 nos. 241-83 (I. Pini).

1981   Tamvaki, A. "Preliminary Notes on the Seals from Armenoi," in *Studien zur minoischen und helladischen Glyptik, CMS* Beiheft 1, ed. W.-D. Niemeier (Berlin) 207-23.

IX. FINDS

Chania Museum; Rethymno Museum.

X. DATE OF PHOTOGRAPHY

July 5, 1984.

METAXIA TSIPOPOULOU

35°11′ N, 26°09′ E

I. IMPORTANCE

On the headland at Ayia Photia in eastern Crete is a unique fortified rectangular building with a central court of the later Prepalatial period, discovered recently during a rescue excavation before the proposed erection of a hotel. This building, ascribed to Middle Minoan IA, with thirty-seven rooms and areas, will increase our understanding of the social organization of Prepalatial Crete. Features of special interest in the building are its stout outer wall; its primitive central court; its division into smaller units that communicate with the central court but not with each other; and its symmetrical arrangement, facing in on itself. These features are otherwise unknown in Minoan architecture of such an early stage. The apsidal buttresses are similar to those on the fortification walls of Lerna in the Argolid and Chalandriani on Syros except that they are solid, with no open space inside.

It is difficult at present to determine the use of the building, but it could have served as a multifamily dwelling for a small clan. It seems certain that it was connected with the agricultural exploitation of the neighboring large plain, which is the only plain between Siteia and Palaikastro.

Two circular structures belong to a later phase and are probably the most northerly and easterly tholos tombs in Crete. Two caves on the hill, their entrances facing the sea, contained Neolithic as well as Prepalatial and Old Palace period remains.

A cemetery of at least 252 tombs, mainly of Early Minoan I date but continuing into Early Minoan II, lies 150 m to the east, at Glyphada. Most tombs are small rock-cut chamber tombs with a small antechamber. The many finds include imported Cycladic vases and other artifacts of Cycladic type; and it has been suggested that there was a Cycladic colony here. One tomb contained Late Minoan III vases, and a 7th-century vase was found near another tomb.

An intensive survey over an area of 1,000 ha, including the whole of the plain and two hills, Kouphota with the rectangular building and Ayia Photia above the modern village, has revealed traces of occupation from Prepalatial and Old Palace through New Palace and Postpalatial to Archaic and Hellenistic and Roman times.

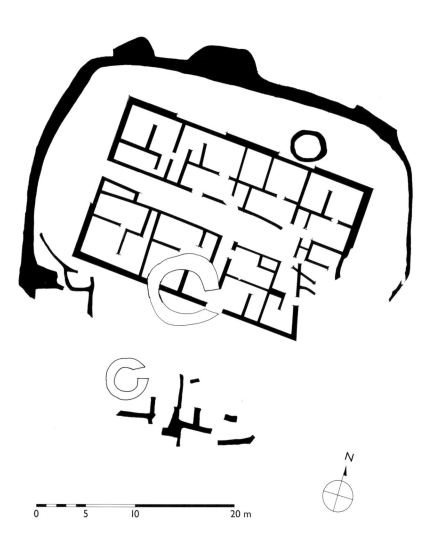

0   5   10   20 m

N

Figure 6.1 Ayia Photia fortified
building
Figure 6.2 Fortified building

Figure 6.3   Fortified building and two circular structures

Figure 6.4   Cemetery E to east of fortified building

II. USE

N traces in Kouphota cave; EM I–II cemetery at Glyphada; MM IA large building on Kouphota hill; MM IIA circular structures over it; MM IIA traces in caves; MM III–LM I, LM III, A, H and R traces of occupation in locality.

III. SITUATION

On the low (25-m) hill of Kouphota beside the sea about 5 km east of Siteia and north-northeast of the village of Ayia Photia.

IV. GEOMORPHOLOGY

The bedrock of the headland consists of the Late Miocene Toplou formation, as defined and described by Gradstein and Van Gelder (1971): a 20-m-thick section of massive silty marls containing marine mollusc shells and wood fragments. This section is overlain by a caprock deposit: a 3–4-m-thick sheet of limestone conglomerate exhibiting giant foreset beds. It was on the upper surface of the conglomerate unit that the Minoan structures were built. The ephemeral stream channels to the east and west of the headland could have supplied some water to the settlement during the winter months.

V. EXCAVATION HISTORY

M. Tsipopoulou, 1984–85, for the Archaeological Service; cemetery: C. Davaras, 1971, for the Archaeological Society. Surveys: N. Platon, 1959, for the Archaeological Society; M. Tsipopoulou, 1985, for the Archaeological Service.

VI. BUILDINGS

MM IA   Large building, 18 by 27.5 m, with an area of about 500 sq m and thirty-seven rooms or areas. The internal walls, of medium-sized rough stones, are .45–.50 m wide and the exterior (with setbacks) 0.75–1.1 m. Floors of beaten earth and, occasionally, pebbles. The entrance on the west leads to a long and narrow court (3.5 by 21 m) with traces of paving. In the eastern part of the building a second entrance was made and a small external court, also with traces of paving, in a limited reconstruction during this phase. The building, one storey high, was probably built of stone throughout. A circular structure used for storage on the west side is an early version of the kouloura, or round pit (compare especially Knossos and Phaistos).

The outer wall around the building was constructed during this phase. It is 1.3–1.5 m thick and preserved on three sides of the building (as foundations of undressed stones). There are three apsidal buttresses on the north side facing the sea and another at the southwest corner, presumably near the entrance (not preserved) from the plain.

Abandonment, after a short period of use.

MM IIA   Two stout circular structures (external d: 7.5 m and 5 m; wall thickness: 1.2–1.5 m), the larger one built partly over the foundations of the earlier rectangular building. Entrances on the east. Probably tombs, but no clear indications. Also of this phase: curvilinear walls, not identifiable with any building, that cut the earlier outer wall by the southwest corner.

VIII. BIBLIOGRAPHY

General

1959   Platon, N. "Ayia Phothia," *PAE* 266.

1971   Davaras, C. "Perisyllogi archaion anatolikis Kritis," *PAE* 301–3.

       ———. "Protominoikon nekrotapheion Ayias Photias Siteias," *AAA* 4:392–97.

1972   ———. "Archaiotites kai mnimeia anatolikis Kritis," *Arch-Delt* 27, pt. 2:648–50.

1976   ———. *Guide to Cretan Antiquities* (Park Ridge, N.J.) 128–29.

       Doumas, C. "Proistoriki Kykladites stin Kriti," *AAA* 9: 69–80.

1979   ———. "Proistoriki Kykladites stin Kriti II," *AAA* 12: 104–9.

1984   Warren, P. M. "Early Minoan–Early Cycladic Chronological Correlations," in *The Prehistoric Cyclades* 55–62.

1987   Sakellaraki, E. "New Evidence from the Early Bronze Age Cemetery at Manika, Chalkis," *BSA* 82:257–64.

1988   Tsipopoulou, M. "Ayia Photia Siteias: To neo evrima," in *Problems in Greek Prehistory* 31–47.

1989   ———. *Archaeological Survey at Ayia Photia, Siteia, SIMA PB* 76 (Partille).

1991   ———. "Recenti scoperte di epoca minoica nel golfo di Sitia," in *Consiglio Nazionale delle Richerche—Istituto per gli Studi Micenei ed Egeo-Anatolici, Seminari anno 1990,* ed. M. Rocchi and L. Vagnetti (Rome) 105–21.

n.d.   Davaras, C. *Mouseion Ayiou Nikolaou* (Athens) figs. 2–11.

Geomorphology

1971   Gradstein, F. M., and A. Van Gelder. "Prograding Clastic Fans and Transition from a Fluviatile to a Marine Environment in Neogene Deposits of Eastern Crete," *Geologie en Mijnbouw* 50:383–92.

IX. FINDS

Siteia Museum; Ayios Nikolaos Museum.

X. DATE OF PHOTOGRAPHY

November 3, 1987.

VINCENZO LA ROSA

35°03′ N, 24°48′ E

I. IMPORTANCE

Ayia Triada has not yet been completely studied because of vicissitudes in the excavation and its publication. In recent years a program of tests inside the excavation area has allowed a more precise chronology for its monumental structures and a preliminary outline of the changes its urban center underwent. Both old and new excavations, however, have revealed the now well known individual character of Ayia Triada in the New Palace period and in Postpalatial times. Its finds are of very high quality (and in some cases unique), and the plans of the different buildings show a remarkable originality. Ayia Triada is also of great interest for its proximity to the far better known center at Phaistos and its relative proximity to the newly excavated settlement at Kommos. The data of the three sites, compared and related to the topographical setting of the Mesara plain, point to some fundamental conclusions about the political history of the whole island.

Perhaps settled at the end of the Neolithic period, Ayia Triada was a place of considerable prosperity in Early Minoan times. A rich debris level of Early Minoan I date has been identified to the south of the Piazzale dei Sacelli, "Court of the Shrines." Part of the Early Minoan II settlement has been excavated to the east of the cemetery area. The two tholos tombs, found in the first excavations of 1903–4, were placed equidistant between the two nuclei of the Early Minoan settlement and, like other tholos tombs, such as those at Lebena, Odigitria, and Platanos, were used for collective burial. The poorly preserved remains make it difficult to connect the cemetery to these two nuclei, from which Ayia Triada's subsequent urban growth spread.

The center of Ayia Triada was inhabited throughout Middle Minoan times, but evidence is insufficient at present to establish the importance of the settlement. The remains do not suggest monumental buildings like the New Palace period "Royal Villa," but they show that the settlement's extent—at least in its excavated part—was no less at this time than in succeeding periods. The gypsum quarry found in 1951 not far from the church of Ayia Triada, "Holy Trinity," was probably already in use in this period. We do not know where the dead were buried, apart from the few last burials inside the large Tholos Tomb A. Ayia Triada in Middle Minoan times seems to have had an organization completely different from that of Phaistos, a palatial center with an impressive archive.

At the end of the Middle Minoan period the Villa was built. Its plan is that of a half-palace, with buildings on two sides of a courtyard. It had at least two floors, with courts and paved streets on every side. Divided by Banti (1977) into four wings, the building certainly underwent changes in its life, as Late Minoan I sherds found beneath some of the pavements show. It is the most important New Palace period building at Ayia Triada and may not be explained simply as "the country seat" of the lords of Phaistos (Halbherr 1903) or "the seaside villa of the lords of the Mesara" (Pernier 1904). The recent theory of Watrous (1984) that the building resulted from the joining of two originally separate but adjacent country houses (as at Tylissos) does not agree with construction evidence from along its north wall (at rooms 62 and 65, excavated in 1980).

The Villa was destroyed by fire at the end of Late Minoan IB and, like Zakro, was not ransacked even though the foundations of Postpalatial buildings were dug into the ruins. In fact, nineteen copper ingots (total weight: 556 kg) were found in a narrow compartment in the NW quarter; in a similar room nearby were bronze figurines (men, women, and animals) and pieces of gold leaf. Three relief vases in serpentine, masterpieces of Minoan art, must have had a ritual use: the Boxer Vase (rhyton), the Harvester Vase (rhyton), and the Chieftain Cup, which Warren (1969) assigns to workshops of Knossos of Middle Minoan IIIB–Late Minoan IA.

One small room (14) with brick partitions had its walls decorated with frescoes with figured scenes (a cat pouncing on a partridge; a seated woman, richly dressed) and plant motifs. Fresco fragments with plant motifs, found below the paving of this room, are evidence of its continuing role as an important place that needed periodic redecoration.

A plaster skirting with polychrome bands in room 54 had three graffiti in Linear A. The sealings (about seven hundred) and Linear A tablets concentrated in this northwest part of the building (mainly on the upper floor) are evidence of the recording and storing of produce. Of about fifty pithoi, or storage jars, one from room 5 has the inscription *su-ki-ri-te-i-ja*, which is also found on a sealing in a fill level in the Old Palace of Phaistos. It recalls the Greek place-name Sybrita (a city southwest of Psiloriti).

The finds, taken as a whole, and the quality of the architecture and the evidence of crafts at Ayia Triada allow us to ascribe to the Villa functions similar to those of the palaces. The contents are markedly similar to those of the palace of Zakro, which also was not sacked. And all that seems to be lacking in the room plans—if we omit the Old Palace period kouloures, or round pits, of Knossos and Phaistos—is lustral basins.

The number of places dedicated as storerooms, in relation to the size of the complex, was considerable, even if they were not always arranged in a regular system. This fact, along with the sealings, Linear A tablets, and imports, suggests that the building was used mainly for recording, collecting, and depositing goods and produce.

In the New Palace period Ayia Triada was markedly different from Phaistos, as the finds suggest: they are much richer at Ayia Triada and fewer and poorer at Phaistos, which continued nonetheless to be a monumental palace. This is a change from Middle Minoan times, when finds were richer—and architecture grander—at Phaistos. The growth, moreover, and the organization of the two settlements in the New Palace period provide revealing contrasts. Whereas at Phaistos only sporadic evidence of inhabitation survives in the different sectors, at Ayia Triada the settlement forms a dense, continuous web, divided only by a long wall with setbacks that runs east–west along the slope of the hill. The wall continued to be an important point of reference in Postpalatial times.

The so-called Bastion links the Villa and the town. It is a narrow elongated building on two levels that had practically no contents when excavated. Recently it has been proposed that it had a commercial use as a warehouse "for the storage of local produce and products" (Watrous 1984) and that it formed part of a group of structures with the Lower Court and the pillared stoa 10. Trials in 1986 showed that the Bastion is on the same alignment as the Villa and belongs to the second New Palace phase (Late Minoan IA–IB).

The area south of the great wall with setbacks has building remains with two alignments. The more recent remains, with a Late Minoan IB destruction level contemporary with that of the Villa, are those of the Casa del Lebete, "House of the Cauldron," with rich contents and some sixty Linear A tablets; the Casa del Pistrinum, "House of the Oven"; the Casa delle Sfere Fittili, "House of the Clay Balls"; the Bastion; and the Casa dei Fichi, "House of the Figs," found in 1978 west of the Shrine. The earlier phase, with an alignment that may be the same as that of the buildings of the end of the Middle Minoan period beneath the Shrine, is represented by poor

remains west and northwest of the Bastion, the Cyclopean Building (excavated in 1979, facing on the west the three southernmost shops of the large Stoa) and by the pillar room south of the Bastion (excavated in 1986) whose destruction level has plenty of pottery assignable to Late Minoan IA.

The Bastion's monumental appearance, together with its links to buildings outside the Villa through stoa 10 and the rich furnishings and Linear A archive in the Casa del Lebete, let us imagine that the whole group of buildings south of the great wall with setbacks, at least in the later phases of the New Palace period, was closely tied to the Villa. On one tablet from the House of the Cauldron the reading *pa-i-to* has been proposed, referring to Phaistos.

Remains of the Late Minoan I town are much scarcer north of the great wall with setbacks, and many buildings shown in Stefani's final plan (1914) in fact belong to the Late Minoan IIIA settlement and lie directly on the rock, as trials in 1981–85 have shown. No burials of the New Palace period are known at Ayia Triada. On the downward slope east of the Villa is a potter's kiln of Late Minoan I date.

Late Minoan II, the phase following the destruction of the Villa and settlement, is at present known only from chance finds of pottery.

From Late Minoan IIIA1 onward there are several buildings, some of them sufficiently imposing to be without doubt public buildings.

The period of greatest magnificence is Late Minoan IIIA2 (a little after the destruction of the palace of Knossos, according to Popham's chronology). The settlement underwent a monumental rebuilding. It has architectural designs unique in Crete, in some cases inspired by models in mainland Greece. Buildings of this phase are the so-called Megaron built over the Villa, the stoa east of it, the Shrine with a frescoed floor (with octopus and dolphin), the large Stoa with eight shops (or were they really storerooms?) and the court in front of it, the odd building with nine rooms (excavated in 1983–84), Building P (somewhat like a megaron), and the Bastion originally built in the New Palace period.

The famous Ayia Triada sarcophagus, a limestone larnax painted with funerary rituals, is probably of Late Minoan IIIA1 date rather than IIIA2. It shows gifts being presented, the sacrifice of a bull, and libations and purifications. It was found in a tomb, robbed in antiquity, immediately south of Tholos Tomb B, which was reused at this period. Also of the 14th century B.C. are some buildings in the southeast sector of the cemetery, including the so-called Tomb 5: in one of its four rooms was a scarab with the cartouche of Queen Tiy, wife of Amenophis III of Egypt.

Evidence of Late Minoan IIIB occupation and destruction has been recovered recently from spots where there had been no previous excavation. No monumental building has yet been proved at Phaistos in Late Minoan III, a period when there were apparently

A   Great wall with setbacks
B   Casa del Lebete

0   5   10   20   30 m

N

Stoa

A

Agora

B

Bastion

Lower Court

10

Villa

Megaron

14

Piazzale dei Sacelli

Court

Shrine

Ayios Yeoryios Galatas

Figure 7.1   Ayia Triada, excavation
plan through 1914

Figure 7.2   Ayia Triada, with Tholos
Tombs A (larger) and B
at northeast corner of
photograph

Figure 7.3 "Royal Villa" with Megaron and Piazzale dei Sacelli

Figure 7.4 Town and stoa

only simple houses there. In Late Minoan IIIC Ayia Triada had an out-of-doors cult in the Piazzale dei Sacelli. Several hundred statuettes have been found.

The differences between Ayia Triada and Phaistos through Late Minoan I–III times suggest that the two sites had closely complementary functions, which was inevitable because they were neighbors. Phaistos, without doubt the center of power in the Old Palace period and perhaps even at the beginning of the New Palace period, steadily incorporated Ayia Triada during the New Palace period—at least in the spheres of economics and administration.

This hypothesis of the new, enhanced, role of Ayia Triada should be tested against research on the important harbor of Kommos and on the organization of the territories around the three Mesara centers. As far as Ayia Triada is concerned, theories or commonly repeated statements such as that one site was nearer the sea and so more active in trade need to take account of the geomorphology, including such factors as changes in the coastline and the possibility of navigating the river Yeropotamos.

A situation in some ways uncertain in Late Minoan I—though by the end of that period the economic and political fortunes of Ayia Triada were clearly rising and those of Phaistos dipping—is clear enough in Late Minoan III. Following the destruction of Knossos,

economic and political power in the Mesara seems to have centered at Ayia Triada through Late Minoan IIIB. (The monumental building phase of Late Minoan IIIA2 may indirectly confirm Popham's Late Minoan IIIA1/2 dating of the destruction of Knossos.) The process of integration begun in Late Minoan I could mean that the place name *pa-i-to* in the Knossos Linear B tablets refers to a combined territorial and political unit of Phaistos/Ayia Triada. (Note: there is an alternative suggestion that the name for Ayia Triada was *da-wo*, but the evidence is indecisive.) Ayia Triada's holding the reins of power through Late Minoan IIIB raises the question of its relations with the growing power of Chania, whose role in crafts, commerce, and politics appears important.

After Late Minoan IIIB Phaistos regained its old leading role. At Ayia Triada the cult in the Piazzale dei Sacelli, which still flourished in Protogeometric times, is the sole solid evidence of use at the beginning of the historical period. In Hellenistic times there was a small village over the Minoan ruins, completely removed in the early excavations. A small shrine dedicated to Zeus Velchanos, as the inscriptions on its tiles show, was built over stoa 10 and then rebuilt in the 2nd century B.C., as the inscription of Arkesilas shows. Probably in the same period, an altar was built at the northwest corner of the Piazzale dei Sacelli. The village was destroyed, as was the large

Hellenistic settlement of Phaistos, probably by Gortyn at the middle of the 2nd century B.C. Later, workshops were put on the site. One of them, which had a wine press, was built over the shrine of Zeus Velchanos, probably in the time of Augustus.

Venetian remains in the area of the excavation are the little church of Ayios Yeoryios Galatas and a group of tombs nearby. The Turkish village that followed was abandoned in the troubles of 1897.

II. USE

(FN?–) EM I–LM IIIB settlement; EM II–MM IB (with some use in MM II) and LM IIIA2 cemetery; LM IIIC, PG, and H shrines; R farms; V church and tombs.

III. SITUATION

On the west slope of a low *kouskouras*, "marl," hill sloping down to the plain of the Yeropotamos river, 2.2 km from Phaistos and 800 m from Patrikies (for which see Phaistos), at 30–40 m above sea level. Excavated area in settlement about 135 by 135 m.

IV. GEOMORPHOLOGY

At the western tip of a ridge of Neogene marine limestones, Ayia Triada lies on the same fault scarp as Phaistos. Such locations, which provide access to a variety of rock types within a short distance, are often associated with springs or seeps and offer commanding vistas; they may be the focus of intense earth motions as well.

Both the storerooms of the Villa and the storerooms of the adjacent town are cut into the limestone bedrock of the ridge, which also supplied the raw material for the finished ashlar blocks used in the Villa's walls.

An extensive use of gypsum in the architecture was possible thanks to outcrops of selenitic gypsum less than 1 km from the site that are associated with upper Miocene marls, which form the primary bedrock type of the ridge.

It is unlikely that in Minoan times any sort of embayment of the Libyan Sea occupied the alluvial plain of the Yeropotamos at the base of the Ayia Triada-Phaistos ridge. Ground levels measured at the foot of the ridge below Ayia Triada are some 15–20 m above present sea level, and although Crete has been (and still is) tectonically active, it is difficult to imagine an elevation of the ridge by that much in the past three thousand years. Moreover, the surface sediments between Ayia Triada and the present coastline—Pleistocene and Holocene alluvium—argue against a recent marine incursion west of the site. It would seem that Kommos served as the port site for both Ayia Triada and Phaistos.

Figure 7.5   Town and stoa

V. EXCAVATION HISTORY

F. Halbherr, R. Paribeni, and E. Stefani, 1902–14, for the Italian Archaeological Mission; D. Levi and C. Laviosa, 1970, 1973, 1976, and V. La Rosa, 1977–, for the Italian School.

VI. BUILDINGS

EM I–MM IA   Small nucleated settlements to north of the Villa and south of the Piazzale dei Sacelli; houses to east of cemetery. In cemetery, Tholos Tombs A (internal d about 9 m) and B (EM II[?]–MM IB[?]).

MM IB(?)–IIIA   Houses, some with plaster floors—beneath Villa, Northeast House, and Bastion; beneath and to south of Shrine (1978 excavation); beneath room 66 of Villa (1980 excavation) and the threshold and gypsum paving at north edge of excavation area (1985)—attest a settlement as large as in the New Palace period. Few last burials in Tholos Tomb A. Gypsum quarry near chapel of Ayia Triada probably already in use.

MM IIIB–LM IB   Villa with two main phases and at least two floors, and town around. Streets and ramps; courts to north and south of Villa.

MM IIIB–LM IA   Poor building remains west and northwest of Bastion; Cyclopean Building (excavated 1979); pillared room south of Bastion (excavated 1986).

LM IA–IB   Great wall with setbacks running east–west in north part of excavation area. Bastion to northeast of Lower Court: two floors and long narrow plan. Casa del Lebete; Casa del Pistrinum; Casa delle Sfere Fittili; Casa dei Fichi (west of Shrine). Few buildings north of great wall with setbacks: walls and pavements at west edge of excavation area beneath Northwest Building and West Building. Potter's kiln to east of modern guardhouse.

LM IB (end)   Destruction by fire.

LM II   Chance finds of pottery.

LM IIIA1   House inside the Cyclopean Building.
Painted sarcophagus in tomb (robbed in antiquity) immediately south of Tholos Tomb B.

LM IIIA2 (beginning)   Casa delle Tre Camere Decapitate below north part of Agora. Other buildings of similar plan to west of it.

LM IIIA2–IIIB   Carefully laid out monumental building phase in LM IIIA2, with open spaces and drains: Megaron (Mycenaean-style hall) over ruins of Villa; stoa to east of Megaron; Piazzale dei Sacelli repaved. Shrine to southeast of Court of Villa, with painted plaster floor. Large Stoa with eight shops (or storerooms?) and Agora (court) in front. Building with nine rooms at northwest of excavated area. Building P with long rectangular megaronlike plan. Reuse of Bastion.
Late use of Tholos Tomb B. Burial debris in building ("Tomb 5") in southeast part of cemetery.

LM IIIC–PG   Open-air cult with votive deposit in and around Piazzale dei Sacelli. Abandonment.

H   Houses; shrine of Zeus Velchanos by stoa; altar in northeast corner of Piazzale dei Sacelli.

R   Farms and workshops by Stoa, by Bastion, and to northeast of Tholos Tomb A.

V   Early 14th–17th century tombs around Ayios Yeoryios church.

VIII. BIBLIOGRAPHY

MINOAN

General

1903   Halbherr, F. "Resti dell'età micenea: Scoperti ad Haghia Triada presso Phaestos," *MonAnt* 13:6–74.

1904   Pernier, L. "Il palazzo, la villa, e le necropoli di Phaestos," in *Atti del Congresso Internazionale di Scienze Storiche* (Rome) 5:642.

1941–43   Banti, L. "I culti minoici e greci di Haghia Triada," *ASAtene* n.s. 3–5:9–74.

1960   *EAA* 3:1087–93 (L. Banti).

1961–62   Levi, D. "Atti della Scuola," *ASAtene* 39–40:671.

1969   Warren, P. M. *Minoan Stone Vases* (Cambridge) 37, 84–85, 88, 174–81.

1969–70   Laviosa, C. "Saggi di scavo ad Haghia Triada," *ASAtene* 47–48:407–15.

1972–73   ———. "L'abitato prepalaziale di Haghia Triada," *ASAtene* 50–51:503–13.

1973   Banti, L. "L'agora di Haghia Triada: La datazione," in *Antichità Cretesi* 1:38–40.

1977   Halbherr, F., E. Stefani, and L. Banti. "Haghia Triada nel periodo tardo palaziale," *ASAtene* 55:13–296.

La Rosa, V. "La ripresa dei lavori ad Haghia Triada: Relazione preliminare sui saggi del 1977," *ASAtene* 55:297–342.

1979   McEnroe, J. C. *Minoan House and Town Arrangement*, Ph.D. diss., University of Toronto.

1979–80   Follieri, M. "Provviste alimentari vegetali in una casa minoica ad Haghia Triada," *ASAtene* 57–58:165–72.

La Rosa, V. "Haghia Triada II: Relazione preliminare sui saggi del 1978 e 1979," *ASAtene* 57–58:49–164.

Levi, D., and C. Laviosa. "Il forno minoico da vasaio di Haghia Triada," *ASAtene* 57–58:7–47.

1980   Hirsch, E. S. "Another Look at Minoan and Mycenaean Interrelationships in Floor Decoration," *AJA* 84:459–61.

Kanta, A. *The Late Minoan III Period in Crete: A Survey of Sites, Pottery, and Their Distribution*, SIMA 58 (Gothenburg) 102–4.

1981   Hayden, B. J. *The Development of Cretan Architecture from the LM III A through the Geometric Periods*, Ph.D. diss., University of Pennsylvania 50–59.

1982   ———. "The Derivation and Architectural Context of Cretan Bronze Age Stoas," *Archaeological News* 11:1–7.

1983   Downey, W. S. *Magnetic Studies of Santorini Minoan Tephra and Cretan Archaeological Materials*, Ph.D. diss., University of Newcastle upon Tyne 526–60.

1984   *Creta antica* 35–42 (V. La Rosa), 161–94 (V. La Rosa with A. L. D'Agata).

Liritzis, Y. "Reappraisal of Minoan Kilns by Thermoluminescence and Neutron Activation/XRF Analyses," *RdArchéom* 8:7–20.

Watrous, L. V. "Ayia Triada: A New Perspective on the Minoan Villa," *AJA* 88:123–34.

1985   *Ancient Crete* 108–36 (V. La Rosa with A. L. D'Agata).

Gesell, G. C. *Town, Palace, and House Cult in Minoan Crete,* SIMA 67 (Gothenburg) 73–77.

La Rosa, V. "Le nuovi indagini ad Hagia Triadha," in *5 Cretological* 1:190–98.

———. "Preliminary Considerations on the Problem of the Relationship between Phaistos and Hagia Triadha," *Scripta Mediterranea* 6:45–54.

1987   D'Agata, A. L. "Un vano di culto TMIII nell'abitato di Haghia Triada," *Sileno* 13.

La Rosa, V. "Spigolature vecchie e nuove da Haghia Triada," in *Eilapini* 383–90.

1989   D'Agata, A. L. "Some MM IIIB/LM IA Pottery from Haghia Triada," *Aegaeum* 3:93–98.

La Rosa, V. "Nouvelles données du Bronze moyen au Bronze récent à Haghia Triada," *Aegaeum* 3:81–92.

1990   ———. "Recenti acquisizioni nel settore nord dell'abitato di Haghia Triada," in *6 Cretological* 1, pt. 1:411–18.

Frescoes

1990   Immerwahr, S. A. *Aegean Painting in the Bronze Age* (University Park, Pa.) 49–50, 54, 100–103, 161, 165, 180–81.

Cemetery

1904   Paribeni, R. "Ricerche nel sepolcreto di Haghia Triada presso Phaestos," *MonAnt* 14:677–756.

1930–31   Stefani, E., and L. Banti. "La grande tomba a tholos di Haghia Triada," *ASAtene* 13–14:146–251.

1959   Long, C. R. "Shrines in Sepulchres? A Re-Examination of Three Middle to Late Minoan Tombs," *AJA* 63:59–65.

1974   ———. *The Ayia Triadha Sarcophagus: A Study of Late Minoan and Mycenaean Funerary Practices and Beliefs,* SIMA 41 (Gothenburg).

1976   Pelon, O. *Tholoi, tumuli et cercles funéraires* (Athens) 8–11.

Scripts and Seals

1925–26   Levi, D. "Le cretule di Haghia Triada e di Zakro," *ASAtene* 8–9:71–156.

1945   Pugliese Carratelli, G. "Le iscrizioni preelleniche di Haghia Triada in Crete e della Grecia peninsulare," *MonAnt* 40:421–610.

1965   Cameron, M. A. S. "Four Fragments of Wall Paintings with Linear A Inscriptions," *Kadmos* 4:7–15.

1969   *CMS* 2.1:12–117 nos. 6–103 (N. Platon).

1976   *GORILA* 1:1–251.

1979   *GORILA* 2:3–78.

1982   *GORILA* 4:63–69, 129–35.

1984   *CMS* 2.3:135–40 nos. 116–19 (N. Platon and I. Pini).

1985   *CMS* 2.4:195–96 no. 153 (N. Platon and I. Pini).

GORILA 5:13–14.

1987   La Rosa, V., and G. Pugliese Carratelli. "Nuove iscrizioni in lineare A dalla 'Villa Reale' di Haghia Triada," *PP* 127:463–68.

Weingarten, J. "Seal-Use at Late Minoan IB Ayia Triada: A Minoan Elite in Action. I. Administrative Considerations," *Kadmos* 26:1–38.

1988   Militello, P. "Riconsiderazioni preliminari sulla documentazione in lineare A da Haghia Triada," *Sileno* 14.

Weingarten, J. "Seal-Use at Late Minoan IB Ayia Triada: A Minoan Elite in Action. II. Aesthetic Considerations," *Kadmos* 27:89–114.

1989   Hallager, E., L. Godart, and J.-P. Olivier. "La rondelle en linéaire A d'Aghia Triada," *BCH* 113:431–37.

POST-MINOAN

1935   *IC* 1:273–74, 278 (= *IC* I. XXIII. 4–5, 24).

1982   Sanders, I. F. *Roman Crete* (Warminster) 160–61.

1989   La Rosa, V. "L'altare del Piazzale dei Sacelli ad Haghia Triada," in *Aphieroma sto Styliano Alexiou, Ariadne* 5:93–98.

Forthcoming   ———. "Considerazioni sul sito di Haghia Triada in età ellenistico-romana," *ASAtene*.

IX. FINDS

Herakleion Museum; Pigorini Museum, Rome.

X. DATE OF PHOTOGRAPHY

April 26, 1984.

COSTIS DAVARAS

35°10′ N, 26°01′ E

I. IMPORTANCE

The grand Middle Minoan IA building set on a high hill in open country near Chamaizi has had an important role in the history of Minoan architecture. Its excavation in 1903 led to a debate on the significance of its oval shape, which Mackenzie concluded by suggesting that it was determined by the slope of the ground, which, at more than 30 degrees, offers limited room for building. This is now seen to be part of the explanation, as new work shows that for most of the perimeter the builders followed the plans of earlier houses with curved walls on the same spot. Curving the walls was one way, but not the only one, of coping with the site (see Fig. 8.3).

This important Prepalatial building was surely not a peak sanctuary, as several scholars have thought, but rather the last of a series of freestanding houses, the country dwelling, perhaps, of an extended family or clan. It was well suited for defense, with a strong outer wall, and, having a splendid view over the Bay of Siteia and the mouth of the Piskokephalo valley, it would have been an excellent lookout post.

II. USE

EM–MM IA building(s).

III. SITUATION

On steep, flat-topped Souvloto Mouri, "pointed hill," 501 m high, 1 km south of Chamaizi and on the land route to far eastern Crete. Rich arable land and pasture around. Likely water sources: springs, wells, and cisterns.

IV. GEOMORPHOLOGY

From the west the hill is asymmetrical, with a relatively gentle north slope of phyllite and a steep south slope predominantly of limestone. The bedrock of the hill represents a widespread phyllite-quartzite rock known east of the isthmus of Ierapetra and centered on the Ornon mountains. On the hilltop the bedrock is mainly phyllite

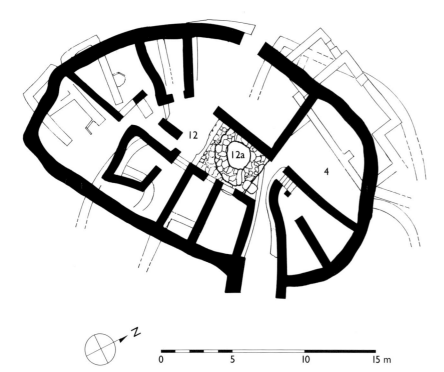

Figure 8.1 Plan of Chamaizi
Figure 8.2 Middle Minoan IA building (and Early Minoan buildings)

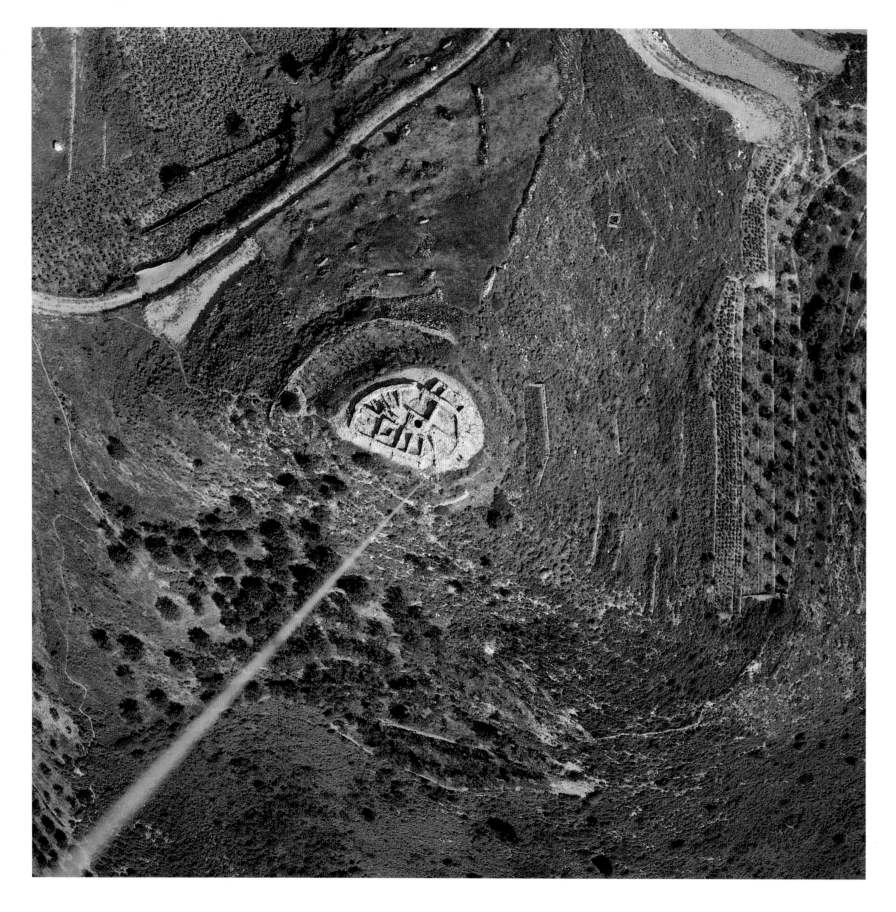

Figure 8.3 High aerial view

(unsuitable for building stone); but there are outcrops of flaggy, slightly metamorphosed limestone on the southwest slope and across the stream valley to the southeast.

The complete absence of springs and wells on the hilltop explains the central cistern, which presumably collected water from a circumferential inward-sloping roof. The cistern, which must have been plastered to minimize water loss, was excavated into phyllite bedrock, but its upper part is built up of limestone blocks.

V. EXCAVATION HISTORY

S. Xanthoudides, 1903, and C. Davaras, 1971, for the Archaeological Service.

VI. BUILDINGS

EM buildings (building phases I–III) below MM IA building (phase IV) with additions (phase V) about 21 by 15 m. Thick outer wall. The rooms set radially around a small courtyard (12) with a cistern (12a) include a possible shrine (4).

VIII. BIBLIOGRAPHY

General

1906 Xanthoudides, S. "Ek Kritis. III. Proistoriki ikia eis Chamaizi Siteias," *ArchEph* 117–56.

1907–8 Mackenzie, D. "Cretan Palaces and the Aegean Civilization. IV," *BSA* 14:411–22.

1908 Noack, F. *Ovalhaus und Palast in Kreta* (Berlin) 53–57.

1921 Evans, A. J. *The Palace of Minos at Knossos* (London) 1: 147–48.

1951 Platon, N. "To ieron Maza kai ta minoika iera koryphis," *KrChron* 5:122–24.

1972 Davaras, C. "The Oval House at Chamaizi Reconsidered," *AAA* 5:283–88.

1973 ———. "Neai erevnai eis tin elleipsoeidi ikian Chamaiziou," in *3 Cretological* 1:46–53.

1975 Höckmann, O. "Zu dem kykladischen Gebäudemodell von Melos," *IstMitt* 25:287.

1978 Sariyannis, G. M. "I protes morphes poleos kai i syllogiki domi tis ikogeneias: Symvoli sto provlima tis ikias tou Chamaiziou," *TechChron* 64–83.

Figure 8.4 Chamaizi, above Piskokephalo valley and Siteia

1985 Gesell, G. C. *Town, Palace, and House Cult in Minoan Crete,* *SIMA* 67 (Gothenburg) 14–16, 18n.33, 83.

Seals

1975 *CMS* 5.1:18–19 nos. 21–22 (I. Pini).

IX. FINDS

Herakleion Museum; Ayios Nikolaos Museum.

X. DATE OF PHOTOGRAPHY

May 9, 1981.

NIKOLAOS PLATON

35°02′ N, 25°22′ E

I. IMPORTANCE

Although badly preserved, the remains on the Kephala saddle near Chondros are important because they belong almost completely to the Postpalatial Late Minoan IIIA2 phase, of whose settlements we know in general too little. The groups of buildings suggest a community of several extended families, and the dais in one room may identify the house of the local ruler. Close to it was a shrine, whose contents included a tubular stand, fragments of an offering table with lions in relief, and a figurine of a woman giving birth. Many clay loom weights show that the settlement wove wool, presumably from its own sheep.

Kephala had a short life, probably not more than a century. We do not know whether earthquake or an attack caused its destruction by fire. There are no signs of the displacement of foundations that earthquake often brings, but the settlement was not reinhabited, as one might expect after an attack.

On the higher point of Kephali Lazana to the west was a New Palace period country house or farmstead, which may be seen as a predecessor to Kephala. It may have been abandoned in Late Minoan I as insufficiently secure.

II. USE

Kephali Lazana: MM IIIB–LM I country house or farmstead; LM III traces of buildings; Kephala: LM IIIA settlement.

III. SITUATION

On the low east–west saddle at Kephala in the valley around the village of Chondros (0.5 km southeast) in the foothills on the southwest side of the Lasithi mountains. Saddle leveled to take the buildings. Heavy erosion exposed buildings before excavation. The flat ground surrounding the hill bears traces of buildings. Buildings also on Kephali Lazana, which is the high point to the west.

IV. GEOMORPHOLOGY

Both Kephala and Kephali Lazana are eroded knobs of the local flysch bedrock, a fine-grained homogeneous sandstone. The 35–40 degree east slope of Kephali Lazana is too steep for large building foundations, although there are some small structures. Sandstone bedrock crops out at two points on this slope.

Wall blocks were easily set into the fractured bedrock of Kephala. Almost all the blocks are flysch sandstone: the largest of them (about 1 by 0.5 by 0.3 m) shows extensive spallation as a result of high temperatures (fire?) nearby. Some occasional use was made also of large pieces of an igneous extrusive rock—pillow lava—obtained from small outcrops common in the vicinity.

There is a small colluvium-filled basin of internal drainage south of the site, where olives are grown now and could have been in antiquity. The hills to the south and southeast, klippes of dense limestone from the Pindos-Ethia nappe, are likely to have many springs at their base.

V. EXCAVATION HISTORY

N. Platon, 1956–60, for the Archaeological Society.

VI. BUILDINGS

MM IIIB–LM I Country house or farmstead on Kephali Lazana. Destruction by earthquake in LM I(A?). Abandonment.

Kephala: traces of buildings with pavements (at lower level).

LM IIIA Settlement (50 by 15–17.5 m; total area: 785 sq m) on Kephala with two principal groups of houses (east: at least seven houses, with twenty areas; west: four to five houses, with twenty-five areas; the two groups separated by a double wall, with no clear communication between them). East group: paved rooms (some with earlier, lower pavements); rooms with benches; a few rooms with built storage

Figure 9.1 Kephala and Kephali Lazana (to the west)

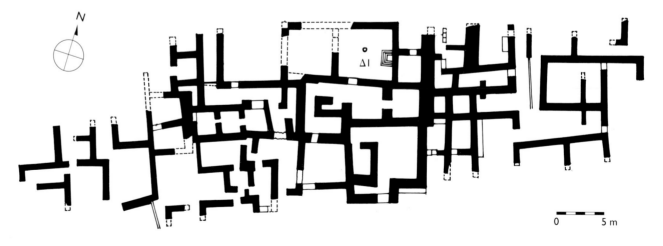

Figure 9.2 Kephala

Figure 9.3 Kephala

Figure 9.4 Chondros village and Kephala

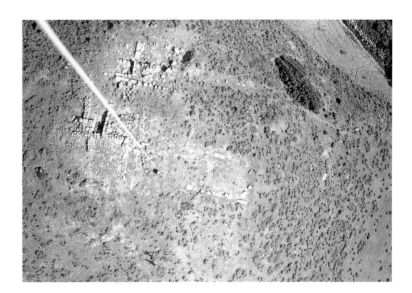

Figure 9.5 Kephali Lazana farmstead

places; base for roof support found in only one room; no staircases or signs of upper floors. West group: similar pavements, storage places, and benches; also (a few) steps to slightly higher rooms and to the notably grander central area, which had an upper floor shrine and a dais in room Δ1. Evidence of minor repairs and rebuilding. Destruction by fire in LM IIIA2. Abandonment.

Traces of another group of buildings to west, extending up to Kephali Lazana.

VIII. BIBLIOGRAPHY

1957   Platon, N. "Anaskaphi Chondrou Viannou," *PAE* 136–45.

1959   ———. "Anaskaphi metanaktorikou synikismou eis Kephali Chondrou, 1959," *PAE* 197–205.

1960   ———. "Anaskaphi Chondrou Viannou," *PAE* 283–86.

1964   Hood, M. S. F., P. M. Warren, and G. Cadogan. "Travels in Crete, 1962," *BSA* 59:81–82.

1980   Kanta, A. *The Late Minoan III Period in Crete: A Survey of Sites, Pottery, and Their Distribution*, SIMA 57 (Gothenburg) 114–17.

1985   Gesell, G. C. *Town, Palace, and House Cult in Minoan Crete*, SIMA 67 (Gothenburg) 41–42, 45, 47, 49–52, 54, 65, 82–83.

1989   Warren, P. M., and V. Hankey. *Aegean Bronze Age Chronology* (Bristol) 85.

1990   Hayden, B. J. "Aspects of Village Architecture in the Cretan Postpalatial Period," in *L'habitat égéen préhistorique*, *BCH* Supplement 19, ed. P. Darcque and R. Treuil (Athens) 203–13.

IX. FINDS

Herakleion Museum.

X. DATE OF PHOTOGRAPHY

April 24, 1983.

HENRI VAN EFFENTERRE

35°16′ N, 25°37′ E

I. IMPORTANCE

Dreros is a remarkable small inland city of east central Crete, on a double acropolis overlooking the valley of Neapolis and the Bay of Mirabello. It features little in ancient testimonia but became famous in 1855, when a *kyrbis*, "inscribed pillar," of rectangular shape was found there. The pillar, with inscriptions on each of its four sides, was dated to the end of the 3rd century B.C. It has the civic oath of the city's 180 ephebes, young men newly become citizens who were grouped in *agelai*, "herds," and it also claims friendship with Knossos and hatred of neighboring Lyttos.

Since 1932 chance discoveries and regular excavations have shown that Dreros is one of the most typical Archaic cities of Crete, though its whole history stretches from Late Minoan IIIC to Hellenistic times.

Above its stepped square agora is a Geometric temple of Apollo Delphinios (the Delphinion), which is now roofed. One of the oldest temples to survive in Greece, it has a central square hearth (*eschara*) between two stone bases for wooden columns on the temple's axis. Its finds are Late Geometric. Standing on a bench in the southwest corner were exceptional bronze statues (*sphyrelata*) of the Apolline triad: Apollo, Artemis, and Leto. The male statue is 80 cm high; the female statues are 50 cm. Nearby was a *keraton*, a stone box-shaped altar containing the horns of young goats. A bronze *gorgoneion*, "gorgon's face," was also found in the temple.

A huge Hellenistic cistern dominates the agora, as at Lato. Called a *lakkos*, "pit," in inscriptions, it was built to ensure a supply of rain-water for the city, as there was no other source at the spot. Inside the cistern Archaic inscribed blocks were found, which had fallen in—perhaps from the temple walls; the blocks record the first known constitutional law of a Greek city. Among other documents on stone in the cistern is a short bilingual(?) text in Greek and Eteocretan.

Other buildings nearby may include a prytaneion for the magistrates, and there was a small cemetery at the foot of the hill. Today we may imagine Dreros as combining ancient Cretan traditions with those of the Dorian (post-Minoan) population of the island.

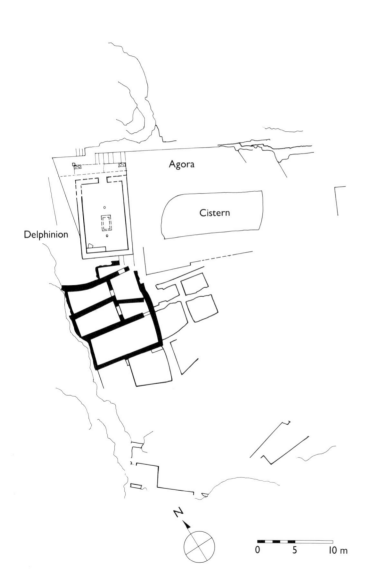

Figure 10.1   Plan of Dreros

Figure 10.2   High aerial view

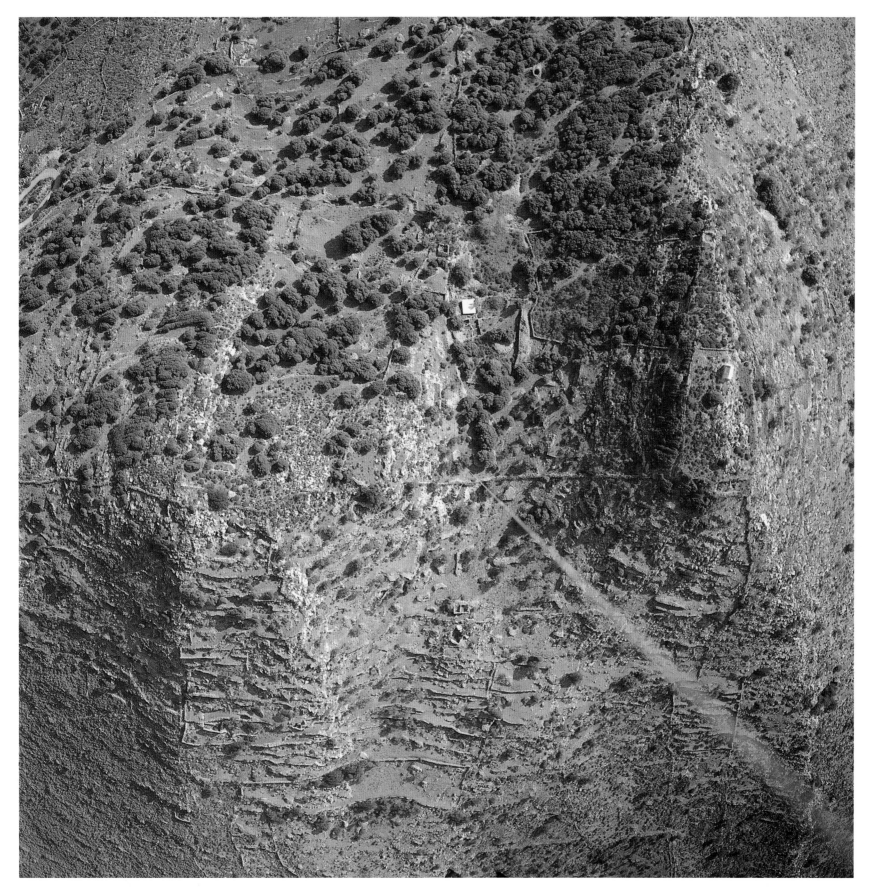

Figure 10.3 Low aerial view

II. USE

LM IIIC and G cemetery; G–H city; R and LByz traces.

III. SITUATION

Two peaks and the saddle between them rise (to the north) above the national road and overlook modern Neapolis and its fertile valley. The agora is in the saddle.

IV. GEOMORPHOLOGY

The peaks of Dreros represent the Plattenkalk series of limestones (Crete's basement rocks), which form the bedrock from the Neapolis valley in a northeast direction toward the Ayios Ioannis peninsula (ancient Cadiston). Defense must have been a prime factor in the selection of this site.

Structures at Dreros are made of relatively small angular limestone blocks, of which there is an unlimited supply. In addition to the many (historically) recent agricultural terrace and sheepfold walls around the ancient site, ancient terrace walls of quite large stones are visible on the north slope between the peaks.

V. EXCAVATION HISTORY

S. Xanthoudides, 1917, for the Archaeological Service; P. Demargne, 1932; S. Marinatos, 1935–36, for the Archaeological Service; P. Demargne and H. Van Effenterre, 1936–38, for the French School.

VI. BUILDINGS

C and G   About twenty-five ossuaries (bone enclosures) and pithos burials inside a rectangular circuit wall. Place for votive offerings nearby.

middle of (century)   Delphinion temple, 11 by 7 m, a simple cella on north–south axis, entered perhaps from the north through a porch—but this part was destroyed by a lime kiln. Inside: square pit lined with small stone slabs, full of ash, between two axial columns (but only one base was in situ); altar with goat horns in southwest corner, and bench for bronze statues.

(century)   Agora beside temple, with a few steps up to its porch. Unpaved, but marked out (30 by 40 m) by a stepped structure with one side and two short returns on the south and a retaining wall on the north.

H   Large rectangular cistern (13 by 5.5 by 6 m). Unroofed. Border of dressed stones along the edge, one of them a kind of measure

Figure 10.4   Looking across town saddle from the west

(*sikoma*), possibly for water rations. To the southwest a few other buildings.

R and LByz   R (1st century) coins and LByz traces on top of east hill near chapel of Ayios Antonios.

VIII. BIBLIOGRAPHY

1890   Svoronos 125–26.

1905   *RE* 5 : 1699 (E. Bürchner).

1935   *IC* 1 : 83–88 (= *IC* I. IX. 1–2).
     Marinatos, S. "Le temple et les statuettes archaïques en bronze de Dréros," *CRAI* 478–89.

1936   ———. "Le temple géométrique de Dréros," *BCH* 60 : 214–85.

1937   Van Effenterre, H. "A propos du serment des Drériens," *BCH* 61 : 327–32.
     Van Effenterre, H., and P. Demargne. "Recherches à Dréros," *BCH* 61 : 5–32, 333–48.

1938   ———. "Recherches à Dréros," *BCH* 62 : 194–95.

1940   *RE* Supplement 7 : 128–49 (E. Kirsten).

1946   Van Effenterre, H. "Inscriptions archaïques crétoises," *BCH* 70 : 588–606.

1948   ———. *Nécropoles du Mirabello*, EtCr 8 (Paris) 15–46, 50–66.
     ———. "Une bilingue étéocrétoise?" *RPhil* 131–38.

1956   Macdonald, W. A. "Note on a Fragment of an Archaic Inscription from Dreros," *Hesperia* 25:69–72.

1960   Van Effenterre, H. "Un sèkôma crétois," *BCH* 84:233–41.

———. "Une copie grecque d'une fresque minoenne?" *CRAI* 117–27.

1961   ———. "Pierres inscrites de Dréros," *BCH* 85:544–68.

1969   Van Effenterre, H., and M. Bougrat. "Les frontières de Latô," *KrChron* 21:28–32.

1976   Beyer, I. *Die Tempel von Dreros und Prinias A, und die Chronologie der kretischen Kunst des 8. und 7. Jhs. v. Chr.* (Freiburg).

Davaras, C. *Guide to Cretan Antiquities* (Park Ridge, N.J.) 75.

PECS 283–84 (D. J. Blackman).

1980   Kanta, A. *The Late Minoan III Period in Crete: A Survey of Sites, Pottery, and Their Distribution, SIMA* 57 (Gothenburg) 133.

1982   Sanders, I. F. *Roman Crete* (Warminster) 141.

1983   Tiré, C., and H. Van Effenterre. *Guide des fouilles françaises en Crète*, 3rd ed. (Paris) 93–96.

1989   Van Effenterre, H. "De l'étéocrétois à la selle d'agneau," *BCH* 113:447–49.

IX. FINDS

Herakleion Museum; Ayios Nikolaos Museum; Neapolis antiquities collection; Istanbul Museum.

X. DATE OF PHOTOGRAPHY

April 21, 1982.

PETROS THEMELIS

34°19′ N, 24°40′ E

I. IMPORTANCE

Eleutherna—known also as Satra, (S)aoros, and Apollonia—a large inland city of central Crete well fortified by nature and man, with rich pasture and arable land around, played an important role in the history of the island during the Archaic, Hellenistic, and Late Roman periods. It was known as the birthplace of Ametor and of Linos, son of Apollo, both famous singers and musicians of Archaic times. An important male limestone torso, in the Daedalic style of Crete of the 7th century B.C., was found at Orthi Petra, "standing stone," where the early cemetery of Eleutherna was located. This cemetery had adult cremation and child inhumation burials.

In the 3rd and 2nd centuries B.C. the city kept contact with mainland Greece, the islands, Asia Minor, Palestine, and Egypt and shared in the politics of the period. In 68/67 B.C. Quintus Caecilius Metellus (Creticus) took Eleutherna by a cunning trick, softening the fortification wall with vinegar to make it easier to breach.

Life continued at Eleutherna during the Roman Empire as well as the Early Byzantine and Late Byzantine periods and probably the Medieval, if the solid ruined and partly restored tower of mixed masonry commanding the narrow approach to the acropolis is really Venetian.

Eleutherna is famous for two important monuments, first noticed by travelers in the 19th century. Down the valley and below the junction of the streams flowing on either side of the acropolis is a Hellenistic bridge with a triangular arch; and in the soft limestone on the west side of the acropolis hill is a pair of huge rectangular cisterns, divided into three aisles—like basilicas—by pillars measuring 3.5 by 3.5 m. A vaulted aqueduct (about 1.5 m wide and 2 m high) takes the water under the acropolis from the cisterns down to the city terraces on the east side.

The abundance of Early Byzantine tombs is another remarkable feature of the site.

II. USE

EM chance finds; G, A, C, H, and R city; EByz basilica; LByz church.

III. SITUATION

On a long, narrow flat-topped ridge about 40 m high with steep sides, at the northwest base of Psiloriti and in the hinterland of Rethymno. Streams at either side, Halopota to the west and Kyriaki to the east. Two water sources on the east slope, by Ayia Sotira church and at Katsivelos by Kyriaki stream. Wells and cisterns, especially on the acropolis.

IV. GEOMORPHOLOGY

If any single site in Crete exemplifies the close relation of geomorphology and location, Eleutherna is that one. The protection normally gained by occupying an eminence was achieved instead by fortifying the root of an elongate erosional spur of Miocene marly limestone and constructing the citadel along its relatively flat top. The valleys to the east and west, occupied by seasonal stream channels, are some 40 m below the spur top. These streams have eroded through the limestone unit and into the underlying slightly metamorphosed rocks of the lower Tripolitza series nappe.

The marly limestone strata are nearly horizontal, which allowed builders to take advantage of the alternating very soft and relatively harder layers for laying out terraces, steps, and building foundations. A secure water supply was assured by the several enormous underground cisterns dug into the west side of the limestone spur. While impressive to view, they must have been relatively easy to excavate because of the soft bedrock. The cisterns were kept full by a short but well-constructed aqueduct tapping the Pigadaki spring up the valley west of the site.

Extensive terracing exists on both the east and west slopes between the valley floors and the vertical or overhanging sides of the spur. These fields are still cultivated, and the maintenance of the terrace walls has prevented extensive soil erosion.

V. EXCAVATION HISTORY

H. Payne, 1928, for the British School; S. Alexiou, 1965, for the Archaeological Service; P. Themelis, T. Kalpaxis, and N. Stampolidis, 1985–, for the University of Crete.

VI. BUILDINGS

LN   Chance find of four stone axes on east terraces.

EM   Sherds and obsidian fragments on acropolis and east terraces.

G–A   Traces of sanctuary on acropolis by Ayia Eirini church; another sanctuary on east side; cemetery at Orthi Petra down west slope near Halopota stream.

H   Monumental terrace walls and building remains on east slope, mainly at Katsivelos. Bridge to north of city hill, below junction of east and west streams.

R   2nd–4th century house at Katsivelos, destroyed by earthquake in 2nd half of 4th century; immediately to east, mosaic floor and stone pavement of large public building (probably a basilica). Large 2nd–4th century bath(?) at Pyrgi (north of acropolis plateau). Parts of fortification wall with square towers preserved on ridge around Pyrgi area. Tombs at Orthi Petra and Katsivelos include a two-room built tomb (Katsivelos).

EByz   Basilica on ruins of R bath; tombs (6th–7th century) on west side of basilica, and on opposite slope near modern village of Eleftherna.

Med? (V?)   Tower.

VIII. BIBLIOGRAPHY

1837   Pashley, R. *Travels in Crete* (London) 1:145.

1865   Spratt, T. A. B. *Travels and Researches in Crete* (London) 2:89–98.

1890   Svoronos 128–36.

1895   Mariani, L. "Antichità cretesi," *MonAnt* 6:193–348.

1905   Gerola, G. *I monumenti veneti dell'isola di Creta* (Venice) 1:81.

   RE 5:2351–53 (E. Bürchner).

1908   Gerola, G. *I monumenti veneti dell'isola di Creta* (Venice) 2:56–57.

1914   Petroulakis, E. N. "I proistoriki yephyra tis Elefthernis," *ArchEph* 230–32.

1915   Karo, G. "Archäologische Funde im Jahre 1914," *AA* 30:198.

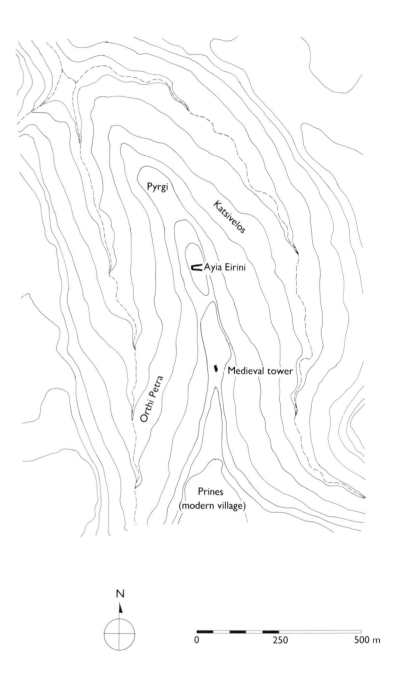

Figure 11.1   Plan of Eleutherna (contour interval 10 m)

Figure 11.2   Aerial view, with arrows at (top) Ayia Eirini and (lower) medieval tower

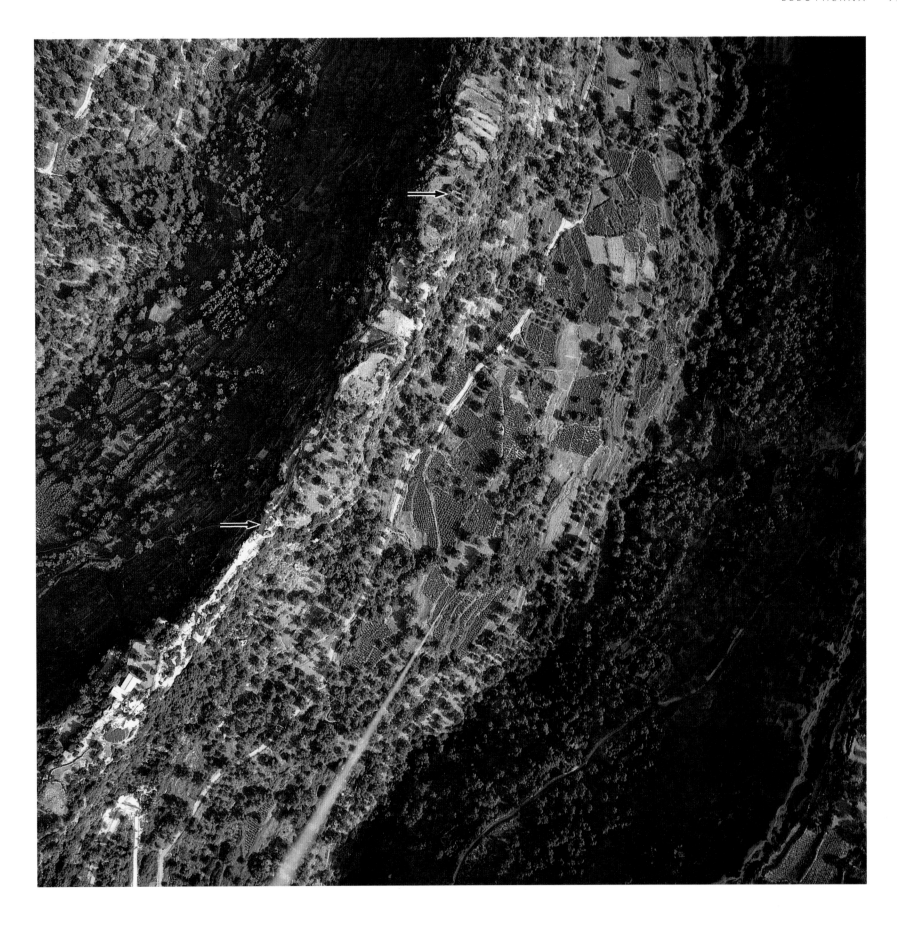

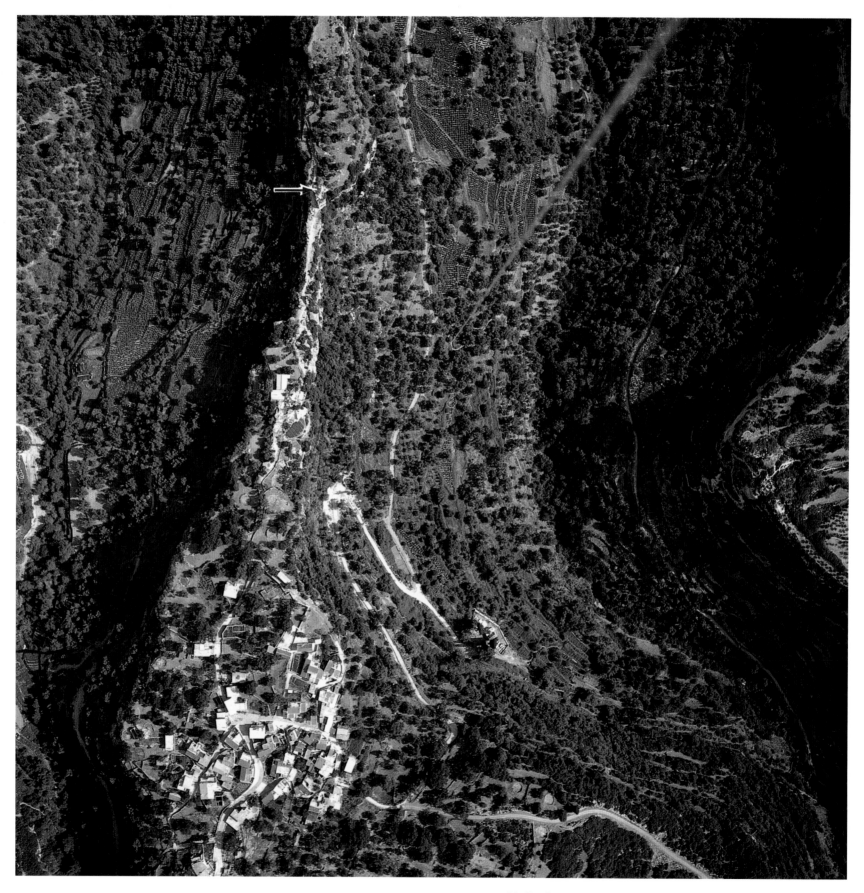

Figure 11.3   Medieval tower (at arrow) and, below it, cuttings on rock causeway to city

Figure 11.4   Causeway and gate tower from the south

1929   Woodward, A. M. "Archaeology in Greece, 1928–29," *JHS* 49:224–26.

1930–31   Hartley, M. "Early Greek Vases from Crete," *BSA* 31: 108–14.

1939   *IC* 2:141–74 (= *IC* II. XII. 1–47).

1948   Platon, N. "Symvoli eis to toponymikon, tin topographian kai tin istorian ton poleon kai ton phrourion tis Kritis," *KrChron* 2:349–65.

1967   Davaras, C. "Archaiotites kai mnimeia dytikis Kritis," *ArchDelt* 22, pt. 2:500–501.

1982   Sanders, I. F. *Roman Crete* (Warminster) 25–26, 120, 162–63.

1990   Gondicas, D. "Mia archaia thesi sto synchrono nekrotapheio tis Elefthernas," in *6 Cretological* 1, pt. 1:179–84.

        Stampolidis, N. "Eleutherna on Crete: An Interim Report on the Geometric-Archaic Cemetery," *BSA* 85: 375–403.

1991   Van Effenterre, H., T. Kalpaxis, A. B. Petropoulou, and E. Stavrianopoulou. *Eleftherna 2.1. Epigraphes apo to Pyrgi kai to Nisi* (Rethymno).

IX. FINDS

Rethymno Museum; Herakleion Museum.

X. DATE OF PHOTOGRAPHY

June 19, 1983.

ANTONINO DI VITA

35°04′ N, 24°57′ E

I. IMPORTANCE

The Gortyn Law Code, found in 1884, is still the queen of Greek inscriptions. A major document of early Greek society datable to about 480 B.C., it has twelve columns of texts that give the laws of the city. Its discovery led to the start of excavations in the Greek, Roman, and Byzantine city that are still continuing. Though there is evidence of inhabitation in Neolithic times and in Late Minoan I and Late Minoan III, the principal period of Gortyn ran from about 700 B.C. to about A.D. 670, when there was a severe earthquake, which was soon followed by the arrival of the Arabs who made Crete the base for their annual attacks on Constantinople.

The first post-Minoan settlement was in Geometric times on the acropolis, where there was a temple of Athena Poliouchos. After the city was settled during the 8th century B.C. at the foot of the acropolis, the temple of Apollo Pythios (the Pythion) was founded on the Pythion hill: it became the most venerated shrine at Gortyn and was known in the whole Greek world. Gortyn is mentioned in the *Iliad* as walled (2 : 646) and in the *Odyssey* (3 : 293–96) is described as ruling the Mesara plain as far as the sea beyond Phaistos.

Gortyn, which remained a leading city of Crete, was frequently a rival and enemy of Knossos and Lyttos. In Hellenistic times the city spread south as far as the higher ground under the modern village of Mitropolis and to the east as far as the shrine of the Egyptian Divinities and the Pythion, in front of which was probably an agora used for commerce only; the political and social center must have been in the area south of the Roman Odeion. Here in a circular *ekklesiasterion*, "assembly building," its walls covered with the city's laws, the council and the citizens met under the direction of the *kosmoi*, "chief magistrates." The Pythion was used as a secure and inviolable depository for the treaties Gortyn made with the leading Hellenistic kingdoms and with the other cities of Crete.

At the end of the 3rd century B.C., with the help of Ptolemy IV Philopator, Gortyn fortified itself with walls along the crest of the hills to the north, giving the city better control of the road that descends from the northern part of the island into the Mesara plain. The walls were being restored around 30 B.C. when an earthquake

struck them down. In the wars of the last years of the Roman republic, Gortyn took sides once again against Knossos and allied itself with Octavian (the later emperor Augustus), while Knossos was a stronghold of the party of Mark Antony and Cleopatra.

Gortyn, made the capital of the province of Crete and Cyrene in 27 B.C. by Augustus, continued in that role until the reforms of Diocletian; it was the principal seat of the proconsul at least until the first half of the 2nd century. The city was at its largest under Roman rule: about 400 ha, including its cemeteries.

The Roman city joined the Hellenistic city on the Pythion hill and spread from there to the southeast. On the edge of the new city an amphitheater arose (recently identified near the old village of Ayii Deka in the suburb known as Aloni, "threshing floor") and also a grand theater, built probably under Antoninus Pius, and a circus that was used into Byzantine times.

The Praetorium, the seat of the proconsul, built beyond a trapezoidal piazza linking the old city with the new, has a large hall of justice and a temple dedicated probably to the deified Augusti. The proconsul's residence was destroyed by earthquake during Trajan's time. In its place grandiose baths were erected, fronted on the north by Nymphaea. Other imposing baths, known as Megali Porta, "great gate," lie 0.5 km south of the Praetorium beside a large rectangular piazza, which was bordered first by public buildings and later partly occupied by a Byzantine basilica.

A small theater beyond the Pythion was used for the competitions attached to the cult of Apollo Pythios; the Greek theater (perhaps originally Classical) was rebuilt on the lower southeast slopes of the acropolis, facing onto the Mitropolianos river and the Odeion. The Odeion, of early Roman date but rebuilt under Trajan, was on the site of the old *ekklesiasterion*.

After Diocletian, Gortyn belonged to the prefecture of Illyricum but remained the capital of Crete. From the 4th to the 7th century the city saw the growth of the new hierarchy of the church. While the old center, destroyed by an earthquake in 365 and then by frequent earthquakes in the following centuries, became an artisans' quarter (including potters' and glassmakers' shops), in the 1-km-long stretch between the Odeion (on the north) and the modern village of Mitropolis (on the south) no fewer than six basilicas were built. One of these is the metropolitan basilica, of which there are significant remains, as there are of mausolea near it and of the Byzantine settlement in general.

Under Heraclius, Gortyn was rebuilt for the last time. The late aqueduct on arches was repaired, many fountains were built in the lower city, and the acropolis was completely fortified with a circuit wall. In the years around 670, when the combination of a damaging earthquake and the Arabs' use of Gortyn as a base for their attacks on Constantinople (between 673 and 677) brought the city to ruin, most of the Gortynians abandoned it, fleeing to the acropolis. There the small settlement resisted all attacks but faded away after the Byzantine recovery of Crete in the 10th century. Gortyn died where it had been born.

II. USE

MN, LN, and FN traces; LM I country house at Kannia, reused in LM IIIB; LM III settlement on acropolis; G–EByz city; Arab–LByz settlement.

III. SITUATION

Gortyn is in the northeast sector of the Mesara plain on a tributary of the Yeropotamos (or Lithaios) river—the Mitropolianos—at the foot of a range of low hills (the eastern foothills of the Psiloriti range) that form the northern boundary of the plain. The river issues from these hills. The westernmost hill became the acropolis. It is separated from those to the east (Pervolopetra, Armi, Prophitis Ilias) by the river, whose course divides the Greek, Roman, and Byzantine city into two unequal parts.

IV. GEOMORPHOLOGY

The river has eroded a small steep-sided gorge through the western end of a fault-bounded ridge of flysch, the south slope of which is mantled by a Pleistocene conglomerate deposit. The first city derived its water from one of the many springs that issue from the ridge. Geologically the site is less than ideal because the contact between the conglomerate and the flysch is marked by a major east–west trending fault that passes right through the Odeion.

The Odeion, whose floor is about 2 m above the elevation of the adjacent river channel, was evidently buried by alluvium before its excavation in 1912. At that time the mill stream (of the old water mill north of the Odeion) covering the site was diverted and the water drained. Apparently the stream's gradient changed sometime between the Odeion's abandonment and the early 20th century, possibly because of human modification of the locality. The fields south of Ayios Titos basilica are now irrigated by the gravity flow of water from the old mill. The modern channel bypasses the bed of the Mitropolianos and flows 3 m higher on an aqueduct that also serves to prevent floodwaters from filling the Odeion excavation area. The water mill, now ruined, was still working twenty years ago.

The flysch above Gortyn consists primarily of a fine-grained sandstone. Many of the building stones used in the city could be from the Pleistocene conglomerate deposit, collected from the slopes above Gortyn. The acropolis has a sandstone flysch bedrock, which was used extensively for the fortification walls.

The Roman ground surface south of the road to Mires is buried beneath about 2 m of alluvium from the Mitropolianos that has accumulated in the past 1,500 years. Over this time, local farmers have worked valiantly to clear the millions of cobble- to small boulder-sized building stones of Roman Gortyn from their fields, piling them up around standing wall remains.

The Pythion was buried beneath 1–2 m of collapsed building debris and colluvium. The Praetorium possessed large monolithic gray granite columns from the Troad; when excavated, these columns were found to be aligned in subparallel fashion toward the northeast. An earthquake having its epicenter in that direction from Gortyn apparently toppled them.

V. EXCAVATION HISTORY

F. Halbherr, 1884–87, 1894; G. De Sanctis, 1899; A. Taramelli and G. Gerola, 1900, for the Italian Archaeological Mission; S. Xanthoudides, 1902, for the Archaeological Service; A. Maiuri, 1910; L. Pernier and others, 1912–14; A. M. Colini, 1925, 1935–36, 1939, 1969–71, 1973, 1975, 1977; M. Guarducci, 1926–28; D. Levi and others, 1954–58, 1961; A. Di Vita and others, 1978–; for the Italian Archaeological Mission, or the Italian School.

VI. BUILDINGS

N Traces of MN and LN on northwest slopes of acropolis and of FN (compare Phaistos and Knossos) on south slopes of Prophitis Ilias.

LM I Country house at Kannia (southwest of Mitropolis village), destroyed in LM IB.

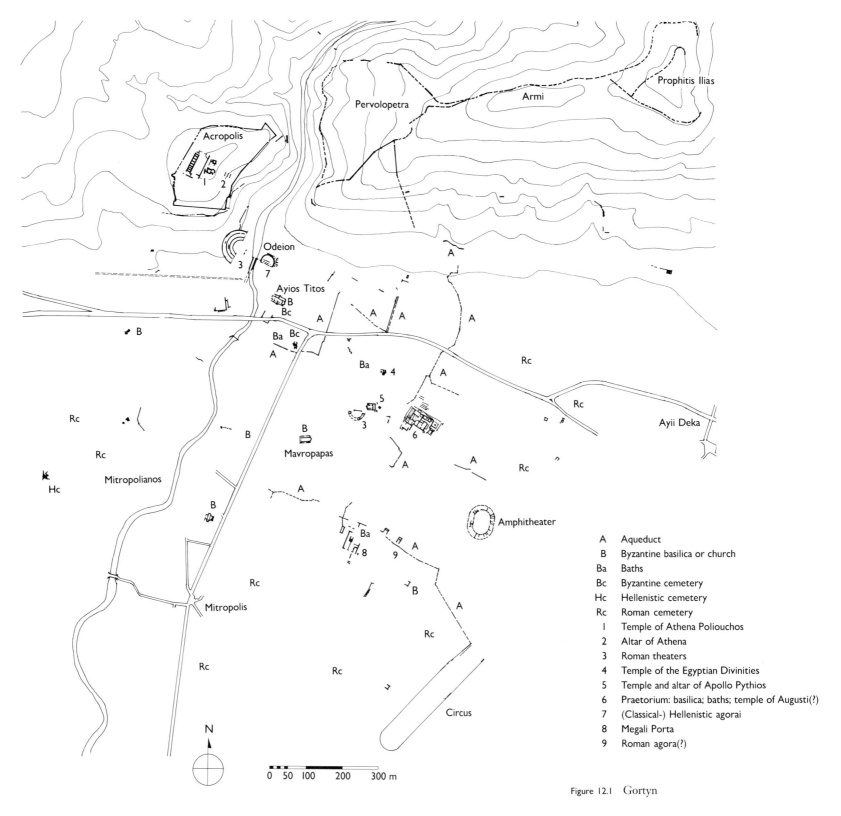

A   Aqueduct
B   Byzantine basilica or church
Ba   Baths
Bc   Byzantine cemetery
Hc   Hellenistic cemetery
Rc   Roman cemetery
 1   Temple of Athena Poliouchos
 2   Altar of Athena
 3   Roman theaters
 4   Temple of the Egyptian Divinities
 5   Temple and altar of Apollo Pythios
 6   Praetorium: basilica; baths; temple of Augusti(?)
 7   (Classical-) Hellenistic agorai
 8   Megali Porta
 9   Roman agora(?)

Figure 12.1   Gortyn

Figure 12.2   Acropolis, Odeion, and Basilica of Ayios Titos

Theater on slopes of acropolis, the perimeter of its cavea 120 m. Another theater near Temple of Apollo Pythios with cavea of 102 m. Large R theater (probably 2nd century) on southeastern edge of city: its external walls stand on fifty-six arches in two orders with attic above. Circus (not before late 2nd century) to south, almost 400 m long and 68 m wide. In use at least until 6th century.

Temple of the Egyptian Divinities (1st–2nd century) with podium for statues of Serapis, Isis, and probably Hermes Anubis; the cult is known at Gortyn from at least the 2nd century B.C.

Two monumental Nymphaea (middle of 2nd century). The larger and more important outside the Praetorium to the northeast, with many statues; large fountain nearby in front of a huge basin. Destroyed by earthquake about 618 and made into a cistern-fountain under Heraclius (610–41).

EByz   Dense settlement from 4th century in an area 1 km by 500–600 m to the south of Ayios Titos basilica, with wide streets in grid pattern and at least six churches; after the 618 earthquake, the rest of city reduced to fragmentary nuclei of inhabitation. Water distributed from aqueducts by channels set on high walls; by 7th century these had destroyed the pattern of the R city.

Basilica of Ayios Titos (Latin cross with narthex and exonarthex) founded probably in 6th century; many subsequent alterations. Basilica of Mavropapas near Pythion with three aisles and narthex (6th century). Two other basilicas (6th–7th century) with mosaics. Church (4th century; repairs in 6th century) on site of temple on acropolis.

Second half of 6th century–end of 7th century: cemetery to southeast of Ayios Titos basilica.

Around 670:   lower town destroyed. Acropolis fortified with circuit wall (until at least 11th century) and towers, on highest point.

Figure 12.3   Acropolis

LM III   Settlement on acropolis (LM IIIA and IIIB); partial reoccupation of Kannia house (LM IIIB).

G   Houses on acropolis and adjacent hill; shrine with open-air altar and votive dumps (with LM III–H objects) at southeastern edge and on side of acropolis was original temple of Athena Poliouchos.

A–R   Temple of Apollo Pythios (from second half of 7th century B.C.), enlarged in H times (late 3rd/early 2nd century B.C.) and reconstructed in R times reusing inscribed A blocks, with external altar on four high steps.

(End of) A: cutting of Gortyn Law Code on what was probably the inside face of a circular open-air wall forming part of an *ekklesiasterion.*

H: Odeion (middle of 1st century B.C.) inside earlier H building (law court?) on walls of which the Law Code was set; destroyed by earthquake and rebuilt by Trajan in A.D. 100; alterations in 3rd and 4th centuries.

R (after Augustus):   Praetorium, with two major rebuildings before 384: final phase with basilica, (large) baths, and temple (of deified Augusti?) with adjacent stoas.

VIII. BIBLIOGRAPHY

MINOAN

1959   Levi, D. "La villa rurale minoica di Gortina," *BdA* 44: 237–65.

1980   Kanta, A. *The Late Minoan III Period in Crete: A Survey of Sites, Pottery, and Their Distribution,* SIMA 58 (Gothenburg) 91–92.

1985   Gesell, G. C. *Town, Palace and House Cult in Minoan Crete,* SIMA 67 (Gothenburg) 43–44, 47–53, 62–65, 77–79.

Figure 12.4 Theater, Odeion, and Basilica of Ayios Titos

Figure 12.6 Odeion

Figure 12.5 Odeion

POST-MINOAN

1890   Svoronos 153–82.

1892   Comparetti, D. "Nuovi frammenti d'iscrizioni arcaiche trovate nel Pythion," *MonAnt* 1:77–120.

          Halbherr, F. "Relazioni sugli scavi del tempio di Apollo Pythio in Gortina," *MonAnt* 1:9–76.

1893   Ricci, S. "Il Pretorio di Gortyna secondo un disegno a penna e manoscritti inediti del secolo XVI," *MonAnt* 2:317–34.

1907   Savignoni, L., G. De Sanctis, and R. Paribeni. "Nuovi studii e scoperte in Gortyna," *MonAnt* 18:177–384.

1912   *RE* 7:1666–71 (E. Bürchner).

1925–26   Pernier, L. "L' 'Odeum' nell' 'agora' di Gortina presso il Leteo," *ASAtene* 8–9:1–69.

1950   *IC* 4 (= *IC* IV. 1–582).

1960   *EAA* 3:987–93 (E. Johannowski).

1967   Willetts, R. F. *The Law Code of Gortyn* (Berlin).

1968   Rizza, G., and V. Santa Maria Scrinari. *Il santuario sull'acropoli di Gortina* (Rome).

Figure 12.7 Basilica of Ayios Titos

Figure 12.8 Praetorium and Pythion

1974 Colini, A. M. "Intorno al Pythion di Gortina," in *Antichità cretesi* 2:129–35.

1976 *PECS* 362–63 (K. Branigan).

1979–80 Di Vita, A. "I terremoti a Gortina in età romana e protobizantina," *ASAtene* 57–58:435–40.

1982 Sanders, I. F. *Roman Crete* (Warminster).

1984 *Creta antica* 69–116 (A. Di Vita with M. A. Rizzo).

Di Vita, A. "Atti della Scuola 1981–1984," *ASAtene* 62:216–54.

1985 *Ancient Crete* 39–71 (A. Di Vita with M. A. Rizzo).

Di Vita, A. "Atti della Scuola," *ASAtene* 63:347–65.

———. "Contributi alla conoscenza di Gortina bizantina," in *5 Cretological* 2:137–43.

Ghedini, F. "Sculture dal ninfeo e dal pretorio di Gortina," *ASAtene* 63:63–248.

Ghisellini, E. "Sarcofagi romani di Gortina," *ASAtene* 63:249–335.

1988 Allegro, N., and M. Ricciardi. "Le fortificazione di Gortina in età ellenistica," *CrSt* 1:1–16.

Di Vita, A., ed. *Gortina* 1 (Rome).

IX. FINDS

Herakleion Museum.

X. DATE OF PHOTOGRAPHY

May 17, 1983.

GERALD CADOGAN

35°07′ N, 25°47′ E

I. IMPORTANCE

Gournia is the most completely excavated Minoan lowland town. It is well placed for both east–west and north–south communications because of its location near the north end of the Ierapetra isthmus and the nearby harbor at Sphoungaras. It had a long life from Early Minoan II to Late Minoan I and was resettled in Late Minoan IIIA2 and IIIB.

Gournia was particularly prosperous in Late Minoan I, when an official house (the "Palace") was built at the top of the town, with features imitating those of palaces, such as a grand west facade with setbacks (for windows on floor[s] above). The house looks across a court to the south. It must have been the local seat of government. The buildings around survive mostly as basements but with the paved streets and the packed setting around the hill, they suggest a lively Minoan town in New Palace times.

II. USE

EM II–LM I and LM IIIA2–IIIB settlement. (LN settlement at Sphoungaras nearby, and EM I/IIA–LM I cemetery.)

III. SITUATION

To the west of Pachyammos, well placed for access to the isthmus of Ierapetra and to land and sea routes along the north coast. Arable land around, including a valley to east, which may have been part of the ancient settlement. Likely water source: stream (and wells) in valley to the west (with springs today 1–2 km south). Settlement about 185 m north–south by 135 m east–west, making an area of about 25,000 sq m around the ridge.

Sphoungaras: spur facing southwest 200 m to the north by sea, with a steep rocky slope east of the beach.

IV. GEOMORPHOLOGY

Gournia is on a bedrock spur projecting north into the small coastal valley: an upturned ridge with a crest of resistant uptilted beds of slightly metamorphosed limestone (*sideropetra*) and outcrops of highly weathered igneous diorite along the west and north slopes.

V. EXCAVATION HISTORY

H. A. B. Hawes, 1901–4, and R. B. Seager, 1910, for the American Exploration Society.

VI. BUILDINGS

LN   Deposit at Sphoungaras below EM deposits.

EM II   No buildings, but scattered traces of EM IIA–IIB pottery, and burials at North Spur Cemetery just north of settlement; Sphoungaras: EM I/IIA–IIB rock-shelter burials (and some MM I).

EM III   No buildings; pottery dump in North Trench.

MM   Building sequence difficult to discern; more evidence from Old Palace "Early Gournia" phase than from earlier phases, though pithos burials from MM I exist at Sphoungaras. Probably occupation then as intensive as in LM I and (some at least of) the street and block system laid out. Principal buildings: houses Aa, Ek, and that beneath Ca. North Spur Cemetery in use with built house-tombs. Thick (defense?) wall at north end of settlement probably of this time.

MM III–LM I   Sphoungaras: continued use of cemetery, with pithos burials.

LM I   Grand official house ("Palace") about 50 by 37 m on crest of hill, facing south across Town Court (about 40 by 15 m) and west across paved West Court. Two building phases, with ashlar facade in later phase. Verandah (shrine?) at northwest corner of Town Court in southwest part of Palace, and elegant west facade with storerooms behind and rooms above. Other storerooms; lustral basin; and two central rooms (20–21), of which 21 is a large light well or small inner court. Entrances from south, west, and northeast, the last flanked by tower. Town around, mostly preserved as basements, divided into blocks by streets following contours or running up ridge. "Hill House" on slope across valley to east. LM IB destruction by fire and abandonment.

IIIA2–IIIB Resettlement, including probably ashlar House He at south end of Town Court (megaron? [Ölmann 1912]; post–Bronze Age? [Hood 1983]); also houses Eh, Ei, and Ej. Small Shrine at end of short lane in use in LM IIIB, probably built after LM I (Russell 1979) rather than in LM I (Hawes et al. 1908). Larnax burials: in settlement, and on opposite slope of valley to the west.

VIII. BIBLIOGRAPHY

General

1908 Hawes, H. A. B., B. E. Williams, R. B. Seager, and E. H. Hall. *Gournia, Vasiliki, and Other Prehistoric Sites on the Isthmus of Hierapetra, Crete* (Philadelphia).

1912 Hall, E. H. *Excavations in Eastern Crete: Sphoungaras*, University of Pennsylvania, The Museum, Anthropological Publications 3.2 (Philadelphia).
      Ölmann, N. "Ein achäisches Herrenhaus auf Kreta," *JdI* 27:38–51.

1965 Hawes, H. A. B. "Memoirs of a Pioneer Excavator in Crete," *Archaeology* 18:94–101, and "Memoirs of a Pioneer Excavator in Crete (Part II)," 268–76.

1968 Graham, J. W. "The Cretan Palace: Sixty-seven Years of Exploration," in *A Land Called Crete* 17–44.

1972 Branigan, K. "Minoan Settlements in East Crete," in *Man, Settlement, and Urbanism*. Proceedings of a meeting of the Research Seminar in Archaeology and Related Subjects held at the Institute of Archaeology, London University, ed. P. J. Ucko, R. Tringham, and G. W. Dimbleby (London) 751–59.

1979 Soles, J. S. "The Early Gournia Town," *AJA* 83:149–67.
      TUAS 4, including
        Betancourt, P. P. "The Pottery Chronology of Gournia: A Brief Sketch," 7–10.
        Russell, P. "The Date of the Gournia Shrine," 27–33.
        Silverman, J. S. "Excavating at Gournia, 1901–1904," 2–6.
        Soles, J. S. "Towards a Reconstruction of the Palace of Gournia," 11–17.

1980 Kanta, A. *The Late Minoan III Period in Crete: A Survey of Sites, Pottery, and Their Distribution*, SIMA 58 (Gothenburg) 139–40.

1983 Betancourt, P. P. *Minoan Objects Excavated from Vasilike, Pseira, Sphoungaras, Priniatikos Pyrgos, and Other Sites* (Philadelphia) 43–51.
      Hood, M. S. F. "The Country House," in *Minoan Society* 133.

1984 Damiani Indelicato, S. "Gournia, cité minoenne," in *Aux origines de l'hellénisme* 47–54.

1985 Gesell, G. C. *Town, Palace, and House Cult in Minoan Crete*, SIMA 67 (Gothenburg) 43, 70–73, 145, 147–49.

1989 Hood, M. S. F. "A Baetyl at Gournia?" in *Aphieroma ston Styliano Alexiou, Ariadne* 5:17–21.

1991 Betancourt, P. P., and J. S. Silverman. *Pottery from Gournia* (Philadelphia).
      Soles, J. S. "The Gournia Palace," *AJA* 95:17–78.

Forthcoming ———. *Prepalatial Cemeteries at Mochlos and Gournia, Hesperia* Supplement 24 (Princeton).

Scripts and Seals

1969 *CMS* 2.1:552–60 nos. 464–70 (N. Platon).

1977 *CMS* 2.2:351–53 nos. 247–48 (N. Platon, I. Pini, and G. Salies).

1979 *GORILA* 2:1–2.

1984 *CMS* 2.3:269–92 nos. 231–49 (N. Platon and I. Pini).

1985 *CMS* 2.4:79–81 nos. 60–61, 255–58 nos. 204–5 (N. Platon and I. Pini).

IX. FINDS

Herakleion Museum; University Museum, University of Pennsylvania, Philadelphia.

X. DATE OF PHOTOGRAPHY

April 16, 1981.

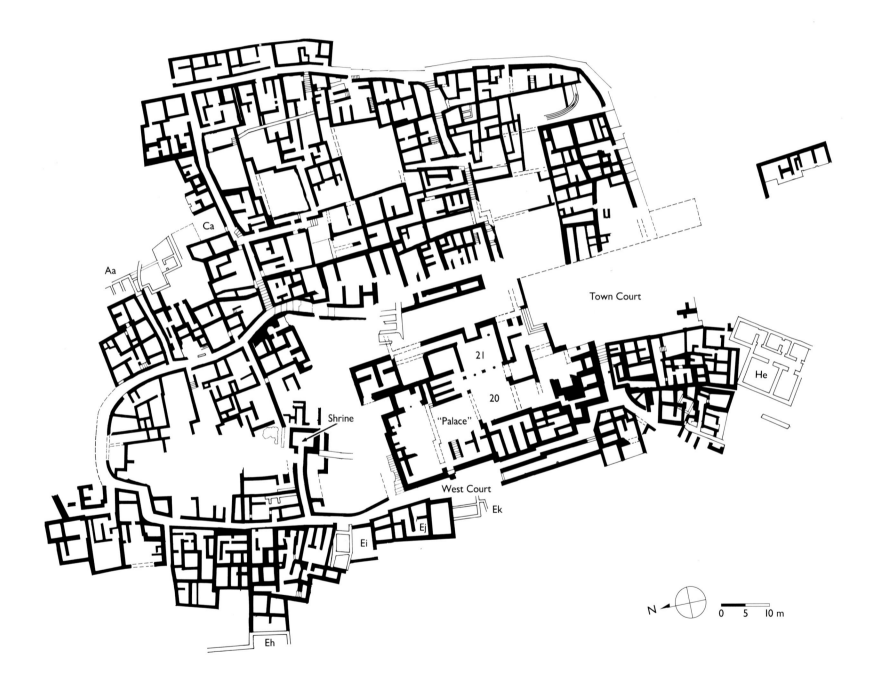

Figure 13.1 Plan of Gournia

Figure 13.2 Gournia and surroundings

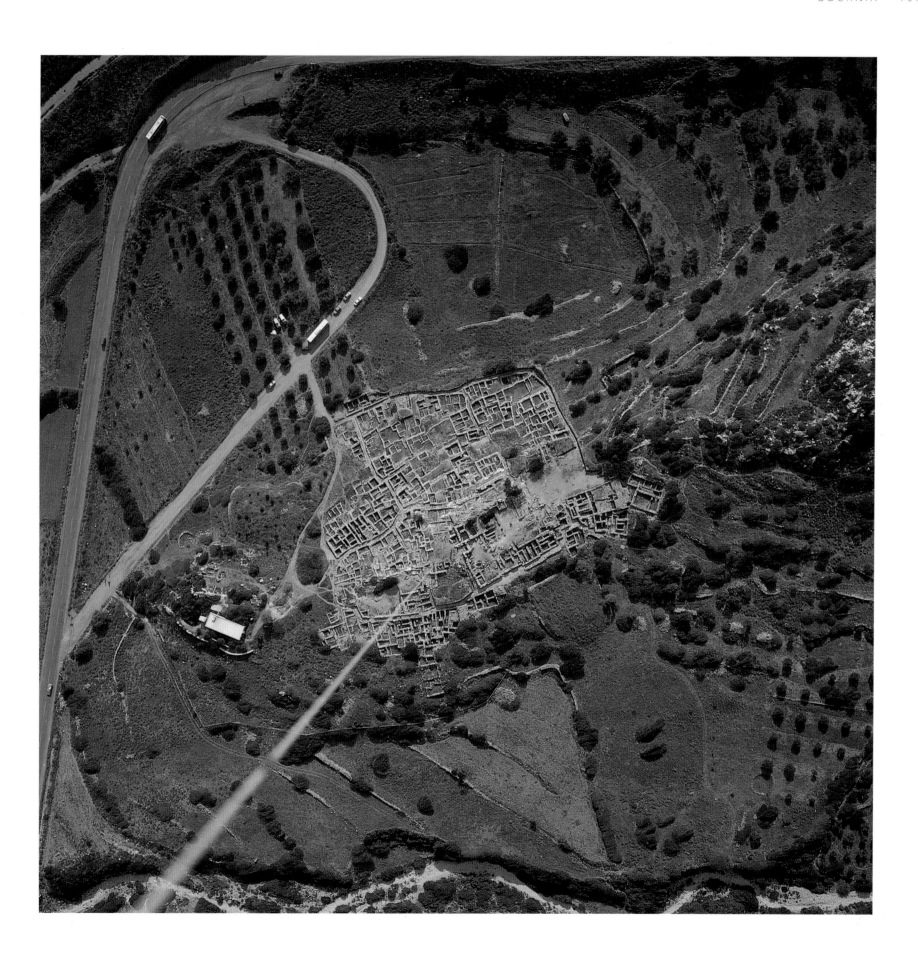

Figure 13.3 The Minoan town

Figure 13.4   Gournia, looking north toward Sphoungaras and the
Bay of Mirabello

Figure 13.5 "Palace"

Figure 13.6   Shrine

Figure 13.7   House He

VINCENZO LA ROSA

35°02′ N, 24°48′ E

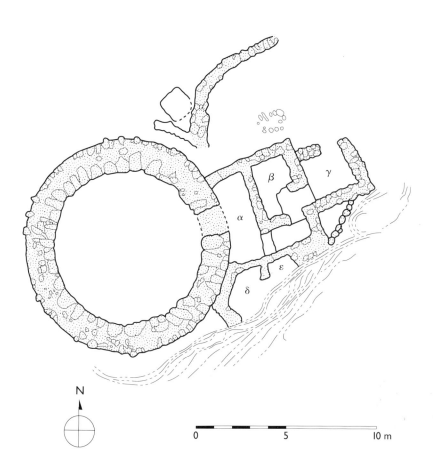

Figure 14.1   Kamilari tholos tomb

Figure 14.2   Tomb

I. IMPORTANCE

The tholos tomb at Kamilari has produced clear evidence that such tombs originally had stone roofs. It is also notable for its long, and not necessarily intermittent, use.

The tomb was partly disturbed in ancient times, when its five annexes, intended originally for votive offerings, were used as ossuaries. North of these was an "enclosure for offerings," with the earliest pottery from the tomb and many small stone vases, all upside down. About 500 vases have been found in this complex, with a further 250 inside the tomb, along with about 500 conical cups and 70 stone vases and 20 clay sealings.

Of special interest are clay models, found in the annexes, which belong to the last (Late Minoan IIIA) burials and probably were part of a cult of the dead. The best known of these are an offering scene inside a small sanctuary and a group of dancers circling and performing a ritual dance.

II. USE

MM IB–LM IIIA₂ tomb.

III. SITUATION

On the low hill of Grigori Koryphi, 1.6 km northwest of Kamilari village and 1.9 km southwest of Ayia Triada.

IV. GEOMORPHOLOGY

The foundations of the tholos tomb were set on an artificially leveled bedrock platform cut into the soft marl-limestone bedrock of the area, which on the 1:50,000 Geological Map of Crete (Tymbakion region) is mapped as "white marly limestone and marls" of lower Pliocene age. This rock unit is very likely correlative with the early Pliocene Kourtes formation just east of the town of Mires, mapped and described by Meulenkamp et al. (1977). The marl bedrock was

Figure 14.3   Tomb and entrance

used as a wall for some of the exterior rooms on the east side of the tholos. With an unlimited quantity of such bedrock available, it was not difficult to quarry, dress, and set the large blocking slab that was found still covering the entrance to the tholos.

V. EXCAVATION HISTORY

D. Levi, 1959, for the Italian School.

VI. BUILDINGS

MM IB–LM IIIA2   Tholos tomb, internal d 7.65 m, with stone roof; and ossuaries α, β; with γ, δ, ε, added in MM IIIA (?).

VIII. BIBLIOGRAPHY

General

1961–62   Levi, D. "La tomba a tholos di Kamilari presso Festòs," *ASAtene* 39–40:7–148.

1976   ———. *Festòs e la civiltà minoica* I, *Incunabula Graeca* 60 (Rome) 703–41.

Pelon, O. *Tholoi, tumuli et cercles funéraires* (Athens) 19–22.

1979–80   Mallegni, F. "Su alcuni reperti ossei umani della tholos di Kamilari," *ASAtene* 57–58:187–95.

1980   Kanta, A. *The Late Minoan III Period in Crete: A Survey of Sites, Pottery, and Their Distribution*, *SIMA* 58 (Gothenburg) 101–2.

1984   *Creta antica* 197–201 (V. La Rosa).

1985   *Ancient Crete* 139–42 (V. La Rosa).

Seals

1977   *CMS* 2.2:29–30 no. 25 (N. Platon, I. Pini, and G. Salies).

Geomorphology

1977   Meulenkamp, J. E., A. Jonkers, and P. Spaak. "Late Miocene to Early Pliocene Development of Crete," in *Proceedings of the Sixth Colloquium on the Geology of the Aegean Region.* (Athens) 1:137–49.

IX. FINDS

Herakleion Museum.

X. DATE OF PHOTOGRAPHY

May 7, 1984.

GERALD CADOGAN

35°13′ N, 25°28′ E

I, 16–17, 27, 57–58, 85, 106, 116   Shrines
8–9, 11–18   "Great House"
21–23, 29–31, 33–37   Storerooms
58–61, 80   "Priest's House"
138–40   Megaron (eastern area)

0   10   20   30 m

Figure 15.1   Plan of Karphi

I. IMPORTANCE

Karphi is important as an extensively excavated large town from the very end of the Minoan era, Late Minoan IIIC—and thus comparable to, though larger than, Myrtos–Phournou Koryphi at the beginning (Early Minoan II). An abundance of pottery and some bronze dress ornaments show links with the rest of Crete and with the southern Aegean and Cyprus. Besides herding and hunting, its inhabitants (whom the excavators estimated at 3,500) cultivated olives, at an altitude considerably lower than that of the town itself (1,100 m).

The position of the town is remarkable for its elevation, and for its site on a prominent rock called Karphi, "nail," which is visible from the east beyond the isthmus of Ierapetra and from as far west as the region of Herakleion. Though cold in winter, it could have been inhabited year-round because the settlement itself is out of the north wind.

The Late Minoan IIIC settlers may have chosen Karphi for defense as a place of refuge, or it may have been a base for brigands—as the Lasithi plain became later. Two pieces of evidence suggest that there may also have been religious reasons for choosing the site: in Middle Minoan times there seems to have been a mountain shrine at the summit; and during the life of the town there was again a shrine there, with cult statues of goddesses with raised arms. (And

Figure 15.2   Aerial view

there were other shrines in the town.) The summit shrine could have been a holy place far and wide.

The aerial photograph made in 1983 shows the erosion of the site since the 1939 excavation, which explains the apparent differences between the plan and the photograph.

II. USE

MM shrine; LM IIIC(–PG?) settlement and cemeteries; A–C shrine at Vitzelovrysis spring?

III. SITUATION

On the prominent peak of Karphi and the adjacent peaks of Mikri Koprana and Megali Koprana, projecting north from the Lasithi massif, about 1,100 m high. Karphi, 1.4 km north of Lagou, commands the entrance to the Lasithi plain (and routes to southern Crete) and overlooks all of north central Crete from near Herakleion and Knossos to the Bay of Mirabello. Grazing land around. Arable land below to the north and in the Lasithi plain. Springs nearby at Vitzelovrysis and Astividero. About a third of the settlement has been excavated. Maximum dimensions of excavation: main area 130 by 130 m; east area 150 by 70 m; Mikri Koprana 40 by 30 m.

IV. GEOMORPHOLOGY

Karphi is a knob of limestone of the Tripolitza series, just at its contact with rocks of the Phyllite-Quartzite series of the same tectonic unit. Although the Phyllite-Quartzite series rocks—metamorphic conglomerates, sandstones, and volcanics—are older than the Tripolitza limestones, at this locality they appear at the surface a few hundred meters east of the limestone. Springs and seeps are common along the contact between the two units.

There is no doubt that the north wall of the summit shrine (1 on Fig. 15.1) has been lost to erosion down the steep north slope.

V. EXCAVATION HISTORY

J. D. S. Pendlebury and others, 1937–39, for the British School.

VI. BUILDINGS

MM   Scanty finds suggest mountain shrine at summit.

LM IIIC   Town with houses, paved streets, and yards. Buildings on all three peaks, of local hard limestone, split but not dressed: mainly of one storey, but some basements; chimneys made from broken pithoi. Summit shrine; "Great House" with shrine; "Priest's House" with shrine; other shrines; storerooms. Apparent megaron in eastern area. Large buildings on Mikri Koprana (147–50; not in Fig. 15.1) and Megali Koprana. Some evidence of two (or more) phases in the area of rooms 70, 71, and 73. PG pottery reported (but not published) suggests settlement and cemeteries could have continued into 10th century B.C.

Cemeteries of wholly or partly freestanding small tholos tombs, seventeen around Vitzelovrysis spring to the southwest and four near Astividero spring to the east.

(A–C)   Scanty finds suggest shrine at Vitzelovrysis.

VIII. BIBLIOGRAPHY

General

1937–38   Pendlebury, H. W., J. D. S. Pendlebury, and M. B. Money-Coutts, "Excavations in the Plain of Lasithi. III. Karphi: A City of Refuge in the Early Iron Age in Crete. Excavated by Students of the British School of Archaeology at Athens, 1937–39," *BSA* 38:57–145.

1960   Seiradaki, M. B. "Pottery from Karphi," *BSA* 55:1–37.

1972   Desborough, V. R. d'A. *The Greek Dark Ages* (London) 58–62, 120–29, 372.

1977   Watrous, L. V. "Aegean Settlements and Transhumance," *TUAS* 2:2–6.

1980   Kanta, A. *The Late Minoan III Period in Crete: A Survey of Sites, Pottery, and Their Distribution*, SIMA 58 (Gothenburg) 121.

1982   Watrous, L. V. *Lasithi: A History of Settlement on a Highland Plain in Crete*, Hesperia Supplement 18 (Princeton) 8, 13, 19–20.

1985   Gesell, G. C. *Town, Palace, and House Cult in Minoan Crete*, SIMA 67 (Gothenburg) 45–46, 79–83, 147.

1987   Nowicki, K. "The History and Setting of the Town at Karphi," *SMEA* 26:235–56.

———. "Topography of Refuge Settlement in Crete," *JRGZM* 34:213–34.

Rutkowski, B. "The Temple at Karphi," *SMEA* 26:257–79.

Figure 15.3   Karphi, "the nail"

Seals

1977   *CMS* 2.2:271–72 no. 199 (N. Platon, I. Pini, and G. Salies).

1984   *CMS* 2.3:263–64 no. 227 (N. Platon and I. Pini).

IX. FINDS

Herakleion Museum.

X. DATE OF PHOTOGRAPHY

July 2, 1983.

Figure 15.4   Tholos tombs at Vitzelovrysis

Figure 15.5   Tholos tombs at Vitzelovrysis

GERALDINE C. GESELL, LESLIE P. DAY, AND WILLIAM D. E. COULSON

35°06′ N, 25°52′ E

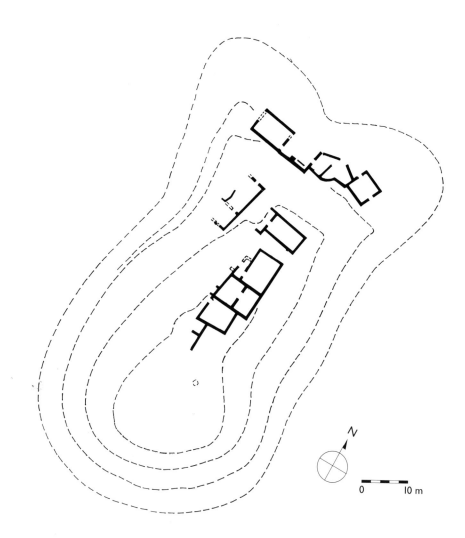

Figure 16.1   Kavousi, Kastro

Figure 16.2   Kavousi, Kastro

I. IMPORTANCE

At Kavousi two important Early Iron Age settlements have strategic positions overlooking the coast, the plains, and mountain passes at the eastern end of the Bay of Mirabello. The upper site, the Kastro, "castle," is illustrated here; an associated site, Vronda, is further down the mountain. Finds from houses include domestic pottery, stone tools, loom weights, and spindle whorls. One room on the Kastro contained a deposit of small, crude terracotta female figurines, another a stone kernos for offerings. Bones and microfaunal remains from both sites indicate the exploitation of a wide area from upland terraces to seashore. Finds in tombs on nearby slopes include fine pottery, bronze jewelry and armor, and iron tools and weapons.

Settlements on high strategic sites are characteristic of the period. Vrokastro at the western end of the Bay of Mirabello; Dreros, west of Ayios Nikolaos; and Prinias in central Crete are other well-known examples.

II. USE

Kastro: LM IIIC–O settlement; Vronda LM IIIC–SM settlement. (At Vronda, LM IIIC–SM settlement with cemetery; the abandoned houses were reused for LG cremation burials.)

III. SITUATION

On the craggy peak of Kastro in the Thripti range of the Siteia mountains, 710 m high. Overlooks the north pass from the isthmus of Ierapetra to far eastern Crete. About 1 km to the southeast are upland terraces for farming, and directly to the south and southwest are steep terraces for vines. The nearest water sources today are at Xerambela, near Vronda ridge, 400 m high and 45 minutes' walk below Kastro, and Mylora, southeast of Kastro, higher up the mountain above the terracing. Settlement about 70 m north–south by 40 m east–west.

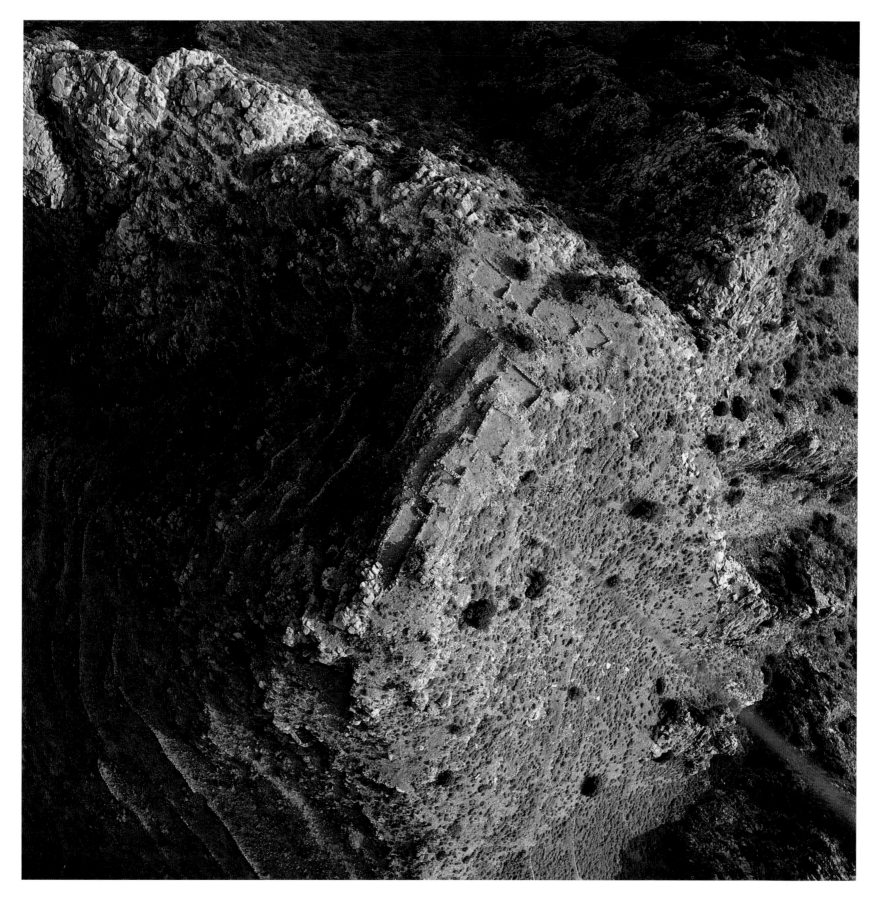

Figure 16.3 Kavousi, Kastro

IV. GEOMORPHOLOGY

The Kastro site is located on a northward-jutting spur of the Plattenkalk series (Jurassic-Eocene), which is the "basement" tectonic unit of Crete, the lowest in the series of nappes that form the pre–Neogene age rocks of the island. Although these rocks were identified on the 1955 Geological Map of Crete (Ierapetra region) as "Metamorphic Series of Sitia, Upper Phyllites," further study has correlated them with the more widespread Plattenkalk series. The Thripti mountains, which are the topographic expression of the Plattenkalk series in this area, are composed of flaggy limestones and phyllites, with local gypsum and chert-rich dolomite beds intercalated.

The balloon photograph (Fig. 16.2) shows how the site buildings cling to the crest of a narrow ridge of upturned, vertically dipping limestone that is harder than the adjacent, differentially weathered, phyllite beds. Evidence of jointing is clearly visible in the limestone. It is interesting that the wall stones are made mostly of natural flags of phyllite whereas the structures they form were founded on the more stable limestone bedrock.

V. EXCAVATION HISTORY

H. A. Boyd, 1900, for the American Exploration Society; G. C. Gesell, L. P. Day, and W. D. E. Coulson, 1981–84, 1987–90, for the American School.

VI. BUILDINGS

LM IIIC–O Settlement (with cemeteries of small tholos tombs to the south at Plaï tou Kastrou, to the southwest at Aloni, and to the east at Skouriasmenos and a shrine at Plaï tou Kastrou). In excavated area, eight houses on six terraces, but settlement continues down slopes and probably across saddle to Plaï tou Kastrou. Houses of undressed limestone with mud mortar; many floors, benches, and lower walls cut out of bedrock.

VIII. BIBLIOGRAPHY

General

1901 Boyd, H. A. "Excavations at Kavousi, Crete, in 1900," *AJA* 5:137–43.

1927–29 Levi, D. "Lo stile geometrico cretese," *ASAtene* 10–12: 562–67.

1983 Gesell, G. C., L. P. Day, and W. D. E. Coulson. "Excavations and Survey at Kavousi, 1978–1981," *Hesperia* 52: 389–420.

1985 ———. "Kavousi, 1982–1983: The Kastro," *Hesperia* 54:327–55.

1986 Day, L. P., W. D. E. Coulson, and G. C. Gesell. "Kavousi 1983–1984: The Settlement at Vronda," *Hesperia* 55: 355–87.

1988 Gesell, G. C., L. P. Day, and W. D. E. Coulson. "Excavations at Kavousi, Crete, 1987," *Hesperia* 57:279–301.

1991 Gesell, G. C., W. D. E. Coulson, and L. P. Day. "Excavations at Kavousi, Crete, 1988," *Hesperia* 60:145–77.

 Klippel, W. E., and L. M. Snyder. "Dark-Age Fauna from Kavousi, Crete: The Vertebrates from the 1987 and 1988 Excavations," *Hesperia* 60:179–86.

Seals

1984 *CMS* 2.3:293–94 no. 250 (N. Platon and I. Pini).

Figure 16.4   Kavousi, Kastro (middle peak)

IX. FINDS

Herakleion Museum; Ierapetra Museum; University Museum, University of Pennsylvania, Philadelphia.

X. DATE OF PHOTOGRAPHY

July 10, 1983 (Kastro).

GERALD CADOGAN

35°18′ N, 25°10′ E

1   Roman basilica and forum; Classical agora probably nearby
2   House of the Frescoes
3   Spring Chamber and Caravanserai
4   Sanctuary of Demeter
5   Middle Minoan tholos tomb

0   500   1000 m

Figure 17.1   Knossos area

Figure 17.2   Knossos palace and Kairatos valley

I. IMPORTANCE

Knossos is the longest-inhabited place in Crete, having been settled early in Neolithic times, probably before 7000 B.C. It is famous in classical mythology as the home of Minos and in archaeology as the site of the principal Bronze Age palace of Crete. During the New Palace period it must have been the capital of the island.

Evans started large-scale excavation of the Minoan palace in 1900, calling the building the palace in the title of his first annual report. He used the periods he observed in the stratigraphy in (and around) the palace as the basis of his chronological scheme for the Cretan Bronze Age, which he named Minoan, after King Minos. Excavation and surface exploration still continue at Knossos, and the site is far from fully exposed. Many parts of its long history still need clarifying. The principal lack is probably a detailed and systematic knowledge of the Minoan town around the palace. Reconstructions that show the palace set amid fields are misleading.

The first settlers chose the low freestanding hill in the Kairatos river valley known as Kephala. Near the north coast of Crete and in the center of the island, this hill has as good a situation as may be conceived for communicating by land with the rest of the island, yet it is sufficiently far from the sea so that people could prepare for, or escape from, enemies attacking from that direction. Its key position is reflected today in Herakleion's economic dominance of the island.

The Neolithic settlement is known principally from soundings around the Kephala hill, from which the sequence has been divided into ten principal strata (X–I). The first settlement (Stratum X, and possibly earlier) covered a small area (about 0.25 ha) of what was to be the site of the palace. The (Aceramic Neolithic) settlers did not use pottery but did build with mud brick and had a developed economy with mixed farming. They grew wheat, barley, and lentils and raised sheep and goats, pigs, and some cattle.

During the long Early Neolithic I phase (Strata IX–V) the settlement seems to have grown to cover almost all of the palace site (about 2 ha). During Early Neolithic I the construction of the rectangular buildings changed from mud brick to pisé, or packed mud, laid on a stone foundation; but the principal innovation was the in-

Figure

0   10   20   40 m

1 Royal Road
2 Theatral Area
3 North West Treasury
4 West Court
5 Koulores
6 West Entrance
7 Corridor of the Procession Fresco
8 Storerooms and corridor (west side)
9 Stepped Portico
10 South House
11 Lustral Basin (north end)
12 North Pillar Hall
13 North Entrance Passage
14 Keep
15 Throne Room
16 Vat Room
17 Temple Repositories
18 Tripartite Shrine
19 Pillar Crypts
20 Propylaeum
21 South Porch (south entrance)
22 Central Court
23 Storerooms (east side)
24 Animal Pens(?)
25 Royal Pottery Stores
26 Storerooms of the Giant Pithoi
27 East Hall (siet of)
28 Loom Weight Basement
29 "school Room"
30 Lapidary's Workshop
31 Residential or Domestic Quarter
32 Grand Staircase
33 Hall of the Double Axes
34 Court of the Distaffs
35 Dressing Room (and lavatory)
36 Queen's Hall and Bathroom
37 Monolithic Pillar Basement
38 House of Chancel Screen
39 South East House

Figure 17.4 Palace

troduction of fired pottery at the beginning of the phase. Early Neolithic II (Stratum IV) was also a long phase, by the end of which the settlement had grown to about 3 ha. Near the end of the phase, clay spinning and weaving equipment appeared for the first time at Knossos, foreshadowing the great importance that the Linear B tablets show its wool industry had some three thousand years later. Middle Neolithic (Stratum III), with considerable evidence of technological quickening, was followed by Late Neolithic (Strata II–I), by which time the settlement may have covered 5 ha or more. From a Late Neolithic level comes the earliest metal object from Crete, a copper axe; houses had fixed hearths for the first time; and some of the latest (Final Neolithic) pottery shows close similarities with that of Phaistos. Final Neolithic has also been found at Gortyn.

The transition from Neolithic to Early Minoan at Knossos, probably around the middle of the 4th millennium B.C., is not yet understood. The principal evidence of Early Minoan I is a deep well in the northeastern part of the palace filled with badly burnt pottery of the phase. Whether the destruction resulted from a small or a widespread event is unknown.

The Early Minoan II settlement seems to have been large and prosperous, spreading to both sides of the later Royal Road as well as the south front of the palace, where there are also EM III remains. Finds include imported stone vases from the Cyclades and Egypt and Early Helladic II pottery from mainland Greece. The best Early Minoan II remains belong to a partly excavated and now backfilled building below the West Court, the Early Minoan IIA West Court House, which was destroyed by fire. It may have been a ruler's residence or a center of the community of some other type: the quality of its pottery suggests a special importance.

Early Minoan III seems to have been a short phase at Knossos leading into Middle Minoan IA. A large building of which walls survive at the northwest corner of the palace may be a predecessor of the Old Palace, a "proto-palace." If so, it would represent an intermediate stage between the West Court House and the Old Palace. The thick-walled Keep at the north end of the Central Court may be related to it. Also contemporary may be the Hypogaeum, an underground cistern or granary below the South Porch.

The settlement grew greatly in Middle Minoan IA, the last phase before the Old Palace, both northeast toward Makryteichos village and 500 m west-northwest up the Acropolis hill. The viaduct and roadway crossing the Vlychia stream south of the palace and the Stepped Portico leading up the Kephala hill may be of Middle Minoan IA date.

Figure 17.5 Palace, with Royal Road

How the Old Palace came into being in Middle Minoan IB (Evans's date) is unclear; and the details of its phasing—and building history—are under scrutiny. Little is preserved of the building beneath the New Palace. Its plan is likely to have been similar to that of the New Palace, with the structure surrounding an open space, the Central Court. (The Throne Room opening onto the Central Court dates back to the Old Palace.) Whether the Old Palace grew from a collection of blocks, or insulae, as has often been suggested, is difficult to establish. More certain is that it had (at least) two major building phases, in the later of which the West Court was laid out on a terrace outside the palace and the round pits known as the kouloures were constructed in it (which were probably granaries or possibly places for sacred offerings—compare similar pits at Phaistos and the set of eight circular structures at Mallia). The pits were built over houses of the end of the Prepalatial period.

The West Court must have been used as a place of public assembly and thus was a link between palace and town. Roads from the town lead in the direction of the palace. Inside the building, there is evidence on the west side of administration (Hieroglyphic tablets), storage (early storerooms), and, probably, cult practice; the Vat Room deposit seems to consist of ritual offerings. (This combination of functions is particularly noticeable on the west side in New Palace times.) Other storerooms were on the east side, where the giant pithoi and the so-called Royal Pottery Stores were located.

The Loom Weight Basement on the east side had over four hundred loom weights as substantial evidence for weaving. That almost all the Middle Minoan pottery that went abroad—to the Aegean islands, mainland Greece, and the Levant—came from the Knossos or Phaistos workshops suggests that one or both palaces were the leaders in trade and foreign relations.

It is difficult to know whether life in the Old Palace had a large religious component or was primarily secular and whether such modern distinctions are valid at all in the Middle Bronze Age. By the time of the New Palaces, sacred and secular often appear completely interlinked. Nor is it clear how much Knossos should be seen as the capital of Middle Minoan Crete. The considerable regional cultural diversity of the Old Palace period may reflect different political units, whereas the island-wide homogeneity of the New Palace period supports domination from one center, Knossos.

Little has been recovered of the Old Palace period town. A rescue excavation on the slope west of the palace found well-laid architecture and probable waterworks. Tombs of the period are known on the hill of Ailias east of the palace (the Ailias and Mavro Spelio cemeteries) and on Gypsades to the south.

The Old Palace was destroyed by unknown means at the end of Middle Minoan II or, more probably, early in Middle Minoan III. It was immediately rebuilt (despite—or after—an earthquake whose date in later Middle Minoan III or even at the transition to Late Minoan IA is still to be agreed). This rebuilding and the number of grand houses built in the town of Knossos in Late Minoan I (the probable period when the palace expanded most), along with the splendor and variety of the works of art of the New Palace period, give evidence of the great wealth Knossos must have accumulated by the end of the Old Palace period.

The Minoan town reached its greatest extent, perhaps as much as 75 ha, in Middle Minoan III–Late Minoan I, a time when its population is estimated to have been at around 12,000, similar to that of medieval Herakleion. Isolated farms have been detected on the edge of the main settlement.

The New Palace period building program may have slowed only in later Late Minoan IA after earthquakes that may be associated with the eruption of Thera. It did not pick up significantly in Late Minoan IB or Late Minoan II. The Unexplored Mansion, for instance, was left unfinished in Late Minoan IA.

During Late Minoan IB there was a major destruction by fire in the town of Knossos, the palace apparently being unaffected. Signs of the disaster have been observed in excavations north of the Royal Road, in the South House below the southwest angle of the palace, and, most strikingly, in new excavations behind the Stratigraphical Museum upslope to the west of the Unexplored Mansion. There the bones of at least four children have been found in what appears to be a ritual context. The bones show butchery marks. With them were edible snails and at least one sheep that had been killed. Most likely this evidence denotes ritual cannibalism, perhaps an attempt to avert the disaster that soon overtook the town of Knossos.

Very few tombs are known of Middle Minoan III–Late Minoan I. The most remarkable is the two-storey Temple Tomb, on the east slope of Gypsades, with its burial chamber, courtyard, and pavilion. Late Minoan I saw the last use of the Ailias cemetery and of the Gypsades tholos tomb.

Late Minoan II brought changes in culture that continued into LM IIIA and further destructions by fire (on two separate occasions, as observed in the Unexplored Mansion). One immediate change was that burial grounds were dispersed and graves usually for single or family use, rather than communal use as before. A new custom, probably derived from mainland Greece, where it is known first in the Late Helladic I Shaft Graves of Mycenae, was burial with weapons in the so-called Warrior Graves, indicating Late Minoan II–IIIA1 squires or officers, and/or burial with large numbers of bronze vessels (notably in the Late Minoan IIIA1 Sellopoulo Tombs 3 and 4 and in the Late Minoan IIIA2 Zapher Papoura Tombs 14 and 36). Similar burials with bronzes have been found at Archanes-Phourni, Phaistos (Kalyvia cemetery), and Chania. Some of these bronzes were made by smiths working at the Unexplored Mansion before it burned down during Late Minoan II.

Other changes at Knossos include the introduction of rectangular chamber tombs with long straight dromoi (seen later, for instance, at Armeni) and of built tholos tombs of mainland Mycenaean derivation rather than Early Minoan and Middle Minoan Mesara type (compare Archanes-Phourni, where both varieties of tholos tomb are found). With them should be placed the tholos-like Royal Tomb at Isopata (destroyed in World War II) and, perhaps, the Tomb of the Double Axes, which has a grave in the floor in the shape of a double axe. Finally, the contents of many Late Minoan II–IIIA1 tombs are closely similar to those of tombs in mainland Greece and on Rhodes.

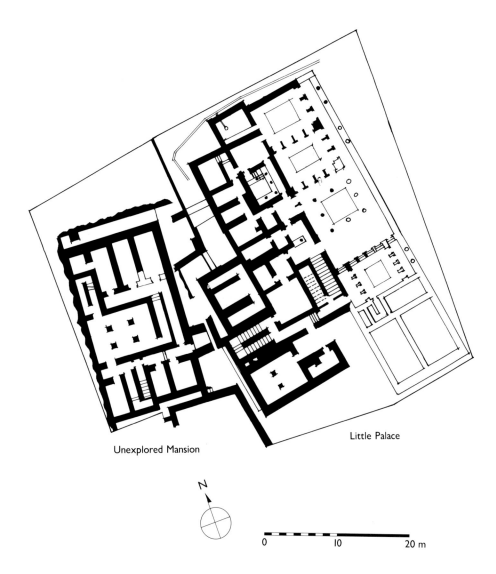

Unexplored Mansion

Little Palace

N

0   10   20 m

Figure 17.6   Little Palace and Unexplored Mansion

The biggest change of all was the appearance of the Greek language in the Linear B script, in a large archive of clay tablets dating from just before the destruction of the palace. The decipherment by Ventris (Ventris and Chadwick 1956) of the script as Greek confirms what the other changes of culture suggest, that Mycenaean Greeks were in charge of Knossos and, probably, of all Crete, which they seem to have controlled by an intensive Knossos-based bureaucracy. They most likely came in the aftermath, or as agents, of the Late Minoan IB destructions by fire that occurred through much of the island.

Late Minoan IIIA1 for many scholars, notably Popham (1970), represents the last phase during which the palace of Knossos func

tioned as a palace. A fierce fire destroyed the palace early in the Late Minoan IIIA2 phase, marking the end of the New Palace period. But others think the palace was destroyed at the transition from Late Minoan IIIA2 to Late Minoan IIIB, or even late in Late Minoan IIIB. Since 1958 the issue has aroused considerable controversy, which has had the benefit of leading to close study both of the stratigraphy and pottery of the destruction deposits in the palace and of their association with the Linear B tablets. Two issues govern individual views on where, between 1370 and 1190 B.C., the tablets are to be dated: what happened in Crete under Mycenaean rule and whether Knossos remained the principal center of the island after 1370 (with a relationship to Chania in western Crete that has yet to be defined) or ceded its leading role at that time to Chania, where Linear B literacy continued after 1370 B.C.

The New Palace and the buildings in the town may be considered an architectural unity, although the period at Knossos spans two centuries (or three, according to the new "high" chronology). Determining the functions of the different parts of the palace, or of other buildings, depends partly on evidence through the Late Minoan IB phase and partly on Late Minoan II–IIIA1/2 evidence, though there is always an uncertainty in extrapolating from one phase to the other. The principal changes of culture are noted above. Life seems to have continued in much the same way after the arrival of Mycenaeans.

The west side of the palace, at ground level, was devoted to shrines and storage (of farm produce, works of art, and probably precious raw materials and textiles), with (Linear B) administration concentrated in the western half of the north end of the building. The parade of storerooms inside the west facade and the great number of boxes (cists) beneath the floors indicate an enormous storage capacity and wealth. The principal shrine may have been the Throne Room, with the throne used for a priestess (and queen or princess?) as the epiphany of the Minoan goddess, rather than for a king, as Evans thought. On the upper floor grand staterooms may be reconstructed, with windows opening onto the West Court that could have been used for ceremonial appearances. Internal approaches to the storerooms are restricted, as the plan (Fig. 17.3) shows. The main approach to this part of the palace was from the West Court by the Corridor of the Procession Fresco, in which life-size figures are depicted entering the palace carrying gifts or offerings. Among the finds from the west side are female faience figures holding snakes from the Temple Repositories—boxes beneath the floor in a small room immediately south of the staircase ascending to the upper west side from the Central Court and behind (west of) the Tripartite Shrine that faces onto the Central Court.

Figure 17.7 Little Palace and Unexplored Mansion

The north end of the palace is divided by a passage coming up from the North Pillar Hall, above which there may have been a dining hall like those that have been inferred over the pillared halls at the north ends of the Central Courts of Mallia and Zakro.

The West Court continued in use from Old Palace to New Palace times (this was not the case at Phaistos). To the northwest is the Theatral Area, used for receptions, assemblies, or performances and approached by the Royal Road from the west. Its line, if prolonged, continues in the street found in the new excavations behind the Stratigraphical Museum.

The east side of the palace has three floor levels preserved, one at the level of the Central Court and two dug into the east slope of the Kephala hill where it drops towards the Kairatos river. Above the level of the Central Court there would have been at least one more floor. The Grand Staircase, a masterpiece of Minoan architecture, descends from the Central Court to the lower floors, which Evans took to be the Residential or Domestic Quarter of the palace. A complex group of rooms is similar—on a larger scale—to those at the north end of Phaistos.

Drainage and water systems are well preserved on the east side. There was a system that brought clean water to the lavatory attached to the Dressing Room in the Domestic Quarter and removed dirty water as well as removing storm water from the light wells; and a drainhead and stone drains probably took storm water away from the East Hall that is presumed to have been immediately north of the Grand Staircase.

Of the south front little is preserved. As on the east side, terraces supported the palace buildings. The magnitude of the earthquake that occurred in Middle Minoan IIIB (or at the beginning of Late Minoan IA) is clear in the House of the Fallen Blocks close to the south front. Here huge stone blocks fell from the palace facade into the house, where they are still to be seen. The blocks themselves are also evidence of the imposing scale of the first phase of the New Palace.

Frescoes adorned the walls of both the palace and other buildings in the town. Study of the Late Cycladic I (Late Minoan IA) frescoes at Akrotiri on Thera suggests that the Knossos frescoes have a thematic character centered on the Minoan goddess and her worship. In the later years of the New Palace period, frescoes of chariot-driving scenes were painted, probably at the command of the Mycenaean rulers.

Little is known of the town of Knossos in the New Palace period. Most buildings excavated are grand town houses, which may be compared to the grand houses in the country such as those at Makryyialos, Myrtos-Pyrgos, Tylissos, or Vathypetro. Some of the town houses, such as the South House and the House of the Chancel Screen, impinge on the palace almost as much as the houses at Zakro do on the palace there. This might indicate the power of a nobility, or it may have some humbler explanation, such as lack of space or force of habit. We know least about the places where ordinary people lived. We have some idea of workshops. Kilns, for instance, have been found southeast of the palace and in the excavations behind the Stratigraphical Museum; and the Unexplored Mansion (so called because for a long time it was known to be there but had not been investigated) had a bronze smithy in Late Minoan II.

Postpalatial Knossos, though still important, was less so than Chania, which, with its evidence for continued Linear B literacy and for trade links with Cyprus and mainland Greece, probably became the capital of Crete when Knossos fell. Ayia Triada, with Kommos nearby, also rose in importance at this time.

Traces of Late Minoan IIIA2–IIIB use are found scattered throughout the town, but it is likely that occupation was much less intensive than before. The palace seems to have been a ruin, with people inhabiting cleared-out parts; most rooms were full of debris. (This story is different for those who date the destruction of the palace to late in Late Minoan IIIB.) Similarly, the Unexplored Mansion, which had some use in Late Minoan IIIA2, was a ruin by Late Minoan IIIB, with a shrine on the upper floor. Another Late Minoan IIIB shrine, set up in the former lustral basin of the Little Palace, was furnished with curious natural stone concretions, which Evans interpreted as fetish symbols.

The new excavations behind the Stratigraphical Museum have revealed no buildings of Late Minoan IIIB date, but there is a new and extensive Late Minoan IIIC settlement, with several phases continuing into Sub-Minoan, that adds greatly to our hitherto scanty knowledge of this time at Knossos. Finds from nearby rescue excavations suggest that this Late Minoan IIIC–Sub-Minoan settlement west of the palace ruins was quite large and could have served as the nucleus for Knossians using widely dispersed cemeteries. Unusual discoveries in the new excavations are a horse's skull and intramural burials of babies under the floor, which was a mainland Mycenaean practice (found at Knossos earlier in the Late Minoan II [Mycenaean] use of the Unexplored Mansion). These burials along with mainland traits in the pottery suggest that some settlers at this new spot were Mycenaeans. Rooted more in the Minoan tradition is the use of the Spring Chamber next to the Caravanserai just above the Vlychia stream as a shrine. It was a fountain house in the New Palace period.

The principal Late Minoan IIIC–Sub-Minoan evidence is from tombs: in the Gypsades cemetery to the south, the Fortetsa cemetery and the newly excavated North Cemetery to the north, some burials in the Mavro Spelio cemetery to the east, and the reuse of the

Figure 17.8   Knossos and Acropolis hill from Ailias (to the east)

Figure 17.9   Royal Road to Palace, from the west

Kephala tholos tomb and the Royal Tomb at Isopata. The Fortetsa cemetery and the North Cemetery, both about 1.5 km northwest of the palace, came into use in this phase (and Gypsades went out of use), and they continued to be used into the Protogeometric period and for a long time thereafter. At Knossos, then, there was continuity both of inhabitation during the transition from the Bronze Age to the Iron Age and of occupation of a long-established lowland center, even if its cemeteries were spread over 5 km. Elsewhere in Crete at this time people retreated to mountain strongholds such as Karphi, Kavousi, and Vrokastro. Political conditions were not the same throughout the island.

In Protogeometric times (Early Protogeometric–Late Protogeometric) three cemeteries came into use, the main part of the Fortetsa cemetery on the west side of the Acropolis hill, the Teke tombs that are a northern outlier of the North Cemetery, and tombs north of the palace along the old Minoan route to the mouth of the Kairatos and the harbor at Poros. There was considerable trade, to judge from many imports, especially from Athens, and a bronze bowl with a Phoenician inscription. Settlement evidence, as before, is concentrated to the west of the palace.

Subsequently, in the Protogeometric B–Middle Geometric phase (c. 840–740 B.C.), tombs at Mastamba and Atsalenio on the outskirts of modern Herakleion began to be used. Too far away to have served a main settlement at Knossos, they may have belonged to a new harbor town founded at Herakleion. But the previous cemeteries continued in use till the last burials in Late Orientalizing. One late 9th-century B.C. (Protogeometric B) burial in a reused Minoan tholos tomb at Teke has been identified as that of an immigrant goldsmith from the Middle East, who was buried with some fine jewelry and gold, silver, and electrum dumps and bars, which were his stock-in-trade.

During Late Geometric and Orientalizing times the settlement west of the palace began to grow to the north, to the area between the palace and the Venizeleion hospital. The population was on the rise. A sign of this may be the appearance of the first offerings in the sanctuary of Demeter, goddess of farming and food and hence of fertility, on the lower slopes of Gypsades opposite the south front of the palace. The sanctuary may be a continuation of the Sub-Minoan goddess cult in the Spring Chamber, which lies downslope toward the palace.

In the late 7th century the archaeological record of Knossos almost ceases. The cemeteries were given up. No buildings of the 6th century survive. In the sanctuary of Demeter there were very few offerings. We do not know what trouble had struck Knossos. Nor are we certain where the Archaic agora of Knossos was, though it was probably part of the expansion north of the palace and on about the same site near the Roman civil basilica as the (presumed) Roman forum. There is evidence of temples and shrines on Gypsades (Demeter) and perhaps near the new excavations behind the Stratigraphical Museum on the lower slopes of the Acropolis (a metope of Herakles and Eurystheus was found near there in 1910). There may have been others on the north (Zeus and Hera?) and south ends of that hilltop and somewhere near the agora (where a shrine to Apollo Delphinios[?] perhaps served as a civic archive). Another (Rhea?) is thought to have been on the palace site.

Hellenistic Knossos is less obscure. The city grew: Strabo estimated a circumference of 30 stades, implying an area of 2.4 sq km, which is larger than the Minoan and Roman towns. To judge from the archaeology, this is an exaggeration. What is certain is that Knossos was the principal city of Crete.

In the new excavations behind the Stratigraphical Museum the next buildings after the 10th century B.C. were Hellenistic. About 200 m to the south a rescue excavation found a shrine of the local hero Glaukos. Its cult ceased in the 1st century B.C., perhaps as a result of the Roman victory in 67 B.C., when Knossos opposed the Romans and was defeated, losing its independence and its primacy. Gortyn, an ally of the Romans, became the capital of the new Roman Crete.

But Knossos soon became a Roman colony, Colonia Julia Nobilis Cnossus, at around the time of Augustus's political settlement of 27 B.C. Some of the colonists were Campanians from the Bay of Naples, probably including Capuans; and some of the territory of Knossos was given to Capua, which held it as an income-producing estate.

The new settlement led to increased building. The Roman city covered the ground from the Kairatos to the lower slopes of the Acropolis hill, an area of 50–60 ha. Several well-appointed houses have been found, including the Villa Dionysos and houses over the Minoan Unexplored Mansion. The center, probably above or close to the Archaic–Hellenistic agora and near the Villa Dionysos with its fine mosaics, included a civil basilica and, doubtless, public baths and a temple or temples, including one of Aesculapius (Asklepios), and a theater or amphitheater. The long wall that gave its name—Makryteichos—to the modern lower village at Knossos may have been part of a stoa. On Gypsades the sanctuary of Demeter continued into the 2nd century.

Roman Knossos, if not so large as Gortyn, was a handsome city rich in statues, many of which were later taken to Venice. Outside the city center there may have been suburban houses (villas) with gardens. There are many Roman tombs, ranging from simple tile graves to rock-cut tombs (which seem to have been the most frequent type) to monumental concrete structures that are now lost, such as the "Tomb of Caiaphas," reported by early travelers, which perhaps dates to the 4th–5th century.

An aqueduct, perhaps 2nd century, curved around the contours of Gypsades to bring water to Knossos, probably from springs at the foot of Mt. Juktas. Knossos also had wells, as there had been since

Early Minoan I, and cisterns, which may have been filled from the aqueduct.

There was a break in occupation during the 5th century, on the evidence of the site behind the Stratigraphical Museum. There may have been an earlier break during the reign of Septimius Severus (193–211), followed by the abandonment of some parts of the city.

The first monuments of Christian Knossos are two basilicas in the cemetery area north of the city. The North Cemetery, in full use again in Hellenistic times, continued to be used into the Roman period. Here a mortuary church was built in the 5th century. The other basilica is east of the Venizeleion hospital and was a martyrion, the church of a martyr whose headless skeleton was found in his grave. It is of early 6th-century date. There was another basilica on the site of Ayia Sophia church in Makryteichos village.

The Roman–Early Byzantine city declined as Herakleion rose. Like Gortyn, it may have suffered from earthquakes but also, being apparently unfortified and difficult to fortify, it was not a safe place when the Arabs attacked. Much of it must have been abandoned.

After their victory in 827, the Arabs made Herakleion (Candax or El Chandak: "ditch" in Arabic; later Candia) their capital. At Knossos the finds of the Arab occupation are a few scattered coins and a cottage by the Kairatos below Makryteichos, which was probably the center of what community there was at Knossos until Bougada Metochi, the modern Knossos village to the west and northwest of the palace, was settled, probably in the 19th century.

The principal Venetian and Ottoman remains are two handsome aqueducts, both built to bring water to Herakleion from Archanes. Francesco Morosini the elder put up the older aqueduct in 1628 to cross the valley between the Gypsades and Baïria hills; Mehemet Ali, the Egyptian ruler of Crete in 1830–40, built the more recent one across the Kairatos valley below Spilia, south of the palace.

Evans came to Knossos for the first time in 1894 and in 1900 started to excavate. Besides the palace and the town houses and the many exquisite finds on display in the Herakleion Museum that are monuments to him, there is also his house, the Villa Ariadne. Its architecture would be at home in British India were it not for such details as relief double axes on the drainheads.

II. USE

Aceramic N–EByz settlement (town/city) (MM IB–LM IIIA1 palace); Arab house; LByz traces; V and Ott aqueducts.

III. SITUATION

The original Neolithic settlement and the later palace at Knossos are

Figure 17.10   West wing floor

on the low hill of Kephala in the Kairatos river valley about 5 km southeast of Herakleion. To the south across the Vlychia stream rises the hill of Gypsades, where the Minoans quarried gypsum for use in their buildings. The Kairatos valley narrows upstream southeast of the palace, Kephala being the last freestanding hill in the valley. East of the palace across the Kairatos the ridge of Ailias rises, its limestone quarried in Minoan and later times. To the north and northwest is rolling country, dipping toward Herakleion and the mouth of the Kairatos at Poros (Katsamba) at the present eastern end of Herakleion harbor. West of the palace is the hill known as the Acropolis.

The *kouskouras* marl of Knossos is excellent for vines and olives, and for the digging of tombs, because it is a soft rock. For water Knossos has depended on wells, the earliest of which is Early Minoan I. The Romans built an aqueduct. The Vlychia is likely to have been seasonal; the Kairatos may have flowed (almost) year-round in antiquity, but it was clearly not sufficient for the needs of the population. The Kairatos would not have been passable to boats.

The modern villages are Makryteichos, on the west bank of the Kairatos northeast of the palace, and Knossos (formerly Bougada Metochi), west of the palace on the lower slope of the Acropolis hill above the main road from Herakleion to Archanes and Viannos.

IV. GEOMORPHOLOGY

The Kairatos river, flowing just east of the palace site, marks a contact between Pliocene marine marls to the west and the older, harder Cretaceous-age limestones to the east that form the ridge of Ailias, which rises some 250 m above sea level. The Pliocene marls are locally termed *kouskouras.* The river was not capable, at least during the late Holocene, of carrying any watercraft, including rafts.

Less than 1 km south of the palace site, on the opposite side of the Vlychia torrent, rises the hill of Gypsades, which represents a concentration of crystalline gypsum (satin spar) within the Pliocene marl. Comparable deposits that exist within 1 km of Ayia Triada were quarried as building stone for that site and for nearby Phaistos. Most of the gypsum used in the architectural elements of the palace and other buildings at Knossos would have been quarried from Gypsades, illustrating again how perceptive the Minoan builders were in locating their sites near inorganic raw materials.

Building stones for the palace would have been quarried from Tripolis limestone bedrock outcrops on the Ailias ridge. The "poros" limestone also used is a Pleistocene eolianite particularly suited for upper floors because of its relatively low density.

V. EXCAVATION HISTORY

M. Kalokairinos, 1878–79; A. J. Evans, 1900–1905, 1907–10, 1913,

1922–31 (with E. J. Forsdyke, 1926–27); D. G. Hogarth, 1900; H. G. G. Payne, 1927, 1929; N. Platon, H. G. G. Payne, A. Blakeway, and J. K. Brock, 1933, 1935; J. D. S. Pendlebury and H. W. Pendlebury, 1931; R. J. H. Jenkins, 1933; R. W. Hutchinson, 1935–40 (with R. Radford, 1937; with T. J. Dunbabin, 1940); N. Platon, 1940, 1956; P. de Jong, 1948–52 (with M. S. F. Hood, 1948, 1951); J. M. Cook, 1949, 1953; M. S. F. Hood, 1950–61 (with S. Alexiou, 1950; with G. L. Huxley and N. K. Sandars, 1955; with J. N. Coldstream, 1957–60), 1963, 1966, 1973 (with J. W. Shaw), 1987; W. H. C. Frend, 1955, 1957–58, 1960; N. Platon and G. L. Huxley, 1957; J. D. Evans, 1957–60, 1969–70; M. Gough, 1957–58, 1961, 1971; G. Cadogan, 1962; S. Alexiou, 1966; J. N. Coldstream and G. L. Huxley, 1967; M. R. Popham and L. H. Sackett, 1967–68, 1972–73, 1976–77; R. J. Howell, 1968, 1976 (with A. Karetsou); C. Ridley and M. A. S. Cameron, 1968; M. R. Popham, 1969; K. A. Wardle, 1970; A. Lebessi, 1971, 1975; P. M. Warren, 1971–72, 1978–82; H. W. Catling, 1974–75; G. Cadogan, V. Hankey, and S. Paton, 1975–76; L. H. Sackett and P. J. Callaghan, 1975; P. J. Callaghan, 1976; R. J. Howell, 1976; M. R. Popham, 1977; J. Carington Smith, 1977, 1978 (with H. W. Catling), principally for the British School or the Archaeological Service.

VI. BUILDINGS

Neolithic

Aceramic N   (Stratum X). Few buildings on palace site; use of mud brick.

EN I   (Strata IX–V). Deep deposit; change from mud brick to pisé.

EN II   (Stratum IV). Substantial deposit.

MN   (Stratum III). Multiple-room rectangular buildings.

LN   (Stratum II–I) and FN. Houses with fixed hearths below Central Court.

Prepalatial

EM I   Well in northeastern part of palace site. Burning (destruction by fire?); scattered finds.

EM II   Scattered traces over most of palace site, including houses by south front (EM IIA and EM IIB). Also three basement rooms of EM IIA West Court House, destroyed by fire; EM II also attested in northeast part of palace site, and on north and south sides of Royal Road.

EM III   Filling level sealed between two plaster floors by south front of palace; and Hypogaeum (a circular underground store assigned to EM III by Evans) below south entrance; well on upper east side; monumental building remains in northwest part, and perhaps Keep at north end of Central Court, belong to a possible protopalace; traces on north side of Royal Road; house below kouloura (round pit) 3 at west edge of West Court (?).

MM IA — Houses below West Court and kouloures, with red plaster; rubbish levels on south side of Royal Road. (Various deposits assigned to MM IA, such as the Monolithic Pillar Basement [outside palace on east side, to the south] and Vat Room deposit [near Pillar Crypts], now appear mixed with later material.)

Considerable growth of town up Acropolis hill to the west as far as about 500 m from palace, for instance in new excavations behind Stratigraphical Museum; also to the northeast in Makryteichos village, and southward on Gypsades to area of House of the High Priest. First burials in large cave-tomb on Acropolis.

Old Palace (MM IB–IIB/IIIA)

MM IB accepted by Evans as time of foundation of palace (though new studies, not yet published, make this MM IIA). Monumental construction with large blocks; also used in bridge across Vlychia, stepped portico, and prominent wall on Ailias above Kairatos.

Palace arranged around Central Court and probably with a plan similar to that of the New Palace, but perhaps set out in separate blocks, of which curved corner of Throne Room block may be a remnant. Throne Room begun. Shrines likely near Vat Room (west side) and Loom Weight Basement (east side). Storerooms on west and east sides, including rooms with giant pithoi. At northeast, so-called Royal Pottery Stores.

Two building phases, West Court with three kouloures laid out in second phase on terrace covering earlier houses. Kouloura also by Theatral Area, of which earlier phase is of Old Palace period, as are Royal Road and road system.

Traces of town west of palace, south to area of House of the High Priest and to the north (as in New Palace period, but evidence scanty because of later building). Isolated farms at Ayia Paraskevi on Ailias and to north on low hill of Zapher Papoura.

Tombs on Ailias (Ailias and Mavro Spelio cemeteries) and on Gypsades, where there was a Mesara-type tholos tomb along with, perhaps, other built tombs.

Destruction in MM IIIA (or MM IIB?).

New Palace (MM III–LM IB–LM IIIA1)

MM III–LM I — Probable greatest extent of Minoan Knossos about 75 ha (4 ha of which were occupied by the palace and its immediate surroundings), extending mainly to west, north, and south. Isolated farms on periphery.

MM III — Rebuilding of palace, though earthquake in MM III (at transition to LM I?) destroyed south front and House of the Sacrificed Oxen and House of the Fallen Blocks below south front of palace.

LM IA — Intensive building at Knossos; probable date of much of (present) palace, and of town houses such as Little Palace, Unexplored Mansion (unfinished), Royal Villa, South House, House of the Chancel Screen, Caravanserai, etc.

Palace: about 135 by 135 m (excluding West Court). Arranged around Central Court (about 50 by 25 m), probably following Old Palace scheme. West Court continued in use from Old Palace.

Grand facade facing onto West Court, with setbacks for windows on presumed rooms on upper floor(s). Entrance from south end of West Court leads down Corridor of Procession Fresco to Central Court and to rooms on first floor, approached through Propylaeum.

Ground floor rooms on west side: long row of eighteen storerooms off corridor (both storerooms and corridor with cists [underfloor boxes]); shrines facing onto Central Court include Tripartite Shrine and Throne Room; Temple Repositories (large underfloor boxes [Evans: MM IIIB]) behind Tripartite Shrine; Throne Room with benches around throne against walls, lustral basin, and anteroom.

North end: archive/administrative area in LM IIIA1 (as in Old Palace; also in MM III–LM I?); lustral basin to west of North Pillar Hall; ramp (North Entrance Passage) from North Pillar Hall, which may be the undercroft of a dining hall, up to Central Court; entrance from north, with pillared building outside to north; later phase(s) of Theatral Area, with terraces and box; North Entrance Passage narrowed on east side during period; part to east of North Entrance Passage unclear; possible animal pens above (west of) earlier rooms with giant pithoi.

East side: presumed East Hall at north end of east side of Central Court; elaborate system for collecting storm water. Grand Staircase: five flights preserved lead down from Central Court to second floor down with Hall of the Double Axes and Evans's Domestic Quarter—a set of rooms, closely linked by passages and staircases, that includes Queen's Hall with Bathroom (formerly a lustral basin [MM III?]), Dressing Room, with its light well (Court of the Distaffs) and lavatory, and Hall of the Double Axes with its light well (with double axes cut on ashlar facing blocks). Rooms on the intermediate floor are perhaps similar to those below. To the north of Domestic Quarter, workshops include Lapidary's Workshop and "School Room." To the south of Domestic Quarter, workshops.

South end: ceremonial entrance to Central Court from end of Corridor of Procession Fresco.

In immediate area of palace, workshops (for instance on north side of Royal Road and, probably, North West Treasury [off north end of West Court], and to southeast where there is a kiln) and some grand town houses, including South House by southwest corner of palace, South East House and House of the Chancel Screen (with its screen and a tripartite shrine) by southeast corner, and earlier houses destroyed by MM III earthquake: House of the Fallen Blocks and House of the Sacrificed Oxen. Other buildings to northwest of palace include House of the Frescoes and a grand upper floor over an ivory workshop on north side of Royal Road; also North Pillar Crypt (shrine?) north of north entrance.

More distant, to the west (northwest): Little Palace, approached from palace by Royal Road, faces east, 40+ by 30+ m, with *polythyron* halls (that is, with multiple pier-and-door partitions forming the walls), peristyle, lustral basin, lavatory, pillar basements, and upper floor(s); from upper floor of Little Palace a bridge led to ground floor of Unexplored Mansion (built after Little Palace), about 24 by 14.5 m and on a higher terrace, with central four-pillared hall, begun and left unfinished in LM IA; higher still up Acropolis slope are houses behind Stratigraphical Museum beside a road that is a straight continuation of the Royal Road, and three kilns for producing fine lime powder (for frescoes).

To the east (northeast): Royal Villa, built into cutting and facing east, with chancel screen and central recess for seat or stand.

To south: Caravanserai and Spring Chamber across Vlychia; House of the High Priest and Hogarth's Houses, and other houses on Gypsades.

Some evidence for earthquake in/at end of LM IA, followed by some rebuilding in palace; but drainage system of east side (Domestic Quarter) had ceased to work.

LM IB   Destruction by fire of places in town, including South House, building with workshop on north side of Royal Road, and buildings behind Stratigraphical Museum; apparently no destruction in palace.

MM III–LM I   Very few tombs. Assignable to MM III: chamber tomb on Gypsades; last use of tomb(s) on Acropolis hill. MM III–LM I: building of two-storey Temple Tomb (with burial chamber, courtyard, and pavilion) on Gypsades and perhaps (but see below) Royal Tomb at Isopata. LM I: last use of Ailias cemetery and Gypsades tholos tomb.

LM II–IIIA1   Palace almost wholly as it now stands. Extent of town uncertain, but considerable scattering of tombs. Appearance of both chamber tombs with long narrow dromoi and rectangular chambers and burials with bronze vessels and weapons. Other tombs are deep, narrow rectangular graves; also tholos and other built tombs, including Kephala and Sellopoulo tholos tombs and, probably, Royal Tomb at Isopata 2.5 km north-northwest of palace. Over a large area principal groups are Isopata, including the Tomb of the Double Axes, with a burial cist shaped like a double axe; Ayios Ioannis, about 2 km northwest of palace; Venizeleion; Zapher Papoura and nearby (with "shaft graves" [Evans] as well as chamber tombs) in rolling country to north of palace, use continuing into LM IIIB; Sellopoulo, opposite Zapher Papoura on east bank of Kairatos; some tombs on Gypsades, including last use of Temple Tomb; Mavro Spelio.

LM II: many houses abandoned and not immediately reused. But in use: Unexplored Mansion, with two destructions by fire (first less severe than second), and people "camping" in it and using it as a bronze-working center; house on south side of road in new excavation behind Stratigraphical Museum. Gypsum House on north side of road. Traces also in trials beneath Stratigraphical Museum between Unexplored Mansion and new excavation. Destruction by fire also in new excavation. Palace presumably in use.

LM IIIA1: last phase of palace; reuse begun of several town houses; some continued use of Unexplored Mansion; in new excavation behind Stratigraphical Museum three circular platforms (Great Circle: d 8.38 m; Small Circle: d 3.22 m; and West Circle: d 3.0 m) built at about end of LM II (West Circle perhaps built in LM II) and in use into LM IIIA2 (Great Circle probably a dancing place; smaller circles for dancing or musicians).

Palace burnt around time of transition to LM IIIA2 (Popham 1970); destruction deposits in several town houses including Little Palace.

Postpalatial (LM IIIA2–SM)

LM IIIA2   Final use of circles in new excavation behind Stratigraphical Museum; also field or garden walls there; use of Unexplored Mansion. Tombs: LM IIIA1 burial grounds generally still in use.

LM IIIB   Last use of palace by "squatters" (Evans) and of Unexplored Mansion (with shrine) and Little Palace (with Fetish Shrine). Extent of occupation difficult to tell. Traces in Makryteichos. Zapher Papoura, Sellopoulo, and Mavro Spelio cemeteries still in use.

LM IIIC   Large settlement in area of Stratigraphical Museum, continuing into SM; last use of Mavro Spelio cemetery; reuse of Kephala tholos tomb and of Royal Tomb at Isopata.

SM   Use of Spring Chamber near Caravanserai as shrine; last use of Gypsades cemetery; beginning of North Cemetery (continuing in use until LO; then very few A burials until H use), principally with chamber tombs (but also "shaft graves" [Evans] as at Zapher Papoura), and of Fortetsa cemetery (continuing in use till LO).

Post-Minoan

PG   Continued settlement traces to west of palace; beginning of part of Fortetsa cemetery on west side of north end of Acropolis hill; North Cemetery and its Teke extension in use, sometimes reusing M chamber tombs and, in one case at Teke, a tholos tomb.

G   Continued settlement to west of palace; beginning of sanctuary of Demeter on Gypsades (continuing in use until middle of 2nd century A.D.); Fortetsa, North Cemetery, and Teke in use; also tombs further out toward Herakleion at Atsalenio and Mastamba.

EO–LO   Some growth of settlement from west of palace to northwest; burials in North Cemetery; last burials (LO) in Fortetsa and Teke cemeteries; some reuse of Mavro Spelio tombs.

A   No 6th-century buildings, and few buildings at all; agora probably to northwest of palace and near later R (civil) basilica; some burials in North Cemetery, ceasing in early 5th century.

C   Temples and shrines (some A foundations?), probably on palace site (Rhea), near agora (Apollo Delphinios?), and on top of Acropolis hill—at north end (Zeus and Hera?) and at south end—and near excavations behind Stratigraphical Museum (Herakles and Eurystheus), as well as sanctuary of Demeter. C(?) kiln southwest of palace. Very few graves.

H   Marked growth of settlement; buildings behind Stratigraphical Museum and house to west of Villa Dionysos; shrine of Glaukos west of palace; other possible shrines, including on Gypsades and at Mavro Spelio cave; continued use of sanctuary of Demeter; kiln to southwest of palace; graves and rock-cut tombs at many sites, including on Ailias, near Spilia (south end of Ailias), and Gypsades, and renewed use of North Cemetery (divided into large plots for groups of graves [rectangular pits]) and Fortetsa cemetery. Tower (fort) on Kephala hill northwest of H city, but no evidence of circuit wall.

Captured by Quintus Caecilius Metellus (Creticus) in 67 B.C.

R   Forum to northwest of palace, with civil basilica, baths, stoa(?), and temple; imposing 2nd-century houses include Villa Dionysos (with fine mosaics) and House of the Diamond Frescoes (beneath Unexplored Mansion); aqueduct (2nd century?) enters Knossos area from the south and probably connected with conduits and cisterns in center. Area of intensive occupation perhaps 50–60 ha. Villas/farms on periphery. Some evidence of disruption in reign of Septimius Severus around 200. Occupation of site behind Stratigraphical Museum ends in 5th century.

Wide spread of tombs (from tile graves to rock-cut tombs and monumental built tombs such as Tomb of Caiaphas, which has disappeared): at Spilia; Gypsades; Baïria hill to southwest of R city; and North Cemetery (where Tomb 244 reused marble blocks from a monumental mid-2nd-century building) and Teke.

EByz   Basilicas at North Cemetery site (5th-century mortuary church: 40 by 18 m, in an enclosure 100 by 65 m), near Venizeleion (6th-century martyrion, over early Christian graves), and at Ayia Sophia church in Makryteichos. Two graves in Knossos village.

Arab   Modest house below Makryteichos by Kairatos, abandoned soon after 900; squatters in North Cemetery basilica; scattered finds of coins.

LByz   Graves at Ayia Sophia in Makryteichos, probable center of community.

V   Aqueduct built by Francesco Morosini the elder, to southwest of palace across valley between Gypsades and Baïria hills, supplying Morosini fountain in Herakleion (1628). Fortetsa hill used as Turkish camp and battery in siege of Herakleion (1648–69).

Ott   Large aqueduct built by Mehemet Ali (1830–40) across Kairatos valley at Spilia, on site of R aqueduct. Bougada Metochi, modern Knossos village, settled, probably in 19th century.

20th century   Villa Ariadne built by Evans (1906).

VII. RADIOCARBON DATES

	B.P.	1σ cal. B.C.	2σ cal. B.C.
Aceramic N			
Stratum X			
BM-124	8050 ± 180	beyond calculable range	b.c.r.
BM-278	7910 ± 140	7050–6568	b.c.r.
BM-436	7740 ± 140	6690–6440	7040–6230
EN I			
Stratum IX			
BM-272	7570 ± 150	6559–6186	6690–6090
Stratum VI			
BM-273	6210 ± 150	5322–4945	5480–4790
Stratum V			
BM-126	7000 ± 180	6077–5650	6180–5530
BM-274	6140 ± 150	5240–4901	5370–4727
EN II			
Stratum IV			
BM-577	5884 ± 188	4998–4530	5230–4350
BM-279	5680 ± 150	4730–4360	4900–4240
MN			
Stratum III (late)			
BM-580	5522 ± 88	4464–4336	4573–4164
MN/LN			
Stratum III/II			
BM-571	5636 ± 94	4657–4363	4720–4340
LN			
Stratum II			
BM-585	5588 ± 145	4658–4340	4780–4047
BM-579	5534 ± 76	4464–4342	4530–4240
EM IIA			
West Court House			
BM-578	3745 ± 137	2454–1970	2573–1772
MM IB			
Palace			
P-2443	3890 ± 70	2471–2288	2577–2144
P-2442	3720 ± 220	—	—
Royal Road			
P-1351	3320 ± 51	1682–1525	1740–1510
MM IIA			
Royal Road			
P-1352	3208 ± 63	1526–1425	1640–1329
MM IIIB			
Royal Road			
P-1353	3029 ± 83	1413–1162	1502–1020
Kiln			
P-2444	3440 ± 90	1886–1673	2020–1520
LM IA			
Royal Road			
P-1354	3565 ± 72	2031–1783	2140–1740
P-1355	3125 ± 64	1492–1321	1520–1260
LM IB			
Royal Road			
P-1356	2964 ± 74	1313–1055	1410–948
LM II			
Unexplored Mansion			
P-2048	4240 ± 70	2917–2703	3029–2618
P-2047	3930 ± 70	2564–2342	2600–2205
P-2046	3820 ± 50	2451–2149	2460–2140
P-2048A	3460 ± 50	1881–1705	1910–1680
P-2045	3320 ± 50	1682–1525	1740–1510
OxA-2098	3220 ± 65	1595–1429	1670–1400
OxA-2097	3190 ± 65	1522–1417	1620–1321
OxA-2096	3070 ± 70	1424–1263	1510–1129
(average of OxA dates:	3177 ± 44	1514–1420	1525–1398)
Royal Road			
P-1357	3096 ± 69	1436–1306	1520–1169
LM IIIA			
Palace destruction			
P-2441	3060 ± 60	1416–1263	1450–1136
Royal Road			
P-1359	3226 ± 43	1526–1445	1618–1422
P-1358	3033 ± 68	1407–1218	1440–1060
C–R kiln			
P-2512	2310 ± 70	405–370	753–200

VIII. BIBLIOGRAPHY

General

1921–36   Evans, A. J. *The Palace of Minos at Knossos* 1–4 and index vol. (London).

1943 Evans, J. *Time and Chance: The Story of Arthur Evans and His Forebears* (London) 308–96.

1973 Powell, D. *The Villa Ariadne* (London).

1979 Roberts, N. "The Location and Environment of Knossos," *BSA* 74:231–41.

1981 Hood, M. S. F., and D. Smyth. *Archaeological Survey of the Knossos Area*, 2nd ed., British School at Athens Supplementary Volume 14 (London).

Horwitz, S. L. *The Find of a Lifetime: Sir Arthur Evans and the Discovery of Knossos* (New York).

1983 Brown, A. *Arthur Evans and the Palace of Minos* (Oxford).

Harden, D. B. *Sir Arthur Evans: A Memoir* (Oxford).

1986 Brown, A. "'I Propose to Begin at Gnossos,'" *BSA* 81:37–44.

1987 Hood, M. S. F. "An Early British Interest in Knossos," *BSA* 82:85–94.

NEOLITHIC

1953 Furness, A. "The Neolithic Pottery of Knossos," *BSA* 48:94–134.

1964 Evans, J. D. "Excavations in the Neolithic Settlement at Knossos, 1957–60. Part I," *BSA* 59:132–240.

1968 Warren, P. M., M. R. Jarman, H. N. Jarman, N. J. Shackleton, and J. D. Evans. "Knossos Neolithic, Part II," *BSA* 63:239–76.

1971 Evans, J. D. "Neolithic Knossos: The Growth of a Settlement," *PPS* 37, pt. 2:95–117.

MINOAN

General

1954 Pendlebury, J. D. S. *A Handbook to the Palace of Minos at Knossos*, new ed. (London).

1961–62 Hood, M. S. F. "Stratigraphic Excavations at Knossos, 1957–61," in *1 Cretological* 1:92–98.

1964 Killen, J. T. "The Wool Industry of Crete in the Late Bronze Age," *BSA* 59:1–15.

1966 Hood, M. S. F. "The Early and Middle Minoan Periods at Knossos," *BICS* 13:110–11.

1981 Warren, P. M. "Knossos and Its Foreign Relations in the Early Bronze Age," in *4 Cretological* 1.2:628–37.

1982 Niemeier, W.-D. "Mycenaean Knossos and the Age of Linear B," *SMEA* 23:219–87.

1983 ———. "The Character of the Knossian Palace: Society in the Second Half of the Fifteenth Century," in *Minoan Society* 217–36.

1984 Driessen, J., and C. Macdonald. "Some Military Aspects of the Aegean in the Late Fifteenth and Early Fourteenth Centuries B.C.," *BSA* 79:49–74.

1985 Bennet, D. J. L. "The Structure of the Linear B Administration at Knossos," *AJA* 89:231–49.

1987 ———. "Knossos and LM III Crete: A Post-Palatial Palace?" in *The Function of the Minoan Palaces* 307–12.

Doxey, D. "Causes and Effects of the Fall of Knossos in 1375 B.C.," *OJA* 6:301–24.

Palaima, T. G. "Preliminary Comparative Textual Evidence for Palatial Control of Economic Activity in Minoan and Mycenaean Crete," in *The Function of the Minoan Palaces* 301–6.

1988 Gale, N. H., H. C. Einfalt, H. W. Hubberten, and R. E. Jones. "The Sources of Mycenaean Gypsum," *JAS* 15:57–72.

Popham, M. R. "The Historical Implications of the Linear B Archive at Knossos Dating to Either c. 1400 B.C. or 1200 B.C.," *CrSt* 1:216–27.

Palace

1899–1900 Evans, A. J. "Knossos. I. The Palace," *BSA* 6:3–70.

1900–1901 ———. "The Palace of Knossos, 1901," *BSA* 7:1–120.

1901–2 ———. "The Palace of Knossos: Provisional Report of the Excavations for the Year 1902," *BSA* 8:1–124.

1902–3 ———. "The Palace of Knossos: Provisional Report for the Year 1903," *BSA* 9:1–153.

1903–4 ———. "The Palace of Knossos," *BSA* 10:1–62.

1904–5 ———. "The Palace of Knossos and Its Dependencies: Provisional Report for the Year 1905," *BSA* 11:1–26.

1963 Palmer, L. R., and J. Boardman. *On the Knossos Tablets: Palmer, The Find-Places of the Knossos Tablets, and Boardman, The Date of the Knossos Tablets* (Oxford).

1964   Popham, M. R. *The Last Days of the Palace of Knossos: Complete Vases of the Late Minoan IIIB Period*, SIMA 5 (Lund).

1967   Warren, P. M. "A Stone Vase Maker's Workshop in the Palace at Knossos," *BSA* 62:195–201.

1969   Palmer, L. R. *The Penultimate Palace of Knossos*, Incunabula Graeca 33 (Rome).

Raison, J. *Le grand palais de Knossos, Répertoire photographique et bibliographique*, Incunabula Graeca 34 (Rome).

1970   Popham, M. R. *The Destruction of the Palace of Knossos*, SIMA 12 (Gothenburg).

1972   Woodard, W. S. "The North Entrance at Knossos," *AJA* 76:113–25.

1973–74   Catling, H. W. "Archaeology in Greece, 1973–74," *AR* 34–35.

1976   Evely, D. "The North Entrance Passage at Knossos," *BSA* 71:57–63.

1977   Hallager, E. *The Mycenaean Palace at Knossos: Evidence for Final Destruction in the IIIB Period*, Medelshavmuseet Memoir 1 (Stockholm).

Popham, M. R. "Notes from Knossos, Part I," *BSA* 72:185–95.

1978   Shaw, J. W. "Sliding Panels at Knossos," *BSA* 73:235–48.

1979   Mirié, S. *Das Thronraumareal des Palastes von Knossos: Versuch einer Neuinterpretation seiner Entstehung und seiner Funktion* (Bonn).

1981   Hood, M. S. F., and W. Taylor. *The Bronze Age Palace at Knossos: Plan and Sections*, British School at Athens Supplementary Volume 13 (London).

1985   Gesell, G. C. *Town, Palace, and House Cult in Minoan Crete*, SIMA 67 (Gothenburg) 84–92.

Niemeier, W.-D. *Die Palaststilkeramik von Knossos* (Berlin) (with refs. on the disputed dating of the destruction of the New Palace).

1986   MacGillivray, J. A. *Pottery of the Old Palace Period at Knossos and Its Implications*, Ph.D. diss., University of Edinburgh.

Niemeier, W.-D. "Zur Deutung des Thronraumes im Palast von Knossos," *AM* 101:63–95.

1987   Begg, D. J. I. "Continuity in the West Wing at Knossos," in *The Function of the Minoan Palaces* 179–84.

Cadogan, G. "What Happened at the Old Palace of Knossos?" in *The Function of the Minoan Palaces* 71–73.

Hägg, R. "On the Reconstruction of the West Facade of the Palace at Knossos," in *The Function of the Minoan Palaces* 129–34.

Hallager, E. "A 'Harvest Festival Room' in the Minoan Palaces? An Architectural Study of the Pillar Crypt Area at Knossos," in *The Function of the Minoan Palaces* 169–77.

Hood, M. S. F. "Mason's Marks in the Palaces," in *The Function of the Minoan Palaces* 205–12.

MacGillivray, J. A. "Pottery Workshops and the Old Palaces in Crete," in *The Function of the Minoan Palaces* 273–78.

Niemeier, W.-D. "On the Function of the 'Throne Room' in the Palace at Knossos," in *The Function of the Minoan Palaces* 163–68.

Popham, M. R. "The Use of the Palace of Knossos at the Time of Its Destruction," in *The Function of the Minoan Palaces* 297–99.

1988   Macdonald, C., and J. Driessen. "The Drainage System of the Domestic Quarter in the Palace at Knossos," *BSA* 83:235–58.

Raison, J. *Le palais du second millénaire à Knossos 1. Le quartier Nord*, EtCr 28 (Paris).

1990   Driessen, J. *An Early Destruction in the Mycenaean Palace at Knossos: A New Interpretation of the Excavation Field-Notes of the South-East Area of the West Wing*, Acta Archaeologica Lovanensia Monographiae 2 (Louvain).

Laffineur, R. "Habitat égéen et reconstitutions: Quelques réflexions méthodologiques à propos du quartier nord-est du palais de Cnossos," in *L'habitat égéen préhistorique*, BCH Supplement 19, ed. P. Darcque and R. Treuil (Athens) 3–19.

Macdonald, C. "Destruction and Construction in the Palace at Knossos," in *3 Thera* 3:82–88.

Town

1899–1900   Hogarth, D. G. "Knossos. II. Early Town and Cemeteries," *BSA* 6:70–85.

1911–14   Evans, A. J. "The 'Tomb of the Double Axes' and Associated Group, and the Pillar Room and Ritual Vessels of the 'Little Palace' at Knossos," *Archaeologia* 65 : 59–94.

1928–30   Pendlebury, H. W., and J. D. S. Pendlebury. "Two Protopalatial Houses at Knossos," *BSA* 30 : 53–73.

1958–59   Hood, M. S. F. "A Late Minoan III 'Kitchen' at Makritikhos (Knossos)," *BSA* 53–54 : 182–93.

1970   Popham, M. R. "A Late Minoan Shrine at Knossos," *BSA* 65 : 191–94.

1971–72   Catling, H. W. "Archaeology in Greece, 1971–72," *AR* 20–21.

1972   Evans, J. D. "The Early Minoan Occupation of Knossos: A Note on Some New Evidence," *AS* 22 : 115–28.

Warren, P. M. "Knossos and the Greek Mainland in the Third Millennium B.C.," *AAA* 5 : 392–98.

1972–73   Catling, H. W. "Archaeology in Greece, 1972–73," *AR* 26–29.

1974   Popham, M. R. "Trial KV (1969): A Middle Minoan Building at Knossos," *BSA* 69 : 181–94.

1975   Graham, J. W. "The Banquet Hall of the Little Palace," *AJA* 79 : 141–46.

1977   Catling, H. W., and R. E. Jones. "Analyses of Copper and Bronze Artefacts from the Unexplored Mansion, Knossos," *Archaeometry* 19 : 57–66.

1979   Catling, E. A., H. W. Catling, and D. Smyth. "Knossos 1975: Middle Minoan III and Late Minoan I Houses by the Acropolis," *BSA* 74 : 1–80.

1980–81   Warren, P. M. "Knossos: Stratigraphical Museum Excavations, 1978–80. Part I," *AR* 73–92.

1981   ———. "Minoan Crete and Ecstatic Religion: Preliminary Observations on the 1979 Excavations at Knossos and Postscript on the 1980 Excavations at Knossos," in *Sanctuaries and Cults in the Aegean Bronze Age* 155–66.

1982–83   ———. "Knossos: Stratigraphical Museum Excavations, 1978–82. Part II," *AR* 63–87.

1984   Popham, M. R., et al. *The Minoan Unexplored Mansion at Knossos*, British School at Athens Supplementary Volume 17 (London).

Warren, P. M. "Knossos: New Excavations and Discoveries," *Archaeology* 37 : 48–55.

1985   Gesell, G. C. *Town, Palace, and House Cult in Minoan Crete*, SIMA 67 (Gothenburg) 93–101.

Wilson, D. E. "The Pottery and Architecture of the EM IIA West Court House at Knossos," *BSA* 80 : 281–364.

1986   Wall, S. M., J. H. Musgrave, and P. M. Warren. "Human Bones from a Late Minoan IB House at Knossos," *BSA* 81 : 333–88.

1987   Foster, K. P. "Reconstructing Minoan Palatial Faience Workshops," in *The Function of the Minoan Palaces* 287–92.

1988   Evely, D. "Unexplored Mansion, Knossos: Note I," *BSA* 83 : 127–33.

1989   Momigliano, N. *MM IA Pottery from Evans's Excavations at Knossos*, Ph.D. diss., University of London.

Tarling, D. H., and W. S. Downey. "Archaeomagnetic Study of the Late Minoan Kiln 2, Stratigraphical Museum Extension, Knossos," *BSA* 84 : 345–52.

Warren, P. M. "Egyptian Stone Vessels from the City of Knossos: Contributions Towards Minoan Economic and Social Structure," in *Aphieroma sto Styliano Alexiou, Ariadne* 5 : 1–9.

Frescoes

1958   Reusch, H. "Zum Wandschmuck des Thronsaales in Knossos," in *Minoica. Festschrift zum 80. Geburtstag von J. Sundwall*, ed. E. Grumach (Berlin) 334–58.

1967   Cameron, M. A. S. "Notes on Some New Joins and Additions to Well Known Frescoes from Knossos," in *Europa. Studien zur Geschichte und Epigraphik der frühen Ägäis. Festschrift für Ernst Grumach*, ed. W. C. Brice (Berlin) 45–74.

———. "Unpublished Fresco Fragments of a Chariot Composition from Knossos," *AA* 330–34.

Evans, A. J. *Knossos Fresco Atlas*, ed. M. A. S. Cameron and M. S. F. Hood (Farnborough).

1968   Cameron, M. A. S. "Unpublished Paintings from the 'House of the Frescoes' at Knossos," *BSA* 63 : 1–31.

1970   ———. "New Restorations of Minoan Frescoes from Knossos," *BICS* 17 : 163–66.

1971   ———. "A Lady in Red: A Complementary Figure to the Ladies in Blue," *Archaeology* 24:35–43.

1976   ———. "Savakis's Bothros: A Minor Sounding at Knossos," *BSA* 71:1–13.

Hawke Smith, C. F. "The Knossos Frescoes: A Revised Chronology," *BSA* 71:65–76.

1977   Cameron, M. A. S., R. E. Jones, and S. E. Philippakis, "Scientific Analyses of Minoan Fresco Samples from Knossos," *BSA* 72:121–84.

1985   Warren, P. M. "The Fresco of the Garlands from Knossos," in *L'iconographie minoenne.* Actes de la Table Ronde d'Athènes (21–22 April 1983), *BCH* Supplement 11, ed. P. Darcque and J.-C. Poursat (Athens) 187–208.

1987   Cameron, M. A. S. "The 'Palatial' Thematic System in the Knossos Murals: Last Notes on the Knossos Frescoes," in *The Function of the Minoan Palaces* 320–28.

Niemeier, W.-D. "Das Stuckrelief des 'Prinzen mit der Federkrone' aus Knossos und minoische Götterdarstellungen," *AM* 102:65–98.

1988   ———. "The 'Priest King' Fresco from Knossos: A New Reconstruction and Interpretation," in *Problems in Greek Prehistory* 235–44.

1990   Immerwahr, S. A. *Aegean Painting in the Bronze Age* (University Park, Pa.) 41–48, 52–54, 58–61, 84–99, 170–79.

Cemeteries

1906   Evans, A. J. "The Prehistoric Tombs of Knossos," *Archaeologia* 59:391–562 (and separately printed [London]).

1913–14   ———. "The 'Tomb of the Double Axes' and Associated Group, and the Pillar Rooms and Ritual Vessels of the 'Little Palace' at Knossos," *Archaeologia* 65:1–59.

1926–27   Forsdyke, E. J. "The Mavro Spelio Cemetery at Knossos," *BSA* 28:243–96.

1952   Hood, M. S. F., and P. de Jong. "Late Minoan Warrior-Graves from Ayios Ioannis and the New Hospital Site at Knossos," *BSA* 47:243–77.

1956   Hood, M. S. F. "Another Warrior-Grave at Ayios Ioannis near Knossos," *BSA* 51:81–99.

Hutchinson, R. W. "A Late Minoan Tomb at Knossos," *BSA* 51:68–73.

———. "A Tholos Tomb on the Kephala," *BSA* 51:74–80.

1958–59   Hood, M. S. F. "A Minoan Shaft-Grave in the Bank with Hogarth's Tombs," *BSA* 53–54:283–84.

———. "A Minoan Shaft-Grave on the Slopes opposite the Temple Tomb," *BSA* 53–54:281–82.

Hood, M. S. F., G. L. Huxley, and N. K. Sandars. "A Minoan Cemetery on Upper Gypsades," *BSA* 53–54:194–262.

1967   Cadogan, G. "Late Minoan IIIC Pottery from the Kephala Tholos Tomb near Knossos," *BSA* 62:257–65.

1968   Hood, M. S. F., and J. N. Coldstream. "A Late Minoan Tomb at Ayios Ioannis near Knossos," *BSA* 63:205–18.

1974   Popham, M. R., E. A. Catling, and H. W. Catling. "Sellopoulo Tombs 3 and 4: Two Late Minoan Graves near Knossos," *BSA* 69:195–257.

1975   Popham, M. R. "A Late Minoan Tomb on Lower Gypsades," *BSA* 80:169–73.

1976   Catling, H. W., and R. E. Jones. "Sellopoulo Tomb 4: Some Analyses," *BSA* 71:21–23.

Pelon, O. *Tholoi, tumuli et cercles funéraires* (Athens) 23, 263–65.

1987   Catling, H. W. "The Society of Antiquaries and the British School at Athens, 1886–1986: The Cemeteries of Knossos and Mycenae," *AntJ* 67:223–36.

Scripts and Seals

1909, 1952   Evans, A. J. *Scripta Minoa* 1–2 (Oxford).

1956   Ventris, M., and J. Chadwick. *Documents in Mycenaean Greek*, 2nd ed. 1973 (Cambridge).

1965   Gill, M. A. V. "The Knossos Sealings: Provenance and Identification," *BSA* 60:58–98.

1967   Betts, J. H. "Some Unpublished Knossos Sealings and Sealstones," *BSA*, 62:27–45.

Olivier, J.-P. *Les scribes de Cnossos, Incunabula Graeca* 17 (Rome).

1968 Cameron, M. A. S. "The Painted Signs on Fresco Fragments from the 'House of the Frescoes,'" *Kadmos* 7: 45–66.

1976 *GORILA* 1:255–65.

1977 *CMS* 2.2:35–87 nos. 28–73 (N. Platon, I. Pini, and G. Salies).

1979 *GORILA* 2:81–85.

Younger, J. G. "The Lapidary's Workshop at Knossos," *BSA* 74:259–68.

1982 *GORILA* 4:7–15, 74–83, 117–25, 137–38, 151–55, 163–64.

1984 *CMS* 2.3:9–112 nos. 8–98 (N. Platon and I. Pini).

1985 *CMS* 2.4:7–22 nos. 3–15, 141–89 nos. 110–49 (N. Platon and I. Pini).

1986 *COMIK* 1.

1987 Hallager, E. "The Knossos Roundels," *BSA* 82:55–70.

1989 Killen, J. T. and J.-P. Olivier. *The Knossos Tablets: A Transliteration*, 5th ed., *Minos* Supplement 11 (Salamanca).

Weingarten, J. "Old and New Elements in the Seals and Sealings of the Temple Repository, Knossos," *Aegaeum* 3:39–52.

1990 Pini, I. "The Hieroglyphic Deposit and the Temple Repositories at Knossos," *Aegaeum* 5:33–60.

POST-MINOAN

General

1890 Svoronos 59–95.

1935 *IC* 1:45–82 (= *IC* I. VIII. 1–59).

1976 *PECS* 459–60 (K. Branigan).

SUB-MINOAN/PROTOGEOMETRIC–HELLENISTIC

1930–31 Hartley, M. "Early Greek Vases from Crete," *BSA* 31: 56–114.

1935 Payne, H. G. G. "Archaeology in Greece, 1934–1935," *JHS* 55:164–67.

1937 Benton, S. "Herakles and Eurystheus at Knossos," *JHS* 57:38–43.

1950 Homann-Wedeking, B. "A Kiln Site at Knossos," *BSA* 45:165–92.

1954 Hutchinson, R. W., and J. Boardman. "The Khaniale Tekke Tombs," *BSA* 49:215–30.

1957 Brock, J. K. *Fortetsa: Early Greek Tombs near Knossos*, British School at Athens Supplementary Paper 2 (Cambridge).

Hood, M. S. F., and J. Boardman. "A Hellenic Fortification Tower on the Kefala Ridge at Knossos," *BSA* 52: 224–30.

1960 Boardman, J. "Protogeometric Graves at Agios Ioannis near Knossos," *BSA* 55:128–48.

Coldstream, J. N. "A Geometric Well at Knossos," *BSA* 55:159–71.

1961 Hood, M. S. F., and J. Boardman. "Early Iron Age Tombs at Knossos," *BSA* 56:68–80.

1963 Coldstream, J. N. "Five Tombs at Knossos," *BSA* 58: 30–43.

1967 Boardman, J. "The Khaniale Tekke Tombs, II," *BSA* 62:57–76.

1968 Davaras, C. "Two Geometric Tombs at Atsalenio near Knossos," *BSA* 63:133–46.

1972 Coldstream, J. N. "Knossos 1951–61: Protogeometric and Geometric Pottery from the Town," *BSA* 67: 63–98.

1973 ———. "Knossos 1951–61: Orientalizing and Archaic Pottery from the Town," *BSA* 68:33–63.

———. *Knossos: The Sanctuary of Demeter*, British School at Athens Supplementary Volume 8 (London).

1976 Sackett, L. H. "A New Figured Krater from Knossos," *BSA* 71:117–29.

1976–77 Catling, H. W. "The Knossos Area, 1974–76," *AR* 3–23.

1978 Callaghan, P. J. "KRS 1976: Excavations at a Shrine of Glaukos, Knossos," *BSA* 73:1–30.

Coldstream, J. N., and L. H. Sackett. "Knossos: Two Deposits of Orientalizing Pottery," *BSA* 73:45–60.

Popham, M. R. "Notes from Knossos, Part II," *BSA* 73:185–87.

1978–79   Catling, H. W. "Knossos, 1978," *AR* 43–58.

1981   Callaghan, P. J. "The Little Palace Well and Knossian Pottery of the Later Third and Second Centuries B.C.," *BSA* 76:35–58.

Catling, H. W., E. A. Catling, P. J. Callaghan, and D. Smyth. "Knossos 1975: Minoan *Paralipomena* and Post-Minoan Remains," *BSA* 76:83–108.

Coldstream, J. N., P. J. Callaghan, and J. H. Musgrave. "Knossos: An Early Greek Tomb on Lower Gypsadhes Hill," *BSA* 76:141–65.

1984   Coldstream, J. N. "Dorian Knossos and Aristotle's Villages," in *Aux origines de l'hellénisme* 313–22.

1984–85   Warren, P. M. "Knossos: Stratigraphical Museum Excavations, 1978–82. Part III," *AR* 124–29.

1988   Liddy, D. J. "A Chemical Study of Early Iron Age Pottery from the North Cemetery, Knossos," in *New Aspects of Archaeological Science in Greece. Proceedings of a meeting held at the British School at Athens January 1987*, ed. R. E. Jones and H. W. Catling (Athens) 29–32.

ROMAN AND LATER

1962   Frend, W. H. C., and D. E. Johnston. "The Byzantine Basilica Church at Knossos," *BSA* 57:186–238.

1971   Hayes, J. W. "Four Early Roman Groups from Knossos," *BSA* 66:249–75.

1972   Wardle, K. A. "Two Notes from Knossos," *BSA* 67:271–84.

Warren, P. M., and G. C. Miles, "An Arab Building at Knossos," *BSA* 67:285–96.

1972–73   Sackett, L. H. "The Unexplored Mansion at Knossos: A Preliminary Report on the Excavations from 1967 to 1972. Part II: Post-Minoan Occupation above the Unexplored Mansion," *AR* 62–71.

1977   Catling, H. W., and G. B. Waywell. "A Find of Roman Marble Statuettes at Knossos," *BSA* 72:85–106.

1982   Carington Smith, J. "A Roman Chamber Tomb on the South-East Slopes of Monasteriaki Kephala, Knossos," *BSA* 77:255–93.

Catling, H. W., C. Ridley, J. Carington Smith, D. Smyth, and A. W. Dunn. "Knossos 1978: Roman Finds at the Venizeleion," *BSA* 77:59–64.

1983   Hayes, J. W. "The Villa Dionysos Excavations, Knossos: The Pottery," *BSA* 78:97–169.

1987–88   Warren, P. M. "Knossos: Stratigraphical Museum Excavations, 1978–82. Part IV," *AR* 86–104.

1988   Evely, D. "Clay Tobacco Pipes from the University of Crete Medical Faculty," *BSA* 83:135–42.

Radiocarbon Dates

1963   Barker, H., and J. Mackey. "British Museum Natural Radiocarbon Measurements IV," *Radiocarbon* 5:104–5.

1969   Barker, H., R. Burleigh, and N. Meeks, "British Museum Natural Radiocarbon Measurements VI," *Radiocarbon* 11:279–80.

Stuckenrath, R., Jr., and B. Lawn. "University of Pennsylvania Radiocarbon Dates XI," *Radiocarbon* 11:157–59.

1971   Evans, J. D. "Neolithic Knossos—the Growth of a Settlement," *PPS* 37, pt. 2:117.

1976   Betancourt, P. P., and G. A. Weinstein. "Carbon-14 and the Beginning of the Late Bronze Age in the Aegean," *AJA* 80:329–48.

1977   Burleigh, R., A. Hewson, and N. Meeks. "British Museum Natural Radiocarbon Measurements IX," *Radiocarbon* 19:145.

1978   Fishman, B., and B. Lawn. "University of Pennsylvania Radiocarbon Dates XX," *Radiocarbon* 20:211–13.

1990   Housley, R. A., R. E. M. Hedges, I. A. Law, and C. R. Bronk. "Radiocarbon Dating by AMS of the Destruction of Akrotiri," in *3 Thera* 3:214–15.

IX. FINDS

Herakleion Museum; Ashmolean Museum, Oxford; British Museum, London.

X. DATE OF PHOTOGRAPHY

June 5, 1976.

JOSEPH W. SHAW

35°01′ N, 24°45′ E

Figure 18.1   Kommos, site before excavation, aerial view

Figure 18.2   High aerial view of excavation

I. IMPORTANCE

The recent excavations at Kommos have exposed Minoan houses and monumental ashlar buildings as well as a Greek sanctuary established in the late 10th or the early 9th century B.C. In the Minoan town, well-preserved contexts have provided a clear definition of Middle Minoan III–Late Minoan I ceramic sequences in the Mesara and information about local industries and domestic architecture. The ashlar buildings of palatial proportions in the south area imply a Minoan preference for developing the seaside here, a situation probably unique along the coast of the Mesara. The variety of imported pottery, especially that dating from Late Minoan I–IIIB, suggests international connections and seafaring associated with a busy local harbor, Kommos, which was presumably the chief harbor town of Phaistos.

The Greek sanctuary with its superposed temples and associated buildings provides a rare sequence of architectural development and stratified pottery deposits, with temple offerings, especially animal figurines, from Protogeometric through Roman times. In the two early temples (Temples A and B), both open to the east, animal bones serve as evidence of ritual sacrifice. A shrine within the second temple, Temple B, founded during the 8th century B.C., has been identified as Phoenician in inspiration, and may have been set up by Phoenicians who landed at the site. The third temple, Temple C, of the 4th century B.C., with its plan similar to that of the earlier Dreros and Prinias temples and the later Lissos temple, helps us to identify the major Cretan temple types unique to Crete.

II. USE

MM–LM III settlement; PG–R sanctuary.

III. SITUATION

Kommos lies 5.5 km south of Ayia Triada, 6 km southwest of Phaistos, and 2 km north of Roman Matala, beside a magnificent beach at the end of the Mesara plain.

IV. GEOMORPHOLOGY

The low hill from which Kommos overlooks the Libyan Sea is composed of the Neogene marine marls and limestones that are the common bedrock type of central Crete, from Herakleion to the Asterousia mountains. These rocks are easily eroded except where they are capped by a better-cemented fossiliferous limestone, as is the case at Kommos. The Minoan residents of Kommos could utilize the natural tabular blocks of local limestone to build walls that were in some cases cut into the bedrock strata.

Buried soils have been found to the north and south of Kommos, under some 1–10 m of windblown sand derived from the alluvium of the Yeropotamos river. This sand has been deposited inland from the coastline continuously but at varying rates. Two major episodes of sand deposition—at the end of the Bronze Age and during Roman times—appear to be related to a relative drop in sea level that exposed a wider beach to eolian deflation and downwind accumulation. Sand deposition in a narrow zone parallel to the low shoreline of the Mesara plain continues to the present, and pockets of windblown

Figure 18.4   Hilltop houses

Figure 18.3   Kommos, excavation plan through 1984 (N.B. Temples A and B lie below Building A2, which is also Temple C.)

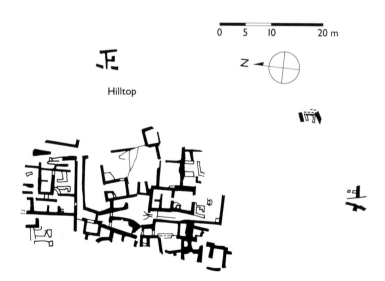

0   5   10   20 m

Z

Hilltop

Hillside

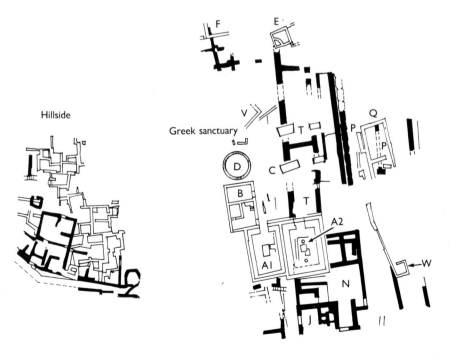

Figure 18.5   Central hillside

Figure 18.6   Building J/T and temples

sand may be seen on ridges 80 m above and 1,500 m inland from the present coastline.

Kommos may owe its importance as a port in the Late Minoan period to a fortuitous combination of geological factors. The bedrock reef, locally the "Pappadoplaka," some 350 m west of the site, rising through 7–8 m of water, is today just awash and apparently the only natural offshore outcrop along the Mesara plain coastline. With a sea level 2 m lower it would constitute a significant barrier to the predominant west-northwest winds and seas, and the shoreline at Kommos could have lain 50–100 m closer to the rock. Thus during the 2nd millennium B.C. a submerged spit or possibly even a tombolo would have extended from the shore at Kommos to the rock, providing a natural shelter for vessels better here than at any other point on the coast of the Mesara plain.

V. EXCAVATION HISTORY

J. W. Shaw, 1976–85, 1991–, for the American School.

VI. BUILDINGS

EM   Scanty traces below houses on hillside.

MM   Town founded in MM I, with rapid growth peaking in MM III. MM houses below LM houses on hilltop and hillside. Probably severe earthquake and abandonment in MM III. To the south MM I–II houses, probably partly razed, below LM I pebble court of Building J/T; no surviving MM III buildings.

LM I   Densely packed houses of rough stone on hilltop, continuing north beyond excavated area and on some of hillside. No evidence of LM IB destruction by fire.

At bottom of slope an east–west paved street, over 2.5 m wide, starts near shore and continues for 60+ m. Bordering street to the south is the monumental Building J/T, with extraordinarily large ashlar orthostats (up to 3.46 m long). On the west, partly destroyed by the sea, is Building J, with a broad entrance from the street. Bordering Building J on the east is Building T: its western part, a long portico with five columns between piers facing south onto a court

(28.75 m east–west by 38+ m north–south), is paved with sea pebbles; storerooms to the east, one with striped frescoes. The eastern part of T went out of use during LM I. East–west, J/T comprises a complex over 80 m wide.

LM II   West part of Building T, probably including portico, and houses on hilltop reused. Building T abandoned.

LM IIIA–IIIB   Roof and upper walls of Building T had largely collapsed before Building J's floor was raised in LM IIIA, its north entrance blocked, and its interior remodeled around a court to form Building N. To the southeast, on a lower (LM I) level, Building P, with long parallel galleries about 5.6 m wide and a maximum length of 38.5 m, with doorless entrances to the west, facing the shore. Buildings N and P abandoned in LM IIIB. Also LM IIIB occupation of hilltop houses.

LM IIIC   Few sherds.

PG   Temple A, a small building with two phases, open to the east and built over M walls: probable rural shrine.

G–A   Temple A succeeded by Temple B, with three phases, also open to the east with a central hearth, probable benches, and a tripillar shrine. Exterior altar added later. In final phase of Temple B, Buildings F, V, and Q were constructed and numerous platforms. Ironworking took place to the east.

A–C (c. 620–400 B.C.)   Occasional use of shrine; only structure perhaps an altar.

C–R   Temple C built over Temple B, also with a central hearth and benches but with double door to the east, opening onto a new exterior altar. Small Building W of unknown use to the south. Six phases. During later phases, other altars added in court, and Buildings B (for storage and, probably, residence) and D (round building, use unclear) to the north. Directly north of Building C another room with a low bench (dining room?) added during a late period.

During last two phases of Temple C (A.D. c. 50–150), C only building in use, perhaps as a residence rather than a shrine.

VIII. BIBLIOGRAPHY

1928   Evans, A. J. *The Palace of Minos at Knossos* (London) 2:88–92.

1977   Shaw, J. W. "Excavations at Kommos (Crete) during 1976," *Hesperia* 46:199–240.

1978   Shaw, J. W., P. P. Betancourt, and L. V. Watrous. "Excavations at Kommos (Crete) during 1977," *Hesperia* 47:111–70.

1979   Shaw, J. W. "Excavations at Kommos (Crete) during 1978," *Hesperia* 48:145–73.

1980   ———. "Excavations at Kommos (Crete) during 1979," *Hesperia* 49:207–50.

1981   ———. "Excavations at Kommos (Crete) during 1980," *Hesperia* 50:211–51.

Shaw, M. C. "Sir Arthur Evans at Kommos: A Cretan Village Remembers Its Past," *Expedition* 23.3:4–12.

1982   Shaw, J. W. "Excavations at Kommos (Crete) during 1981," *Hesperia* 51:164–95.

1984   ———. "Excavations at Kommos (Crete) during 1982–1983," *Hesperia* 53:251–87.

1985   *Scripta Mediterranea* 6, including:
Betancourt, P. P. "A Great Minoan Triangle: The Changing Characters of Phaistos, Hagia Triadha, and Kommos during the Middle Minoan III–Late Minoan III Periods," 31–43.
Shaw, M. C. "Late Minoan I Buildings J/T, and Late Minoan III Buildings N and P at Kommos: Their Nature and Possible Uses as Residences, Palaces, or Emporia," 19–30.
Watrous, L. V. "Late Bronze Age Kommos: Imported Pottery as Evidence for Foreign Contact," 7–18.

1986   Shaw, J. W. "Excavations at Kommos (Crete) during 1984–1985," *Hesperia* 55:219–99.

1987   ———. "A 'Palatial' Stoa at Kommos," in *The Function of the Minoan Palaces* 101–10.

Shaw, M. C. "A Bronze Figurine of a Man from the Sanctuary at Kommos, Crete," in *Eilapini* 371–82.

1989   Shaw, J. W. "Phoenicians in Southern Crete," *AJA* 93:165–83.

1990   Betancourt, P. P. *Kommos 2: The Final Neolithic through Middle Minoan III Pottery* (Princeton).

Shaw, M. C. "Late Minoan Hearths and Ovens at Kommos, Crete," in *L'habitat égéen préhistorique*, *BCH* Supplement 19, ed. P. Darcque and R. Treuil (Athens) 231–54.

Figure 18.7 Kommos site, from the south

Figure 18.9 Reef at Kommos

IX. FINDS

Herakleion Museum.

X. DATES OF PHOTOGRAPHY

June 12–13, 1976 (before excavation); June 5, 1984.

Figure 18.8 Reef at Kommos

OLIVIER PICARD

35°11′ N, 25°39′ E

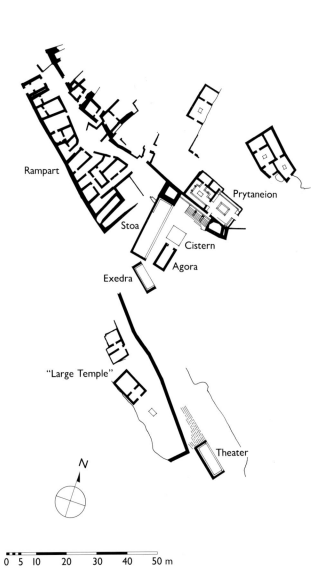

Figure 19.1   Plan of Lato

Figure 19.2   Aerial view

I. IMPORTANCE

Situated in a magnificent position on very steep hills beneath the mountains and above the coastal plain, with views to the sea, Lato is the best preserved ancient Cretan town. Its walls, in places several meters high, make a romantic picture among the rocks and wild-flowers and scrub.

The excavations at Lato let us reconstruct the typical framework of a Classical city. It has its agora; its Prytaneion, where the magistrates sat; temples, the main one of which still has the base of the statue of its god (its inscription too much damaged to be read); and a rustic theater, partly cut into the rock. The powerful fortifications of some houses and of the town as a whole show the warlike nature of the population that controlled the main route from central to eastern Crete. The Latians, who lived principally on agriculture, struck coins only when their political center moved to Kamara (the port of Ayios Nikolaos), for a brief time in the 2nd century B.C.

II. USE

LM III traces; (L)G–H city; R traces.

III. SITUATION

Lato lies at 300–400 m on the slopes of two hills (the north and south acropoleis) about 8 km west of Ayios Nikolaos (ancient Kamara) and 3 km north-northeast of Kritsa.

IV. GEOMORPHOLOGY

These hills form the eastern part of Mt. Phylakas, between the polje of Lakonia to the north and the Xeropotamo valley to the south. A narrow valley, with the road from the north coast to the Ierapetra isthmus, separates Lato from Mt. Kephala and the Lasithi massif. There is no spring at Lato, and cisterns were the only way of getting water; by contrast, Kritsa, the nearest village, enjoys an abundant perennial supply.

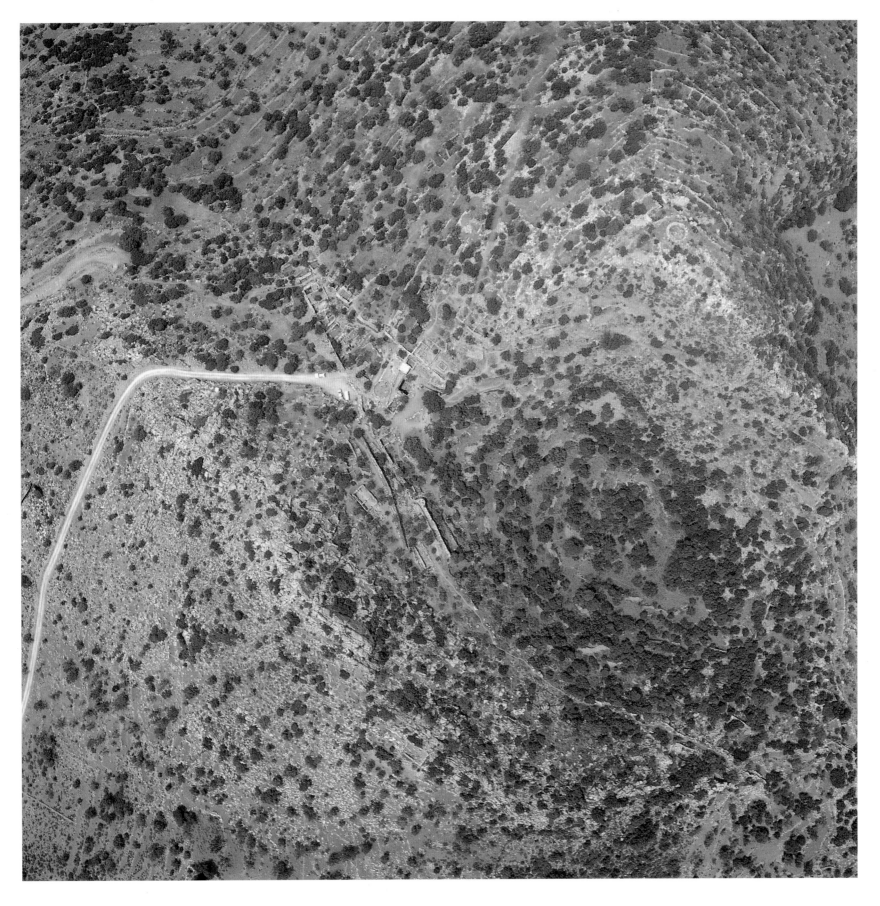

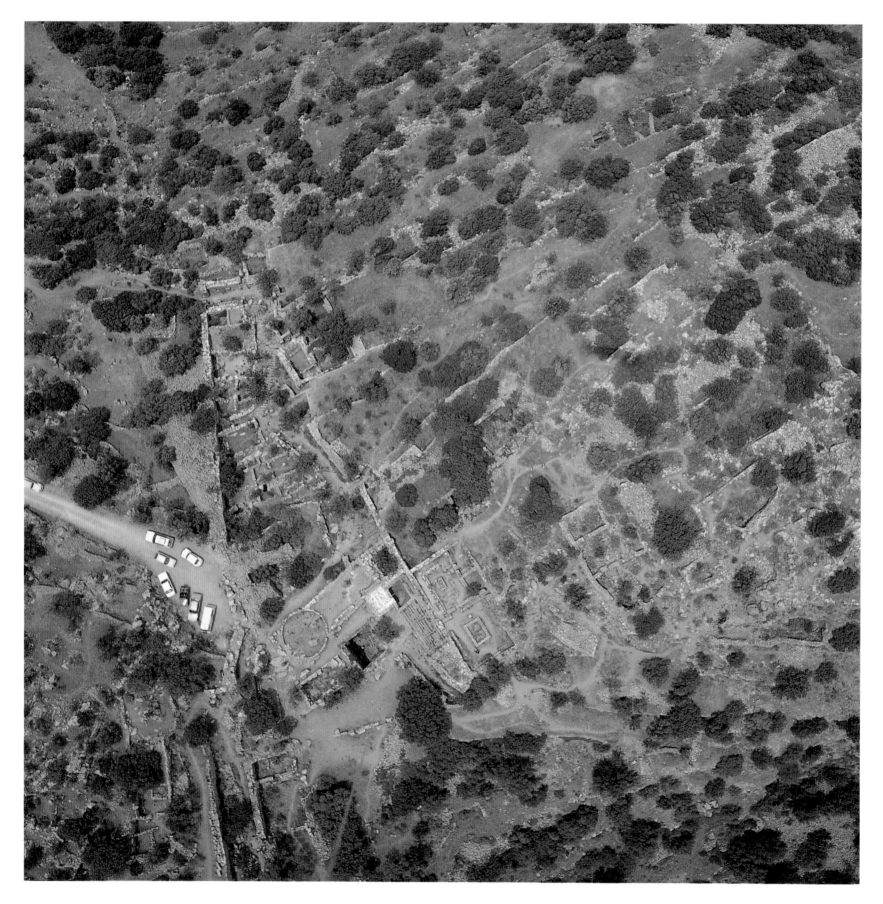

Figure 19.3 Low aerial view

The dark gray massive limestones of the Tripolitza series form the bedrock. The three surrounding hills are tightly folded anticlines, which have been shaped by the dissolution of the limestone washed down into a small central sinkhole. The cistern in the agora, sensibly enough, was constructed within this natural depression. (This feature is identical to the sinkholes [*katavothri*] of the Lasithi plain, some 15 km to the west, which is surrounded by the same limestone unit.)

The builders made extensive use of the local limestone, particularly a brecciated variety that was favored for orthostats and doorsills.

Geologically Lato is the "reverse image" of Eleutherna, which occupies a topographic high, for Lato was planned and built around a natural depression. In both cases the builders seem to have welcomed the challenge presented by local topography of exceptional relief, even for Crete.

V. EXCAVATION HISTORY

J. Demargne, 1899–1900; A.-J. Reinach, 1910; P. Ducrey, V. Hadjimichali, and O. Picard, 1967–71, for the French School.

VI. BUILDINGS

LM III Surface sherds.

century Remains of terraces. Potter's workshop with three kilns beneath the terrace of the "Large Temple" (3rd quarter of 7th century).

century; Main period of Lato.
century) The Agora is trapezoidal (about 30 by 20 m), with a temple in the center and a large cistern (5.25 by 5.25 by 5.25 m). The temple is a simple rectangular cella (4th century[?]; A figurines also found). On the west a stoa with Doric portico and on the south a rectangular exedra.

On the north side of the Agora is the Prytaneion (identified from an inscription), reached by nine or ten steps (2 m high, 8.4 m long), which are divided into three by two landings (meeting places?). West of the steps are two small rooms, and on either side of the steps two massive bastions support the Prytaneion.

The Prytaneion (about 18 by 8 m: end of 4th century through 3rd century) has two large rooms (to the east a peristyle court, to the west an *estiatorion*, "dining hall," with a central hearth and couches [*klinai*] for eight banqueters) and two small rooms on the northwest, one opening into the *estiatorion* and the other into the court, which must have been used as an archive and a *chalcotheke*, "treasury of bronzes."

Figure 19.4 Lato "Large Temple"

Figure 19.5 Lato

The "Large Temple" (10 by 6.5 m) is on a terrace (of a maximum 36 by 16.5 m) south of the agora, with a retaining wall of rustic polygonal masonry capped by a slightly projecting course. Almost square cella, with the remains of an inscribed base of a cult statue, and a pronaos opening to the east. In front of the temple, an altar with three steps. Building technique (large bossed masonry outside, small stones bound with mud on inside), tiles, and pottery indicate a date around the end of the 4th century and the beginning of the 3rd.

An unusual complex (32 by 8 m) at the foot of the east end of the terrace of the large temple combines ten or eleven steps (rock-cut or built) with a rectangular exedra on the same axis; in front of the steps and exedra is a large open space on a terrace (enlarged and supported by two semicircular bastions). At the entrance are the footings of a small altar or statue base. This group of buildings has been interpreted as a theater with steep steps built immediately after the Large Temple.

Many houses visible. Some built against west city wall. Among others, seven (fully recorded) have a terrace wall (of large irregular polygonal masonry) for a narrow terrace, along which are the rooms and courtyard. Several have an upper storey (mud brick?). Almost all have a cistern, and a built hearth in the center of the main room. Terrace roofs of puddled clay.

The defense system has been studied along the street leading down from the agora to the west. The houses, protected from below by their terrace walls, were placed at the end of the terraces in the weakest spot. (Some evolution may be observed from the earlier houses to those of the end of the 4th century.) Next, the outer wall was doubled. Then the entrance was fortified with a chicane. The later houses were like towers, with very strong masonry. Finally (end of the 3rd century?), freestanding rampart built south of street (with gate to inner courtyard), and houses and workshops (one a dyeing works) built between the rampart and the street.

Other sanctuaries, defense walls, houses, and streets visible in city. Lato abandoned in 2nd–1st century.

R Some bronze coins (4th century A.D.) indicate a very limited occupation.

VIII. BIBLIOGRAPHY

1890 Svoronos 217–21.

1901 Demargne, J. "Les ruines de Goulas ou l'ancienne ville de Lato en Crète," *BCH* 25:282–307.

1903 ———. "Fouilles à Lato en Crète," *BCH* 27:206–32.

1913 Reinach, A.-J. "L'autel rustique du mont Phylakas, Crète," *RA* 21:278–300.

1929 Demargne, P. "Terres cuites archaïques de Lato," *BCH* 53:382–429.

1935 *IC* 1:105–30 (= *IC* I. XVI. 1–14).

1940 *RE* Supplement 7:342–65 (E. Kirsten).

1943 Van Effenterre, H. "Documents édilitaires de Latô," *REA* 27–39.

1969 Ducrey, P., and O. Picard. "Recherches à Latô I. Trois fours archaïques," *BCH* 93:792–822.

        Van Effenterre, H., and M. Bougrat. "Les frontières de Latô," *KrChron* 21:9–53.

1970 Ducrey, P., and O. Picard. "Recherches à Latô II. Le grand temple," *BCH* 94:567–90.

1971 ———. "Recherches à Latô IV. Le théâtre," *BCH* 95:513–31.

        Hadjimichali, V. "Recherches à Latô III. Maisons," *BCH* 95:167–222.

1972 Ducrey, P., and O. Picard. "Recherches à Latô V. Le Prytanée," *BCH* 96:567–92.

1974 ———. "A propos de l'histoire de Latô," in *Antichità cretesi* 2:75–80.

        Van Effenterre, H. "Inscription funéraire métrique de Latô," *KrChron* 26:23–31.

1976 Ducrey, P., V. Hadjimichali, and O. Picard. "Recherches à Latô VI. Céramique hellénistique," *BCH* 100:253–67.

        PECS 487 (P. Ducrey and O. Picard).

1984 Tréheux, J. "Les cosmes à Latô," in *Aux origines de l'hellénisme* 329–42.

1986 Van Effenterre, H. "Inscription funéraire métrique de Latô," *KrChron* 27:89–90.

1989 Baldwin Bowsky, M. W. "Epigrams to an Elder Statesman and a Young Noble from Lato pros Kamara," *Hesperia* 58:115–29.

        ———. "Portrait of a *Polis*: Lato pros Kamara," *Hesperia* 58:331–47.

1990 Voutiras, E. "A Funerary Epigram from Latos in Crete," *Hesperia* 59:669–73.

IX. FINDS

Ayios Nikolaos Museum.

X. DATE OF PHOTOGRAPHY

May 23, 1983.

CHIARA TARDITI

34°56′ N, 24°55′ E

I. IMPORTANCE

The Hellenistic and Roman center of Lebena on the south coast of Crete was renowned in antiquity for its sanctuary of Asklepios, the god of healing, which was as important for Crete as the Asklepieion at Pergamon was for Asia. It is mentioned by the ancient geographers and was identified in 1586 by Belli, who made a plan of an extraordinarily grand group of buildings, which are difficult to make out today.

The cult probably originated in the 4th century, when it was superimposed on an earlier cult of the Nymphs and Acheloos. (Water was an essential part of the worship and medicine.) The remains now visible belong mostly to Roman times. There may have been a general refurbishment of the sanctuary after the earthquake and apparent tidal wave in 66. The sanctuary was still flourishing in the 3rd and 4th centuries, as dedicatory inscriptions illustrate.

We do not know how the temples declined and were abandoned. Around 500 a basilica was built on the eastern edge of the sanctuary, maintaining the (now Christian) sanctity of the place.

The remains at Lebena are not completely published.

II. USE

H–R sanctuary, and cemetery; EByz basilica; V church.

III. SITUATION

On the south side of the Asterousia mountains, set around the bay immediately east of Cape Lenda, "lion," or Cape Lebena (also designated Akrotiri Kephalas on many maps), which looks like a resting lion.

IV. GEOMORPHOLOGY

Cape Lenda is an isolated block of the penultimate nappe, or rock unit thrust over the stable basement complex of the island (the Plat-tenkalk series). This nappe consists of marly reddish limestones associated with mafic volcanics forming isolated bodies of rock on the scale of 1–10 sq km in area, named the Arvi unit by Bonneau (1973).

Surrounding the blocks of the Arvi unit is a sedimentary rock type called a flysch, which at Lebena forms the relatively soft bedrock along the shoreline. The headland exists because of the relative resistance of the Arvi unit to weathering. Just inland, at the elevation of the Asklepieion, there is a fault contact between the flysch and the next younger nappe (the Asterousi nappe). Rocks of the Arvi unit, the Asterousi nappe, and two smaller nappes are collectively termed the Serpentinite-Amphibolite association, after the most common metamorphic rocks found therein.

The Asklepieion is behind the bay shore, beside the spring. Much of the building material is limestone, quarried from Cape Lenda or Cape Xammidomouri further east. The water at the spring head seems to have been channeled from upslope at the fault contact between the flysch and the serpentinite-amphibolite rocks.

V. EXCAVATION HISTORY

F. Halbherr, 1900, and L. Pernier, 1910–11, for the Italian Archaeological Mission; S. Alexiou and A. Lebessi, 1971, for the Archaeological Society.

VI. BUILDINGS

H–R Building phases seem early H, late H, and 2nd–3rd century A.D.

Cella (of building generally considered temple of Asklepios) on artificial terrace built out from, and partly cut into, the rock, 11.4 m wide by about 13 m long. Walls stand to 3.4 m; two granite columns 4.7 m high in front of podium (6 by 1.35 m by 0.65 m high) for statue of Asklepios; another statue base in cella; mosaic floor with blue and white geometric patterns.

West stoa to north of temple, 27 m long by 4.3+ m wide, colonnaded to the east and to the south, set over a fine pebble mosaic of a sea horse belonging to a building below stoa, perhaps 3rd century B.C.; and cut by a small treasury (probably the only building datable to first phase of sanctuary). Steps (35 m long) gave access to temple and stoa.

North stoa (to northeast of west stoa), 18 by 5.1 m, and to the east an exedra (perhaps a nymphaion), with the spring 6 m to the south with a facade of dressed limestone and a tiled arch. Remains of other buildings used for bathing or collecting water nearby. Near eastern streambed are traces of a bridge. In the center of the embayment with a sea view, remains of accommodation for pilgrims: two parallel walls, about 100 m long and 10 m apart, divided into rooms. Tombs at east side of sanctuary.

EByz Late 5th/early 6th century basilica, 26 by 14.5 m (external dimensions), partly covered by church of Ayios Ioannis.

V 14th–15th century church of Ayios Ioannis.

VIII. BIBLIOGRAPHY

General

1900 (or later) Taramelli, A. Manuscript account of early work at Lebena, in Italian School library.

1901 Halbherr, F. "Lavori eseguiti dalla missione archeologica italiana nell'Agorà di Gortyna e nell'Asclepieio di Lebena," *RendLinc* 10:300–306.

1914 Porro, G. G. "Il tesoro dell'Asklepieion di Lebena," *StRom* 2:373–83.

1915 Gerola, G. *Le antiche chiese di Lebena a Creta* (Venice).

1934 Guarducci, M. "I miracoli di Asclepio a Lebena," *Historia* 8:410–38.

1935 *IC* 1:150–78 (= *IC* I. XVII. 1–60).

1940 *RE* Supplement 7:366–71 (E. Kirsten).

1961 *EAA* 4:517–19 (I. Baldassarre).

1971 Alexiou, S. "Mikrai anaskaphai kai perisyllogi archaion en Kriti," *PAE* 285–86.

1974 Berti, F. "Il mosaico dell'Asclepieion di Lebena," in *Antichità cretesi* 2:213–18.

1976 *PECS* 493 (K. Branigan).

1982 Sanders, I. F. *Roman Crete* (Warminster) 80–83, 113–14, 159.

1984 *Creta antica* 117–20 (M. A. Rizzo).

1985 *Ancient Crete* 72–74 (M. A. Rizzo).

Geomorphology

1973 Bonneau, M. "Les differentes 'séries ophiolitifères' de la Crète: Une mise au point," *Comptes Rendus, Académie des Sciences* (Paris) 276:1249–52.

1979–80 Di Vita, A. "I terremoti a Gortina in età romana e protobizantina," *ASAtene* 57–58:435–44.

IX. FINDS

Herakleion Museum.

X. DATE OF PHOTOGRAPHY

May 22, 1983.

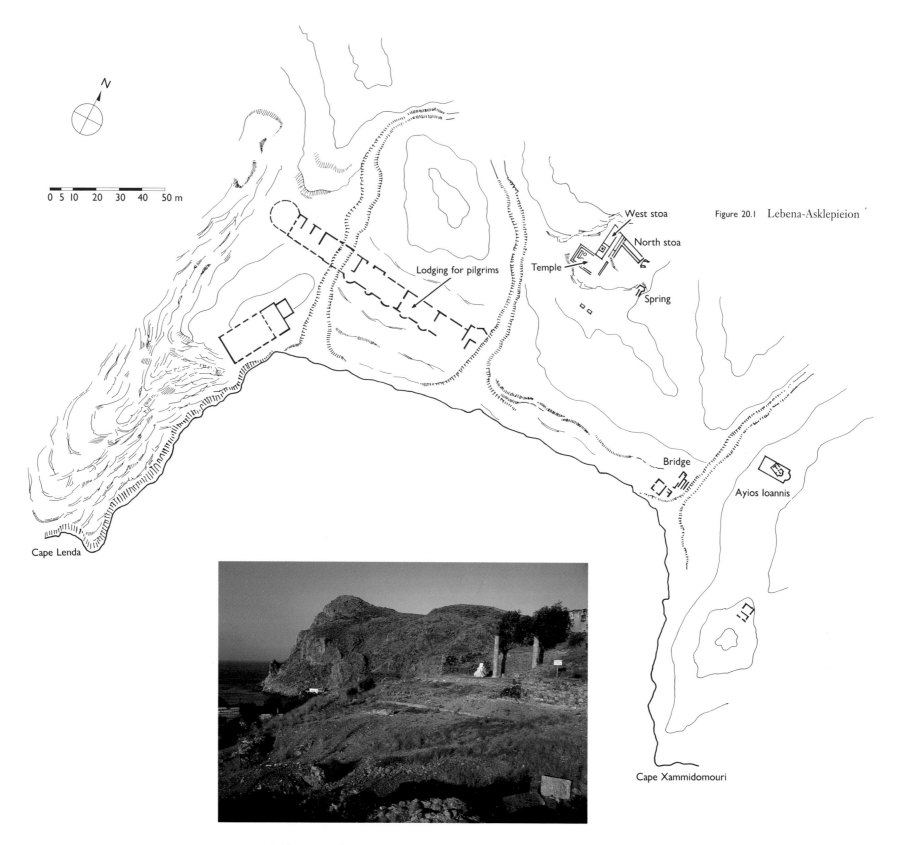

Figure 20.1 Lebena-Asklepieion

Figure 20.2 Asklepieion and Cape Lenda

Figure 20.3 Asklepieion and basilica

STYLIANOS ALEXIOU

34°56′ N, 24°55′ E

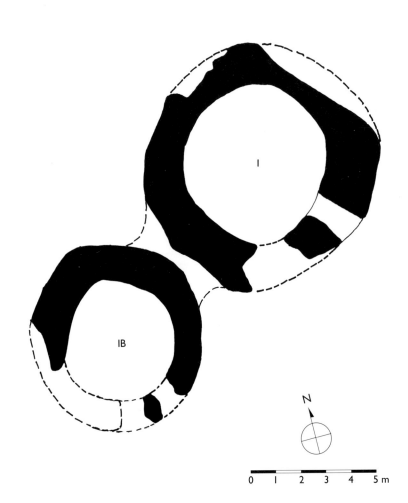

Figure 21.1   Lebena tholos tombs
              at Papoura: Tomb I,
              Tomb IB

Figure 21.2   Tholos tombs at Papoura:
              Tomb I, Tomb IB

I. IMPORTANCE

Prepalatial tholos tombs have been found near Lenda at two separate sites west of the village and at one site east of it (not photographed). Both sites must have been in use in the 3rd millennium B.C. and into the earlier 2nd millennium.

The double tomb (Tombs I, IB) at Papoura belonged to a settlement identified but not excavated at Anginaropapouro, on the north side of the great Cape Lenda, which seems to have been in use until Middle Minoan IA. The burial layer was 0.6 m thick. Ashes found near the entrance on the inside are likely to be evidence of fumigation rather than of cremation. Finds include a gold diadem, seals, an Egyptian scarab, two Cycladic figurines, and beads from necklaces.

At Yerokambos is another double tomb (Tombs II, IIA). Tomb II was in use from Early Minoan I, as the pottery in the lower burial layer shows. Its upper layer contained Early Minoan II–Middle Minoan IA pottery and offerings similar to those at Papoura (despite a modern tomb robbing), including another Egyptian scarab. On the floor of Tomb IIA was a thick layer of burnt bones, with Early Minoan II pottery.

The settlement that was using the Yerokambos tombs has not been located—it was probably by the Kalamitsi stream west of the tombs—nor has that using the Early Minoan II–Middle Minoan IB tomb (Tomb III) at Zervou east of Lenda village (though there are Minoan settlements nearby at Koutrouli Mandra and Pigaïdopoulo).

II. USE

EM I–MM IB tholos tombs.

III. SITUATION

On the south coast of Crete and the south side of the Asterousia mountains, to the west and east of the village of Lenda and of Lebena-Asklepieion. Yerokambos is opposite the rock of Volakas in the sea.

IV. GEOMORPHOLOGY

The Papoura tomb group (Tombs I, IB) 1 km west of the village of Lenda is built on the same geological substrate as the Yerokambos tomb group (Tombs II, IIA) 4 km west of the village, a narrow, fault-bounded coastal pocket of Pleistocene colluvium. Because both sites are only a few hundred meters downslope of the fault contact with the Serpentinite-Amphibolite association, the walls of the tombs show a wide range of metamorphic boulders: serpentinized peridotites, amphibolites, gneisses, mica schists, garnet schists, and marbles. These boulders were obtained by the Early Minoan tomb builders from the bed of an adjacent stream channel.

V. EXCAVATION HISTORY

S. Alexiou, 1958–60, for the Archaeological Service.

VI. BUILDINGS

EM II–MM IA, and MM IB

Five tholos tombs (I, IB, II, IIA, III) at three sites (west of Lenda, at Papoura and Yerokambos; east of Lenda, at Zervou).

Tomb I (Papoura): EM II–MM IA. Internal d 5.15 m; wall thickness 1.9 m; height preserved (on the north), 1.25 m. Low entrance from the east (0.6 m high by 0.9 m wide) closed by slab; large capstones on top. Small compartments (forming Tomb IA) outside.

Tomb IB; adjoins Tomb I on the west: EM II–MM IA. Internal d 4.5 m; wall thickness 1.1–1.4 m and up to 1.9 m (on the south); height preserved, 1.4 m. Entrance from the southeast (1.4 m high by 0.6 m wide).

Tomb II (Yerokambos): EM I–MM IA. Internal d 5.15 m; wall thickness 1.9 m; height preserved (on the north), 1.7 m. Entrance from the east 0.6 m wide, with two monolith doorjambs and monolith capstone; blocking stone has a triangular upper side. Walls mainly of boulders; some facing stones worked. Part of tomb collapse has stones fallen in their rows (as at Kamilari). On northeast side, built against internal face of tomb wall at ground level, is a compartment of thin orthostat slabs (1 m wide). East of tomb entrance are four rooms (A, M, AN, and Δ) built of small stones and probably having had flat wooden roofs.

Tomb IIA: EM II–MM IA; adjoins Tomb II on the southeast. Internal d 3.4 m; wall thickness 1 m; height preserved, 1 m. Entrance possibly from the southwest, now obscured by a modern hut.

Tomb III (Zervou: not photographed): EM II–MM IB. On south (seaward) side of small hillock, south side of tomb almost all destroyed. Internal d 5.4 m; wall thickness 1.5–2 m; wall height (on the north) 1 m. Entrance from the east with two doorjambs (0.5 m high by 0.85 m wide) blocked by slab on outside. Walls of large and small stones (some worked). Additional row of stones added on the north outside to widen tholos wall and improve (corbeled) construction.

VIII. BIBLIOGRAPHY

General

1958   Alexiou, S. "Ein frühminoisches Grab bei Lebena auf Kreta," *AA*: 2–10.

1960   ———. "New Light on Early Minoan Dating: Early Minoan Tombs of Lebena," *ILN* August 6: 225–27.

1961–62   ———. "I protominoiki taphi tis Levinos kai i exelixis ton protominoikon rythmon," in *1 Cretological* 1: 88–91.

1969   Warren, P. M. *Minoan Stone Vases* (Cambridge) 93–94.

1976   Pelon, O. *Tholoi, tumuli et cercles funéraires* (Athens) 27–30.

1984   Belli, P. "Nuovi documenti per lo studio delle tombe circolare cretesi," *SMEA* 25: 101–3, 131–33.

Seals

1969   *CMS* 2.1: 193–247 nos. 170–221 (S. Alexiou).

IX. FINDS

Herakleion Museum.

X. DATE OF PHOTOGRAPHY

May 22, 1983.

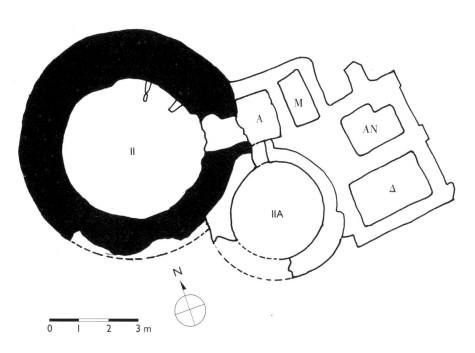

Figure 21.3 Tholos tombs at Yerokambos: Tomb II, Tomb IIA

Figure 21.4 Tholos tombs at Yerokambos: Tomb II, Tomb IIA

NIKOLAOS PLATON

35°15′ N, 23°47′ E

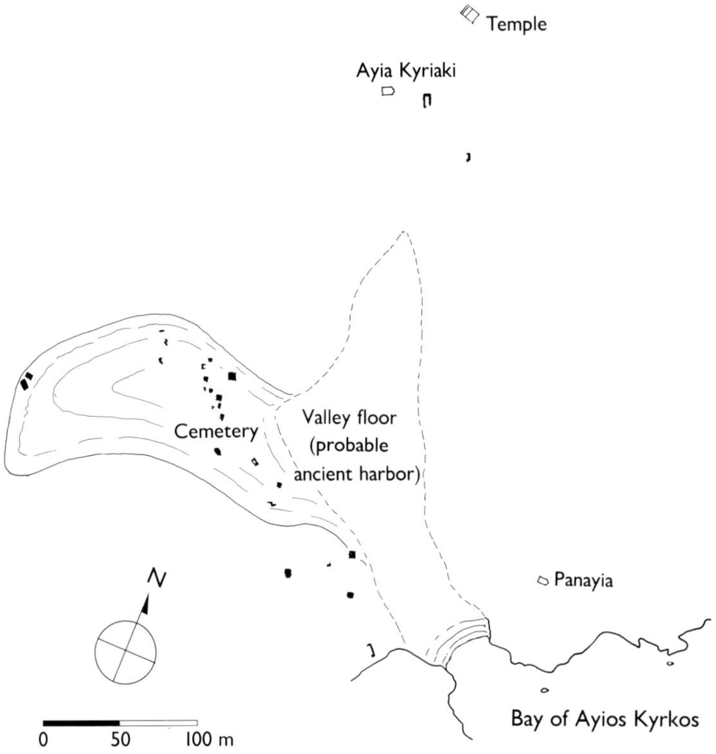

Figure 22.1 Plan of Lissos

Figure 22.2 Aerial view

I. IMPORTANCE

The chance discovery of statuary led to the excavation in 1957–60 of the shrine of Asklepios and Hygeia at Lissos, an important late Hellenistic and early Roman religious center on the south coast of western Crete, which has produced many sculptures (mostly of Asklepios or Hygeia), votive offerings, and inscriptions (including a long inscription honoring Tiberius at the entrance to the shrine's temple). At this shrine, unlike other Asklepieia, however, no inscriptions have been found recording cures.

In the 3rd century B.C. the city was a member of the league of the Oreii (mountain people), when coins show that its main divinity was Dictynna. Lissos had a long life, from at least the 4th century B.C. (any earlier history being unknown) till the Early Byzantine period. Its spring, with an abundant and therapeutic water supply, occasioned the rise of the rich sanctuary of Asklepios and Hygeia.

The whole sanctuary, with the temple, collapsed in an earthquake, probably soon after the end of the 1st century A.D. Later, Christian builders completed the destruction by using many of its stones as building material for a basilica and a church. The same people may have removed the heads of many of the statues from their torsos— the heads were found in a separate heap—and cut the sign of the Cross on the walls of the temple.

II. USE

(C,) H, and R sanctuary of Asklepios and Hygeia (Asklepieion); EByz basilica and church.

III. SITUATION

On the south coast of western Crete on the small bay of Ayios Kyrkos, east of Kastelli Selinou and west of Souyia.

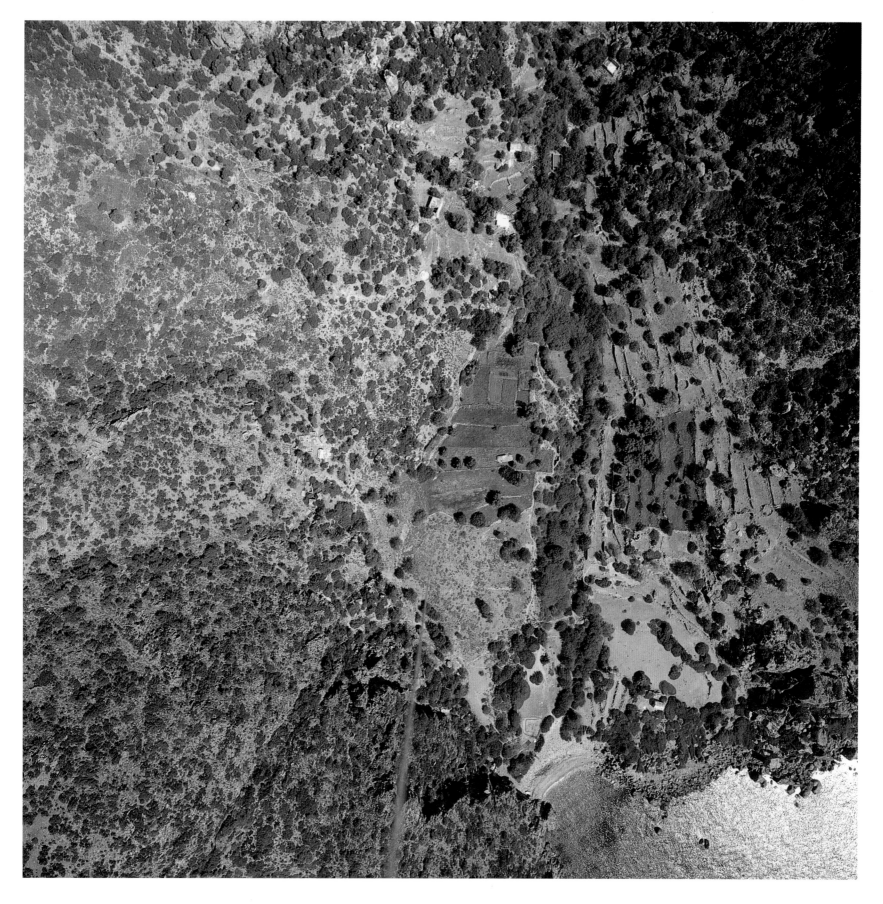

Figure 22.3   Asklepieion

Figure 22.4   Asklepieion

IV. GEOMORPHOLOGY

Along the last few kilometers of road from Moni south to Souyia one passes along a steep-sided valley that marks the fault contact between two nappes: the Phyllite-Quartzite series rocks to the west and the underlying dolomitic limestones of the Trypali nappe to the east. Lissos itself rests in the Phyllite-Quartzite zone, but within a smaller coastal rock unit representing the rapid erosion of massive limestones during the Miocene to form a brecciated limestone bedrock. The small alluvium-floored valley in which Lissos rests was formed in the brecciated limestone by faulting and subsiding of a bedrock block, certainly to the east and probably also to the west. A seasonal stream entering the valley from the north has eroded a nearly vertical gorge into the bedrock: the general physiography resembles that of Zakro. The valley floor may well be the site of the ancient harbor.

The small area of valley-floor alluvium is under cultivation, irrigated by water from the perennial spring on the valley's east slope that supplied the Asklepieion. Although relatively steep, the east slope of the valley was cultivated at some time in the past, as evidenced by deteriorating stone retaining terraces. Where breached, these terraces have disgorged much sediment downslope. More recently, the alluvium in the valley appears to have suffered erosion, visible in the steep channel marking the main natural drainageway to the sea. Along the west rock cliff at the present shoreline one can make out a series of solution notches marking past sea levels. They must correlate in some way with the series visible at other sites in western Crete, such as Phalasarna.

V. EXCAVATION HISTORY

N. Platon, 1957–60, for the Archaeological Service.

VI. BUILDINGS

H–R   Sanctuary of Asklepios and Hygeia (mostly 1st century B.C.–1st century A.D.): Doric temple, cella (9.9 by 6 m) with no internal divisions, with podium for cult images of the two gods at rear and, to their right, a small pit used in the ritual. Entrance from the south up two steps. Mosaic pavement (1st century A.D., with bird, duck, goat, and lion or leopard) occupies main part. (Pavement later cut by pit, in which some statues buried. Earlier [4th–3rd century B.C.] floor below pavement.) East wall preserved to some height in polygonal masonry, with pseudo-isodomic above, in limestone. Other walls (little preserved) would have been similar. On south wall proxeny decrees and inscribed votive stelai built into wall. Many bases of votive statues inside and outside temple.

Small paved forecourt in front of temple, bounded by low walls to the south and west. To the west is the spring, with pipes taking its water beneath the temple to the sanctuary's fountain.

Immediately south of temple is a narrow stoa, on same alignment and of same length as temple, with inscribed architrave.

To the northwest a bath building, and nearby hostel, or priests' house (with alterations during successive phases), approached by steps from an opening in the enclosure wall (which was also the supporting wall of upper terrace).

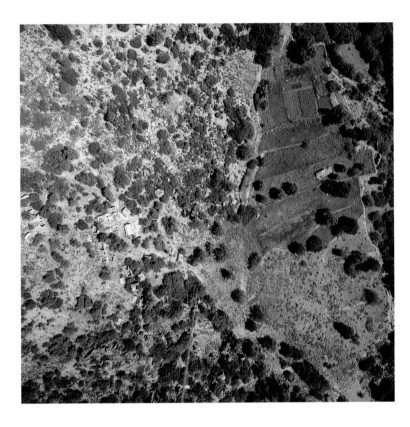

Figure 22.5   Cemetery

Figure 22.6   Raised ancient waterline shows on cliff

Below is fountain. Next to it to the south a cistern and a small cistern and well. Also late R small theater, badly preserved.

Chamber tombs on west side of valley.

Destruction by earthquake in early 2nd century. Sanctuary not rebuilt.

R   Cemetery of freestanding built vaulted tombs (about 2 by 3 by 2 m), arranged on terraces.

EByz   Basilica of Ayia Kyriaki, locally called Ayios Kyrkos (22.8 by 11 m), and church of Panayia (probably 23.3 by 13.6 m) (Asiatic sarcophagus built into Panayia); tombs.

VIII.   BIBLIOGRAPHY

1837   Pashley, R. *Travels in Crete* (London) 2:88–97.

1865   Spratt, T. A. B. *Travels and Researches in Crete* (London) 2: 240–41.

1890   Svoronos 222–24.

1901   Savignoni, L., and G. De Sanctis. "Esplorazione archeologica delle provincie occidentale di Creta," *MonAnt* 11:448–59, 509–50.

1926   *RE* 13:730 (E. Bürchner).

1939   *IC* 2:210–15 (= *IC* II. XVII. 1–9).

1942   *RE* 18:1063–65, s.v. "Orioi" (E. Kirsten).

1957   Platon, N. "I archaiologiki kinisis en Kriti kata to etos 1957," *KrChron* 11:334–37.

1958   ———. "I archaiologiki kinisis en Kriti kata to etos 1958," *KrChron* 12:465–67.

1959   ———. "I archaiologiki kinisis en Kriti kata to etos 1959," *KrChron* 13:376–78.

1960   Platon, N., and C. Davaras. "I archaiologiki kinisis en Kriti kata to etos 1960," *KrChron* 14:516.

1962   Willetts, R. F. *Cretan Cults and Festivals* (London) 191–92.

1976   *PECS* 519–20 (D. J. Blackman).

1982   Sanders, I. F. *Roman Crete* (Warminster) 42–43, 46–47, 84–85, 128, 171–72.

IX.   FINDS

Chania Museum.

X.   DATE OF PHOTOGRAPHY

May 15, 1984.

COSTIS DAVARAS

35°02′ N, 25°58′ E

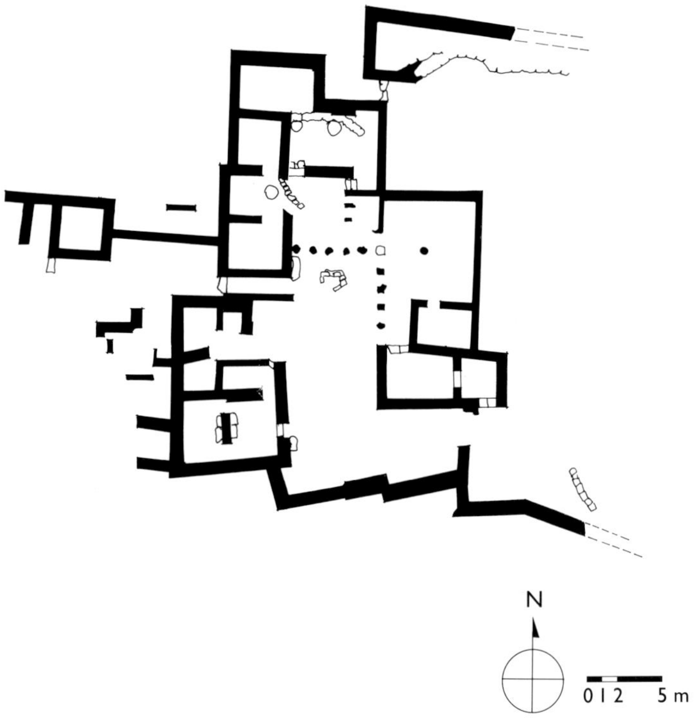

I. IMPORTANCE

The unique Late Minoan I country house at Makryyialos in the rich farming land east of Ierapetra is built in a grand style that imitates that of the Minoan palaces and may even be seen as an epitome of them. (Unfortunately, it has been badly damaged by modern farming.) The house has strong religious associations: in its central court is an altar, the north part of the west side of the court had a bench shrine, and the large room on the east side may have had a ritual use, possibly for banquets. The finds include a bronze female figurine with pronounced genitals, a large stone chalice, a stone (sacred?) anchor, and evidence for the marine links of the Minoan goddess, such as a fine sealstone showing a sacred ship carrying an altar, a sacred palm tree, and an adoring female worshipper.

II. USE

LM I country house.

III. SITUATION

On the south coast east of Ierapetra, Makryyialos lies on flat ground in a valley on the west side of the mouth of a stream, across which is village of Makryyialos. Rich farming in the valley. Useful anchorage.

IV. GEOMORPHOLOGY

The site lies on a bedrock terrace sloping approximately 10 degrees toward the sea. It appears to have been covered by only a few decimeters of pebbly slopewash before excavation. The bedrock is a nodular cream-colored marine limestone of Pliocene age—the Myrtos formation, as mapped by Fortuin (1977).

The largest wall foundation blocks were roughhewn from the local bedrock (not dressed). The main room on the north has a floor of slabs of pebble conglomerate derived from the Pleistocene rock unit that caps much of the Neogene marine limestone in the area. Cisterns are cut into the bedrock around the site. Ashlar building

Figure 23.1   Makryyialos country house

Figure 23.2   Country house

N

0 1 2   5 m

blocks (including a fire-cracked example almost 1.7 m long) were finely finished from a greenish fine-grained sandstone derived from the flysch bedrock on the other side of the Kalonero Bay, about 4 km southeast of the site.

Water may have come from wells in the bed of the small deep valley just east of the site, whose setting is reminiscent of that of Myrtos–Phournou Koryphi.

V. EXCAVATION HISTORY

C. Davaras, 1972, 1977, for the Archaeological Service.

VI. BUILDINGS

LM I Unusual country house with main entrance facing north and a dogleg corridor leading to an east court and east entrance; principal facade on west with large blocks, and west court; corridor from west entrance leads directly to north–south court in center of house: 12.5 by 6 m, with altar and cult bench at west wall, and porticoes with mud-brick pillars (stone socles) at north and north end of east side; main room at northwest corner, finely paved; small stairway nearby to upper floor; in east wing a square room 6 by 6 m with central column; in west wing a large room with central freestanding wall, benches on either side. Mud brick used on upper floor(s). LM IB destruction by fire. Abandonment.

VIII. BIBLIOGRAPHY

General

1973   Davaras, C. "Archaiotites kai mnimeia anatolikis Kritis," *ArchDelt* 28, pt. 2:590–91.

1976   ———. *Guide to Cretan Antiquities* (Park Ridge, N.J.) 326–27.

1980   ———. "Une ancre minoenne sacrée?" *BCH* 104:47–71.

1985   ———. "Architektonika sticheia tis YM IB epavlis tou Makryyialou," in *5 Cretological* 1:77–92.

Geomorphology

1977   Fortuin, A. R. "Stratigraphy and Sedimentary History of the Neogene Deposits in the Irapetra Region, Eastern Crete," *Geologische Uitgaven.* Amsterdam Papers of Geology series 1, 8.

IX. FINDS

Ayios Nikolaos Museum.

X. DATE OF PHOTOGRAPHY

May 28, 1981.

OLIVIER PELON, JEAN-CLAUDE POURSAT, RENÉ TREUIL,

AND HENRI VAN EFFENTERRE

35°18′ N, 25°29′ E

I. IMPORTANCE

If not so old as Knossos and Phaistos, Mallia dates back at least to Early Minoan II. Traces of habitation in that phase are found to some degree almost everywhere in the palace and the surrounding town. It is likely, however, that the town as such did not come into being until Early Minoan III–Middle Minoan IA with the development of a coherent system of paved streets radiating from the palace building.

The Old Palace, which definitely began in this period, is still little known, but its wealth is beyond dispute. On the northwest are large plastered rooms, on the floor of which was found the famous acrobat sword, named after the figure in relief on the pommel. Also of Old Palace date is a long bronze rapier with a schist hilt and amethyst pommel. These objects prove that the palace of Mallia did not fall behind its grand neighbors in conspicuous consumption.

The New Palace is what is visible today. It has all the characteristics of the Cretan palaces: a west facade of ashlar masonry, systematic projections and setbacks on all four facades, a central court, and so forth. The different functions of a palace—political, economic, and religious—are all represented. Cult appears both in traditional form (the Pillar Crypt is like those of Knossos) and in an original way, with the round table of offerings with thirty-four small hollows that is fixed into the paving of a terrace at the southwest corner of the Central Court. The *bothros*, "pit," or *eschara*, "hearth," of square open shape in the middle of the Central Court is also unusual, and so is the small southwest shrine, which contained a concave altar with incised signs. The pillaging that followed the Late Minoan IB destruction left no objects of value of the second phase of the New Palace, but the beautiful leopard's-head axe found west of the Central Court belongs to the first phase. The only relic of the last phase is a magnificent triton shell in chlorite with relief decoration, which happened to fall down near the northeast corner of the palace.

The building was not abandoned altogether. A little while after the destruction, stones from the walls were reused for a small building in the north part of the palace, aligned on a diagonal, that has the plan of a Greek temple in antis.

The town is composed of quarters (*quartiers*) of different periods of use, several of which have been cleared. The houses of Early Minoan III–Middle Minoan I and of Middle Minoan I–II are modest, except for Quartier Mu, whose wealth and special importance are reflected by such features as a dagger with a handle in gold openwork and archives in the Hieroglyphic script that make this quarter an administrative center with the functions one would expect in the palace. A small sanctuary with its furnishing still in situ (a sacrificial table, libation vase, and tables of offerings) is an interesting part of the Old Palace period town of Mallia. Quartier Mu has the oldest lustral basin in Crete: it was roofed.

Large buildings in the town date only from Middle Minoan III–Late Minoan I, principally on the east and south sides of the palace. One of them, House E, continuing into Late Minoan II, is large enough to have been compared even to the Little Palace of Knossos.

The cemeteries of Mallia are to the north by the seashore. Following some primitive ossuaries, the cemetery of Chrysolakkos, "gold pit," is a freestanding rectangular building of several phases, probably beginning in Early Minoan II. Inside, it is divided into rooms. Its facade, of partly dressed limestone blocks, is the earliest evidence for ashlar masonry in Crete. It has yielded the well-known gold pendant of two bees holding a berried fruit or honey cake, another proof of the great dexterity of the craftsmen of Mallia in Middle Minoan II. Chrysolakkos has also been suggested as the ultimate source of the gold jewelry known as the Aegina Treasure that the British Museum acquired in the last century, but a new find from Aegina makes that unlikely. No tombs of Late Minoan I have yet been found. There are some Late Minoan III tombs along the shore.

Although Mallia was less affected by outside influences than Knossos or Phaistos and always had a conservative and rural character throughout its long life, works of art of great quality were produced there.

There is evidence of a Roman settlement of some size at the Mill Beach. Remains include houses, tombs, and an Early Byzantine basilica.

Figure 24.1 Mallia area

Figure 24.2   Aerial view

II. USE

EM II settlement; EM III/MM IA–LM IIIB/C town (EM III–LM IB palace); R settlement; EByz basilica.

III. SITUATION

Mallia lies in a small coastal plain on the north coast, bounded to the south by the Lasithi mountains. Its rich agricultural domain would have included the plain as well as the Lasithi mountains and the valleys leading to them. Two harbors served both fishing and the sea trade: the Mill Beach (*Plage du Moulin*) to the northwest, where there is both evidence of a rise in sea level since the Bronze Age and a freshwater spring now in the sea; and a smaller harbor in the bay of Ayia Varvara to the northeast.

The town, with a likely extent of about 80 ha, was enclosed by a wall, of still uncertain date, whose circuit has not been fully found. Outside the town: cemeteries to the north and isolated buildings, such as a house at Ayia Varvara.

IV. GEOMORPHOLOGY

Mallia is a site of great geologic interest, being on an open bay where there is today no shelter for small vessels. Almost certainly the swampy area 0.5 km northwest of the palace was, during the Bronze Age, an embayment providing excellent natural shelter and a harbor for small boats.

The bedrock beneath Mallia is a bluish gray dense limestone (*sideropetra*) of the Gavrovo-Tripolitza (Tripolis) series, which also forms the Selena (Lasithi) mountains between Mallia and the Lasithi plain to the south. Along the coast north of Mallia this bedrock has been eroded into a steep, rocky shore. Just inland, the bedrock contains a set of deep, nearly vertical, joints; in these joints collective burials were made in Early Minoan and Middle Minoan times.

A deep residual soil developed on the bedrock during the last glacial period or earlier. It is a classic example of the Mediterranean terra rossa soils, and its high fertility is demonstrated by the numerous small farms still to be seen on the Mallia plain. In places around the palace this soil cover is more than 2 m thick.

A second bedrock type in the vicinity of the palace is the cemented "fossil" dune sand, or eolianite, that forms a thin mantle over the coastal limestone outcrops. The Minoans used this easily quarried rock extensively in ashlar constructions at Mallia, and the remains of their quarry cuttings are visible at several points along the shore. The continuation of some of the quarrying below the surface demonstrates a relative rise in sea level of at least 1 m during the past several millennia.

V. EXCAVATION HISTORY

J. Hazzidakis, 1915, 1919, for the Archaeological Service; C. Picard, L. Renaudin, J. Charbonneaux, F. Chapouthier, and P. Demargne, 1921–34; F. Chapouthier, 1936, 1946–49; H. Gallet de Santerre, A. Dessenne, J. Deshayes, and P. Demargne, 1946–49, 1951–54; P. Demargne and A. Dessenne, 1956–57, 1960; H. Van Effenterre, 1956–57, 1960–65; O. Pelon, 1963–69, 1978–; J.-C. Poursat, 1964–; R. Treuil, 1968, 1978; C. Baurain and P. Darcque, 1981–; A. Farnoux and J. Driessen, 1988–, for the French School.

VI. BUILDINGS

Palace

On the low rise of Zourokephali (14.97 m high), about 115 m north–south by 87 m east–west, for approximate area of 8,900 sq m. Not in center of town but at meeting point of a network of (partially explored) paved roads. On flat ground, unlike Knossos and Phaistos, but of similar plan to those palaces, though with a marked rusticity (an almost complete absence of frescoes and luxury materials such as gypsum).

EM II
(Prepalatial)   Remains revealed in trials, including EM II buildings inside the west storerooms.

EM III–MM II
(Old Palace)   Observed at various spots, especially under the staterooms at the northwest (where the sword with the acrobat came from) and the area to the north of them. Plan quite different from that of the New Palace.

MM III (first phase of New Palace)   Identified recently, of almost identical plan to LM I palace except at northwest.

LM I (second phase of New Palace)   Present building, which incorporates a few earlier features.

Several entrances, each with its own distinctive character: north, public/official entrance with double anteroom and dogleg approach; south, religious entrance, leading to spacious anteroom with decorated paved floor; northeast, southeast, and west, service entrances.

Two large courts: West Court with flagstone walkways and cobbled yard; Central Court (48 m north–south by 23 m east–west), partly paved and otherwise with chalk surface, has central square cutting with four square bases; porticoes on north (wooden columns on limestone bases) and east (pillars alternating with columns).

Two lesser courts: North Court with π-shaped portico, and North West Court, or "Keep Court."

Staterooms: at northwest with hall leading to north onto a portico beside an open space, probably gardens.

Cult rooms and places: grouped mainly on west side of the Central Court. At north the Loggia, a small room raised on a platform, opening to the Central Court by a wide flight of steps with a central pillar; in middle, pillar crypt with incised signs on pillars and, unlike Knossos, two pillars on north–south axis; at south, small terrace with round offering table in limestone, with large central hollow and thirty-four hollows around rim; in southwest part, small shrine opening out of doors, with contents including a small altar in sandstone with incised signs (star and cross).

Storerooms: along west facade, long and narrow; on east side of Central Court, plastered rooms with platforms along the sides, channels, and collectors (for spillage); a linked, but less elaborate, group at the northeast; silos (kouloures) at the southwest, a freestanding building with two rows of circular containers with central pillars.

Upper floor: not preserved, but indicated by many staircases; likely banquet room (suggested by Graham 1961) above pillared hall at north end of Central Court.
Destruction in LM IB.

Postpalatial   Small diagonal building in North Court, entrance between antae, on different alignment. Date uncertain, probably LM II.

Agora

Northwest of palace and immediately north (north–northwest) of West Court.

Old Palace period   Three buildings, interconnected and on same alignment (80 degrees) as Chrysolakkos cemetery: (1) the Hypostyle Crypt (now roofed), a row of five basement rooms, their walls plastered, the end rooms with benches running around the walls and a nonaxial column base to support the roof; (2) a similar row of five semibasement storerooms for pithoi; (3) a courtyard 30 by 40 m enclosed by a big stepped wall with three gates, one giving access to the upper floor of the crypt, one opening onto West Court of palace, and one opening in the direction of the Chrysolakkos cemetery. Possible use as political center for town before, or as well as, the Old Palace.

New Palace period   Out of use. Houses built on east side of Agora, but the courtyard itself and crypt left free of rebuilding.

Quartier Mu

Lies 200 m west of palace (and now roofed). Two main buildings (A and B) and seven smaller houses excavated. Approximate area 4,000 sq m.

EM II–MM IA   Chance finds outside the buildings.

MM IB   Traces in trials beneath some MM II rooms; some houses built that were reused in MM II.

MM II   Principal building phase.

Building A (800 sq m): main entrance from the west; east and north service entrances. At northwest, large square room with adjacent sanctuary and a row of small storerooms; *polythyron* hall with light well, paved portico, and a roofed lustral basin. Storerooms to the south. Upper floor attested, as in the other buildings, by numerous staircases.

Building B (450 sq m): main entrance from the south. On the west a large basement (10 by 10 m) with well-preserved walls, doors, and small windows. At the east, a hall and storeroom.

Five smaller buildings: each is 80–100 sq m; identified as craftsmen's houses. Seal engraver's, potter's, and metalworker's shops northeast of Building A; south workshop and Building C (probably another metalworker's shop) south of Building A.

Building D: very badly preserved and function unknown. Building E (not fully excavated) has long storerooms (perhaps an annex of Building A).

All these buildings destroyed by fire at end of MM II.

MM III–LM I Traces of small MM III structures. LM I: very occasional potsherds.

LM II–LM III LM II–IIIA1 pottery; LM III building remains principally to the north of seal engraver's workshop.

Quartier E

Lies 150 m south of palace, bounded to the north by east–west street, not completely excavated.

EM II Pottery only.

MM I–MM II Building remains in eastern part.

MM III–LM I Principal building phase. House E 50 m east–west by 28 m north–south: entrance from the north; angled portico; remains of a *polythyron* hall; lustral basin with niches and painted plaster; House Eα to the east, smaller and separated from House E by an alley.

LM II Pillar room with bench and hearth in eastern part of House E.

LM IIIB/C Apparent series of successive buildings having no connection with earlier plan.

Quartier Zeta

Lies 40 m from southeast entrance to palace. Remains badly preserved.

EM III Paved area (at least 40 by 60 m) closely connected to palace; north–south wall, 1.75 m wide, attested particularly under House Zβ, room XVI, seems to be remains of an early defense wall; sandstone walkway crosses paved area from west to east and crosses the defense wall to northeast of House Zβ.

MM II House Zγ, built over paved yard of about 110 sq m. Entrance from the south, but remains badly destroyed. North facade remodeled in MM III–LM I.

MM III–LM IB House Zα, about 23 by 20 m. Carefully built outside walls on east, south, and west, but north edge uncertain. Two entrances on the south side: one to the west reaches the principal rooms (lustral basin, and hall separated by five pillars from a verandah opening to the west) by a passage; the other leads to the eastern part of the building (service rooms or meeting places?). Destroyed by fierce fire in LM IB.

House Zβ, about 17.9 by 20.7 m. North side fronts onto a street; main entrance from the east leads to staircase I or to room XVII, which leads to all ground-floor rooms. Most rooms on the east side are service rooms. On the west, hall VII and, through four openings, a light well. Room IX perhaps a bath and room V a bronze smithy. Destroyed by fire in LM IB.

Mill Beach and Surrounds

Named after modern water mill, now almost completely covered by sand, at bay west of palace. Sandstone quarry 100 m west of bay probably used by Minoans. Toward eastern end of bay: rectangular building underwater (not in photograph); uncertain date, imposing size. Also at eastern end of bay: later aqueduct, date uncertain. Quartier Theta includes:

Old Palace period: parts of two or three buildings (Maison de la Plage) with two phases, both Old Palace.

New Palace period (or LM III?): traces of later occupation.

R Houses and tombs at eastern end; tomb with Attic sarcophagus 100 m south-southwest of beach at Sta Marmara.

EByz Basilica (partly excavated) built over tomb at Sta Marmara, with
(6th century?) mosaics.

Chrysolakkos Cemetery

By shore, 500 m north of Palace, near EM II–MM I ossuaries.

EM II–MM II Rectangular, 38.8 m north–south by 29.8 m east–west; outer wall of
(use in MM III *sideropetra* blocks, dressed with particular care on north and west,
unlikely) was leveling and bedding course for orthostats that have now almost completely disappeared. Interior divided into compartments by walls at right angles, with two building phases. Cult place in eastern part has a hollow plaster "altar" with fluted outside on a sloping plaster floor with small round hollows. Paving outside on all four sides and

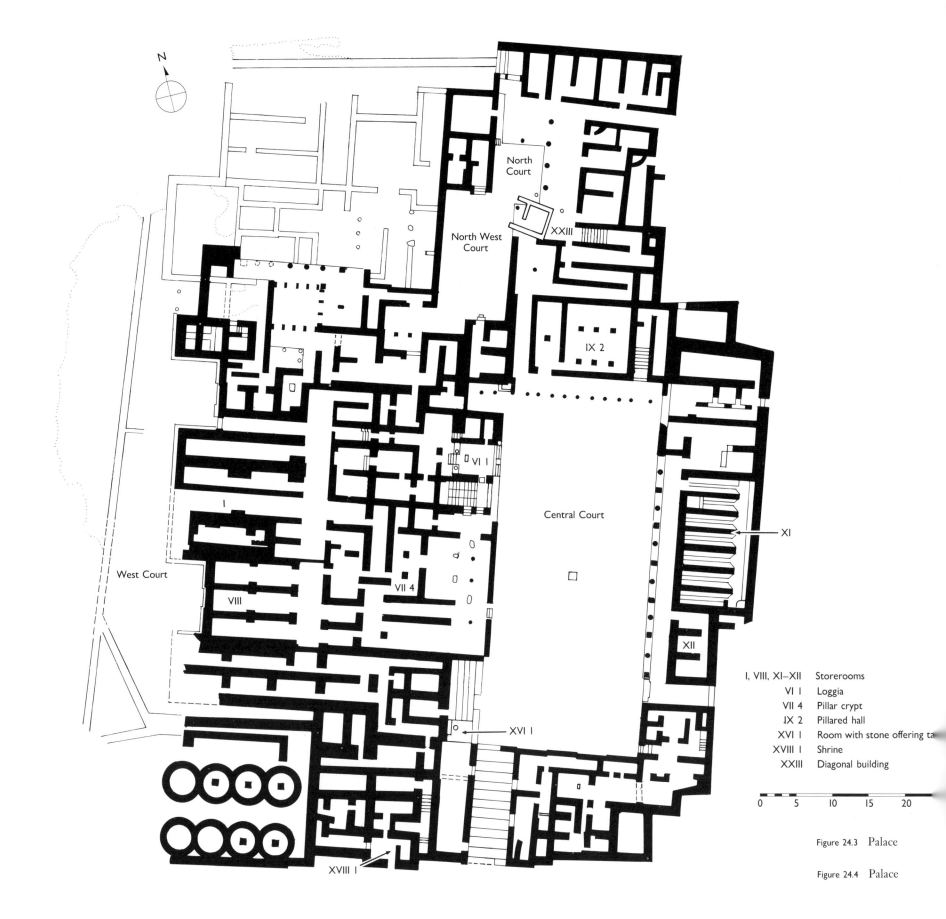

North
Court

North West
Court

XXIII

IX 2

Central Court

VI I

I

West Court

VII 4

VIII

XI

XII

XVI I

XVIII I

I, VIII, XI–XII   Storerooms
VI I   Loggia
VII 4   Pillar crypt
IX 2   Pillared hall
XVI I   Room with stone offering ta
XVIII I   Shrine
XXIII   Diagonal building

0   5   10   15   20

Figure 24.3   Palace

Figure 24.4   Palace

Figure 24.5   Palace

on the east, with a row of pillar bases making a portico. Under the east paving, plastered rooms with benches belong to a first phase that probably had a funerary use.

VII. RADIOCARBON DATES

	B.P.	1σ cal. B.C.	2σ cal. B.C.
EM III destruction, north of palace			
Gif-254	4030 ± 300	—	—
MM II destruction, Quartier Mu			
Gif-448	3905 ± 200	—	—
Gif-447	3800 ± 200	—	—
Gif-875	3780 ± 130	2460–2030	2580–1880
Gif-449	3420 ± 200	—	—
Gif-1279	3410 ± 110	1880–1543	2028–1450
Gif-874	3350 ± 120	1867–1520	1950–1410
MM II(?), Quartier Mu			
Gif-2452	3060 ± 100	1430–1215	1520–1020
MM III destruction			
Quartier E			
Gif-255	3470 ± 250	—	—
Palace			
Gif-1277	3380 ± 110	1875–1530	1960–1430
LM IA, Quartier E			
Gif-256	3200 ± 250	—	—
LM II destruction, Quartier E			
Gif-1521	3100 ± 110	1510–1260	1620–1040

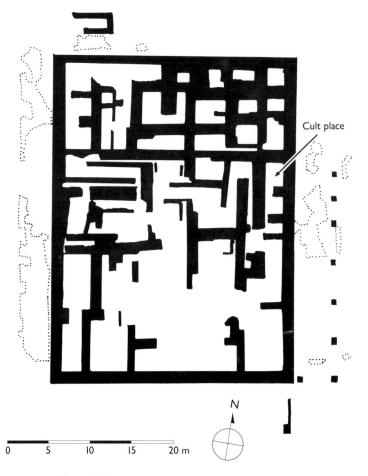

Cult place

N

| 0 | 5 | 10 | 15 | 20 m |

Figure 24.6   Chrysolakkos cemetery

VIII. BIBLIOGRAPHY

General

1949   Gallet de Santerre, H. "Aperçu historique," *KrChron* 3: 363–91.

1974   Ecole Française d'Athènes. "Mallia. Plan du site, plans du palais, indices," *EtCr* 19 (Paris).

1980   Van Effenterre, H. *Le palais de Mallia et la cité minoenne, Incunabula Graeca* 86 (Rome).

1982   Sanders, I. F. *Roman Crete* (Warminster) 101–2, 147.

1983   Van Effenterre, H. "The Economic Pattern of a Minoan District: The Case of Mallia," in *Minoan Society* 61–68.

Tiré, C., and H. Van Effenterre. *Guide des fouilles françaises en Crète*, 3rd ed. (Paris).

1987   Pelon, O. "Crète et Anatolie: Données maliotes," in *Mélanges E. Laroche, Hethitica* 8, ed. R. Lebrun (Louvain) 381–92.

Poursat, J.-C. "Le début de l'époque protopalatiale à Malia," in *Eilapini* 461–66.

Figure 24.7 Chrysolakkos cemetery

Figure 24.8 Cemetery

1988 Pelon, O. "L'autel minoen sur le site de Malia," *Aegaeum* 2:31–46.

Poursat, J.-C. "La ville minoenne de Malia: Recherches et publications récentes," *RA* 61–82.

1989 Guest-Papamanoli, A. "Les carrières de grès dunaire à Malia," *BCH* 113:113–22.

Palace

1928 Chapouthier, F., and J. Charbonneaux. *Mallia. Premier rapport (1922–1924)*, *EtCr* 1 (Paris).

1936 Chapouthier, F., and R. Joly. *Mallia. Deuxième rapport (1925–1926)*, *EtCr* 4 (Paris).

1938 Chapouthier, F. *Deux épées d'apparat découvertes en 1936 au palais de Mallia*, *EtCr* 5 (Paris).

1942 Chapouthier, F., and P. Demargne. *Mallia. Troisième rapport (1927–1932)*, *EtCr* 6 (Paris).

1961 Graham, J. W. "The Minoan Banquet Hall," *AJA* 65:165–72.

1962 Chapouthier, F., and P. Demargne. *Mallia. Quatrième rapport (1929–1935 et 1946–1960)*, *EtCr* 12 (Paris).

1977 Van Effenterre, H., and Y. Tzedakis. "Matériel inédit des premières fouilles au palais de Mallia," *ArchDelt* 32, pt. 1: 156–81.

1979 Olivier, J.-P., O. Pelon, and F. Vandenabeele. "Un nouveau document en Linéaire A au palais de Malia," *BCH* 103:3–27.

1980 Pelon, O. "Aspects de la vie religieuse minoenne à la lumière des recherches récentes au palais de Malia (Crète)," *CRAI* 658–70.

———. *Le palais de Mallia* V, *EtCr* 25 (Paris).

1982 ———. "L'épée à l'acrobate et la chronologie maliote," *BCH* 106:165–90.

———. "Le palais de Malia et les jeux de taureaux," in *Rayonnement grec: Hommages à Charles Delvoye*, ed. L. Hadermann-Misguich, G. Raepsaet, and G. Cambier (Brussels) 45–57.

———. "Palais et palais à Malia (Crète)," *RALouvain* 15: 45–57.

1983 ———. "Fonction politique dans un palais minoen," in *Minoan Society* 251–57.

———. "L'épée à l'acrobate et la chronologie maliote (II)," *BCH* 107:679–703.

Schmid, M.-E. "Les portes multiples au 'megaron' du palais de Malia," *BCH* 107:705–16.

1985 Pelon, O. "L'acrobate de Malia et l'art de l'époque proto-palatiale en Crète," in *L'iconographie minoenne. Actes de la Table Ronde d'Athènes (21–22 April 1983)*, *BCH* Supplement 11, ed. P. Darcque and J.-C. Poursat (Athens) 35–40.

1986 ———. "Publication d'un palais minoen: Eléments pour une chronologie," in *5 Cretological* 1:276–83.

———. "Un dépôt de fondation au palais de Malia," *BCH* 110:3–19.

1987 ———. "Minoan Palaces and Workshops: New Data from Malia," in *The Function of the Minoan Palaces* 268–72.

1990 Spence, Y. "Was There a Guarded Entrance Way to the First Palace at Mallia?" *BSA* 85:369–74.

Town

1953 Demargne, P., and H. Gallet de Santerre. *Mallia. Exploration des maisons et quartiers d'habitation (1921–1948)*, *EtCr* 9 (Paris).

1959 Deshayes, J., and A. Dessenne. *Mallia. Exploration des maisons et quartiers d'habitation (1948–1954)*, *EtCr* 11 (Paris).

1966 Pelon, O. "Maison d'Hagia Varvara et architecture domestique à Malia," *BCH* 90:552–85.

Poursat, J.-C. "Un sanctuaire de Minoen Moyen II à Malia," *BCH* 90:514–51.

1967 Pelon, O. "La Maison E de Malia reconsidérée," *BCH* 91:494–512.

1969 Van Effenterre, H., and M. Van Effenterre. *Mallia. Le centre politique* I. *L'agora (1960–1966)* *EtCr* 17 (Paris).

1970 Amouretti, M.-C. *Mallia. Le centre politique* II. *La crypte hypostyle (1957–1962)*, *EtCr* 18 (Paris).

Pelon, O. *Mallia. Exploration des maisons et quartiers d'habitation (1963–1966)*, *EtCr* 16 (Paris).

1973 Graham, J. W. "A New Arena at Mallia," in *Antichità cretesi* 1:65–73.

Van Effenterre, H. "Arène ou agora?" in *Antichità cretesi* 1:74–78.

1975 Chevallier, H., B. Detournay, S. Dupré, R. Julien, J.-P. Olivier, M. Séfériadès, and R. Treuil. *Mallia. Sondages au sud-ouest du palais (1968)*, *EtCr* 20 (Paris).

1976 Van Effenterre, H., and M. Van Effenterre. *Mallia. Exploration des maisons et quartiers d'habitation (1956–1960)*, *EtCr* 22 (Paris).

1978 Poursat, J.-C., L. Godart, and J.-P. Olivier. *Mallia. Le quartier Mu* I, *EtCr* 23 (Paris).

1980 Detournay, B., J.-C. Poursat, and F. Vandenabeele. *Mallia. Le quartier Mu* II, *EtCr* 26 (Paris).

Guest-Papamanoli, A. "Anaskaphi simantikou ktismatos mesa sti thalassa sta Malia Kritis," *AAA* 13:99–101.

1983 Baurain, C., and P. Darcque. "Un triton en pierre à Malia," *BCH* 107:3–73.

Poursat, J.-C. "Ateliers et sanctuaires à Malia," in *Minoan Society* 277–81.

Frescoes

1990 Immerwahr, S. A. *Aegean Painting in the Bronze Age* (University Park, Pa.) 182.

Cemeteries

1945 Demargne, P. *Mallia. Exploration des nécropoles (1921–1933)*, *EtCr* 7 (Paris).

1963 Van Effenterre, H., and M. Van Effenterre. *Mallia. Etude du site (1956–1957) et exploration des nécropoles (1915–1928)*, *EtCr* 13 (Paris).

1973 Shaw, J. W. "The Chrysolakkos Façades," in *3 Cretological* 1:319–31.

1979 Higgins, R. A. *The Aegina Treasure: An Archaeological Mystery* (London).

1987 Baurain, C. "Les nécropoles de Malia," *Aegaeum* 1:61–73.

De Pierpont, G. "Réflexions sur la destination des édifices de Chrysolakkos," *Aegaeum* 1:79–93.

Higgins, R. A. "A Gold Diadem from Aegina," *JHS* 107:182.

1989 Pelon, O., and V. Stürmer. "Sur les pseudo-trompettes de Malia," *BCH* 113:101–11.

Scripts and Seals

1930 Chapouthier, F. *Les écritures minoennes au palais de Mallia, EtCr* 2 (Paris).

1969 *CMS* 2.1:484–97 nos. 409–20 (N. Platon).

1974 Poursat, J.-C. "L'atelier des sceaux de Malia et la chronologie des sceaux protopalatiaux," in *Die kretisch-mykenische Glyptik und ihre gegenwärtigen Probleme* (Bonn) 111–14.

1976 *GORILA* 1:267–78.

1977 *CMS* 2.2:93–108 nos. 76–85 (N. Platon, I. Pini, and G. Salies) and 109–270 nos. 86–198 (A. Dessenne).

1979 *GORILA* 2:87–88.

1981 Poursat, J.-C. "L'atelier des sceaux et le quartier Mu de Malia: Etude comparée des sceaux découverts," in *Studien zur minoischen und helladischen Glyptik, CMS* Beiheft 1, ed. W.-D. Niemeier (Berlin) 159–65.

1982 *GORILA* 4:80–89, 139–40.

1984 *CMS* 2.3:177–86 nos. 144–52 (N. Platon and I. Pini).

1985 *CMS* 2.4:35–38 nos. 22–24, 207–15 nos. 162–69 (N. Platon and I. Pini).

   GORILA 5:49–54.

1989 Farnoux, A., and J.-P. Olivier. "Trois nouveaux fragments de tablettes en écriture hiéroglyphique crétoise à Malia," *BCH* 113:98–100.

1990 Poursat, J.-C. "Hieroglyphic Documents and Seals from Mallia, Quartier Mu: A Functional Analysis," *Aegaeum* 5:25–32.

Radiocarbon Dates

1970 Delibrias, G., M.-T. Guillier, and J. Labeyrie. "Gif Natural Radiocarbon Measurements V," *Radiocarbon* 12:441.

   Pelon, O. *Mallia. Exploration des maisons et quartiers d'habitation (1963–1966), EtCr* 16 (Paris) 171–72.

1971 Delibrias, G., M.-T. Guillier, and J. Labeyrie. "Gif Natural Radiocarbon Measurements VI," *Radiocarbon* 13:227–28.

1986 ———. "Gif Natural Radiocarbon Measurements X," *Radiocarbon* 28:23.

1989 Warren, P. M., and V. Hankey. *Aegean Bronze Age Chronology* (Bristol) 181.

IX. FINDS

Herakleion Museum; Ayios Nikolaos Museum.

X. DATE OF PHOTOGRAPHY

May 20, 1982.

2 5 M O C H L O S

JEFFREY S. SOLES

35°11' N, 25°54' E

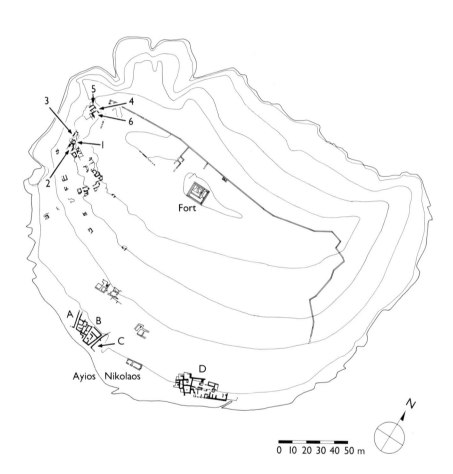

Figure 25.1   Plan of Mochlos

Figure 25.2   Mochlos and spit to mainland

I. IMPORTANCE

The small island of Mochlos, now rocky and dry, was almost certainly connected to Crete in the Bronze Age by a low isthmus. It is known particularly for its rich Early Minoan cemetery of houselike tombs, which have produced gold jewelry, silver cups, a fine group of stone vases and the earliest faience known in Crete. These tombs would have belonged to a small town that became prosperous by trading in the Aegean. It may have had as many as two to three hundred inhabitants, ruled by local chiefs, some of whom were buried in the two largest and richest tombs (Tombs 1-2-3; Tombs 4-5-6).

Mochlos was partly abandoned in the Old Palace period, though there is plenty of evidence for settlement in eastern Crete (including an interesting tholos tomb of the type well known in the Mesara at Galana Charakia about 2.5 km east). In the New Palace period the town flourished again, and some of the tombs came back into use. Four blocks of houses and one large house (or "villa") have been identified on the island; an industrial area was located on the coast opposite, behind the modern village. A sandstone quarry in a ravine on the mainland provided the stone for the ashlar masonry used in the villa and in the "Palace" at Gournia (and in smaller amounts for other buildings at Mochlos and Pseira). Like many other Late Minoan I centers in eastern Crete, Mochlos was destroyed by fire in Late Minoan IB. But at Mochlos, unlike the others, human skeletons were found in the debris.

Fish tanks cut into the rock on the mainland coast are an important feature of the Roman settlement that provide evidence for a rise in sea level since Roman times. The isthmus was probably flooded by the end of the Roman period. The Byzantine fort may have been built in response to the Arab threat of the 8th and 9th centuries. The Byzantine village was on the south slope of the island and on the coast opposite at Loutres.

II. USE

FN, EM II–MM IA, MM IB–II, MM III–LM I, LM IIIA–IIIB, R, and EByz settlement; EByz fort.

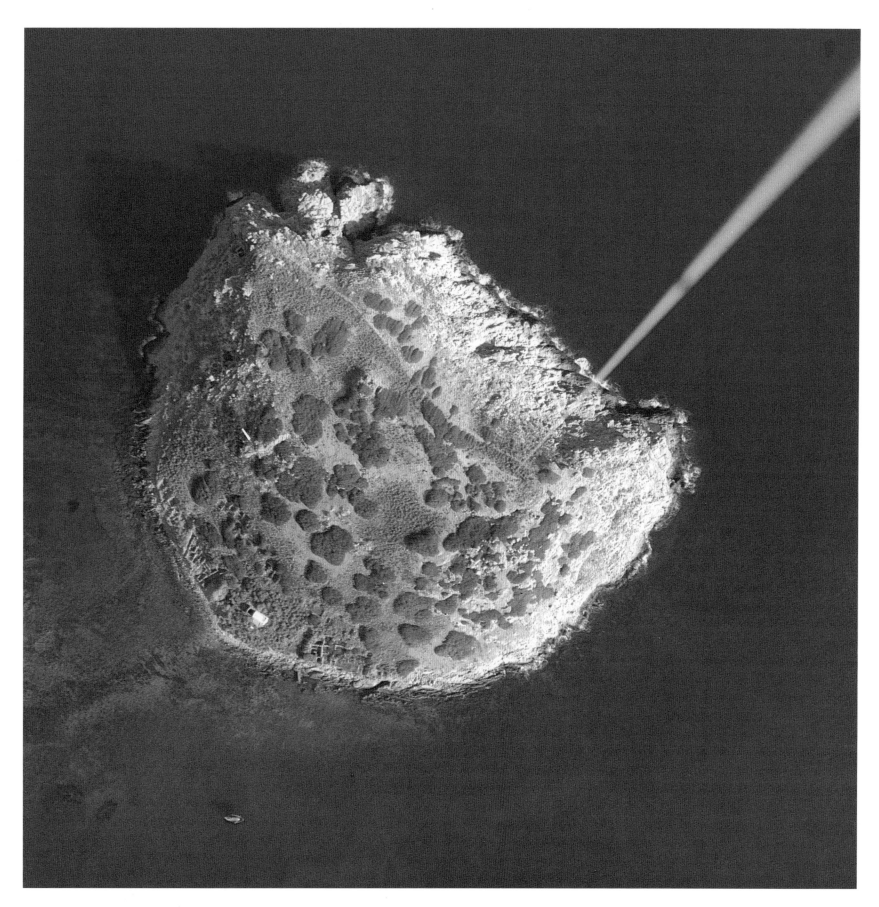

Figure 25.3   View of island

Figure 25.4   Roman fish tanks at Mochlos

III. SITUATION

Mochlos, a small island, about 250 by 300 m, rises to 45 m, off the north coast of Crete at the eastern limit of the Bay of Mirabello. Little vegetation and no water source. In the Bronze Age it was probably connected to Crete by an isthmus about 180 m long. On the mainland opposite, a well-watered and fertile plain extends for about 4 km.

IV. GEOMORPHOLOGY

The bedrock layers of Mochlos are a continuation of those that form the central eastern shore of the Bay of Mirabello: Phyllite-Quartzite rocks overlying the thin-bedded cherty limestones of the Plattenkalk series. The bedrock is identical in this respect to that of Pseira, some 3 km to the west.

Mochlos is the core of an anticline of Plattenkalk limestone whose axial plane trends approximately east–west and is inclined to the south. Whereas the island's north side is quite steep, the south side, which faces the mainland of Crete, is less precipitous because it follows the dip slope of the bedrock.

On the coast opposite the islet, highly deformed (jointed and folded) phyllite bedrock crops out. A resistant ridge of this bedrock extends in a northwest direction toward Mochlos, where it appears just above sea level along the south shore. When sea level was 2–3 m lower in antiquity, a bedrock spit (similar to the one at Traphos on the south coast) extended toward, and may even have reached, the

Figure 25.5 Tombs 4-5-6, etc.

islet. However, there is no evidence of construction on the bedrock ridge crest. The traces of putative structures visible in 2 m of water are only the remnants of a naturally cemented Pleistocene talus breccia deposit whose wave-eroded fragments mimic the appearance of artificial stone walls. It is likely that the small protected anchorage just south of the islet was used by the earliest settlers; its bottom sediments must contain miscellaneous objects of the sort that have always been discarded or lost overboard from ships at anchor.

The Roman fish tanks, now fully submerged, near the shore just east of the modern village indicate a relative rise in sea level of 1–2 m since the 3rd century A.D.

V. EXCAVATION HISTORY

R. B. Seager, 1908, for the American Exploration Society; C. Davaras and J. S. Soles, 1971–72, 1976, for the Archaeological Service and the American School, and 1989–, for the Archaeological Institute of Crete and the American School.

VI. BUILDINGS

FN Traces at northwest and southwest.

Figure 25.6   Settlement east of church

Figure 25.7 Settlement west of church

EM II–MMIA Cemetery with twenty-four house-tombs and two rock-shelter tombs on terraces at northwest. Two largest tombs (Tombs 1-2-3; Tombs 4-5-6) with large orthostat slabs of purple and green schist and gray-blue limestone. Paved entry with outdoor altar in front of Tombs 4-5-6. Traces of settlement along south shore, over an area about 50 m north–south by 150 m east–west, with some house remains and a long paved street.

MM IB–II Cemetery largely abandoned; small scattered deposits from settlement along south shore.

MM III–LM I Town with four blocks of houses along south shore. Blocks A, B, and C to the west of church of Ayios Nikolaos and Block D to the east, covering about same area as Prepalatial settlement. Total of perhaps ten houses exposed by Seager: the largest, in east part of Block D, is over 30 m long east–west, with main entrance from the south leading to a light well with bench, a main room, and stairs to an upper floor. A large house or villa, the main administrative center of the town, was located above Block B. Built with ashlar facades, and with pillar crypts on its ground floor, it was terraced in three stories against the hillside.

Settlement extended in LM IB to coast opposite island, behind modern village, where an industrial establishment, specializing in clay and stone vase making and bronzeworking, was located. Pithos burials in old cemetery area; some tombs (including Tombs 4, 5, and 6) reused. LM IB destruction by fire: skeletons. Abandonment.

LM IIIA–IIIB House on island; small cemetery of chamber tombs on the coast opposite the island, behind the modern village.

R Small settlement of 2nd–4th century. Three fish tanks in rock on coast opposite the island.

EByz Small village along south shore and at Loutres on the coast opposite. Fort with long curtain wall along the top of the island, about 200 m east–west, at east end turning south for 80 m. Remains of three small towers along the wall. One large tower, built with cement, behind the wall on the island's summit.

VIII. BIBLIOGRAPHY

General

1909 Seager, R. B. "Excavations on the Island of Mochlos, Crete, in 1908," *AJA* 13:273–303.

1912 ———. *Explorations in the Island of Mochlos* (Boston and New York).

1955 Platon, N. "I archaiologiki kinisis en Kriti kata to etos 1955," *KrChron* 9:564.

1958–59 Leatham, J., and M. S. F. Hood. "Sub-Marine Exploration in Crete," *BSA* 53–54:273–75.

1970 Kenna, V. E. G. "Richard Berry Seager: American Archaeologist, 1882–1925," *Archaeology* 23:322–32.

1972 Davaras, C. "Archaiotites kai mnimeia anatolikis Kritis," *ArchDelt* 27, pt. 2:654.

1973 ———. "Archaiotites kai mnimeia anatolikis Kritis," *ArchDelt* 28, pt. 2:585–86.

Zois, A. A. *Kriti, Epochi tou lithou*, Ancient Greek Cities 18 (Athens) 98–104.

1974 Davaras, C. "Archaiotites kai mnimeia anatolikis Kritis," *Amaltheia* 5:40–45.

Soles, J. S. "Investigations at Mochlos," *AJA* 78:179–80.

1976 *PECS* 586 (K. Branigan).

1978 Soles, J. S. "Mochlos: A New Look at Old Excavations. The University Museum's Work on Crete," *Expedition* 20.2:4–15.

Vagnetti, L., and P. Belli. "Character and Problems of the Final Neolithic in Crete," *SMEA* 19:137.

1982 Sanders, I. F. *Roman Crete* (Warminster) 136.

1983 Betancourt, P. P. *The Cretan Collection in the University Museum, University of Pennsylvania 1. Minoan Objects Excavated from Vasilike, Pseira, Sphoungaras, Priniatikos Pyrgos, and Other Sites* (Philadelphia) 10–13.

Soles, J. S. "A Bronze Age Quarry in Eastern Crete," *JFA* 10:33–46.

1988 ———. "Social Ranking in Prepalatial Crete," in *Problems in Greek Prehistory* 49–61.

1990 Soles, J. S., and C. Davaras. "Theran Ash in Minoan Crete: New Excavations on Mochlos," in *3 Thera* 3:89–95.

Forthcoming Soles, J. S. *The Prepalatial Cemeteries at Mochlos and Gournia, Hesperia* Supplement 24 (Princeton).

Scripts and Seals

1963   Hughes, H. M. C., and P. M. Warren. "Two Sealstones from Mochlos," *KrChron* 17:352–55.

1969   *CMS* 2.1:561–70 nos. 471–78 (N. Platon).

1973   Davaras, C. "A New Hieroglyphic Seal from Mochlos," *Kadmos* 12:109–13.

1975   *CMS* 5.1:20–23 nos. 24–26 (I. Pini).

1977   *CMS* 2.2:355–64 nos. 249–55 (N. Platon, I. Pini, and G. Salies).

1982   Pini, I. "Zu dem silbernen Rollsiegel aus Mochlos," *AA* 599–602.

1984   Aruz, J. "The Silver Cylinder Seal from Mochlos," *Kadmos* 23:186–88.

         CMS 2.3:295–315 nos. 251–68 (N. Platon and I. Pini).

1985   *CMS* 2.4:83–84 no. 62, 259–62 nos. 206–8 (N. Platon and I. Pini).

1989   Olivier, J.-P. "Le 'Disque de Mochlos': Une nouvelle interpretation en Linéaire A sur un poids en plomb, HM 83/MO Zf 1," *Kadmos* 28:137–45.

IX. FINDS

Herakleion Museum; Ayios Nikolaos Museum; Siteia Museum; University Museum, University of Pennsylvania, Philadelphia.

X. DATE OF PHOTOGRAPHY

April 24, 1981.

ATHANASIA KANTA

35°14′ N, 24°40′ E

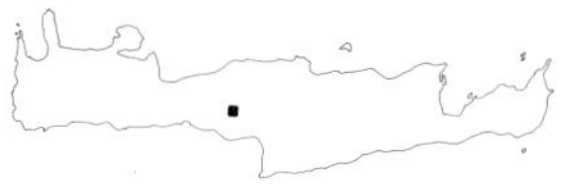

I. IMPORTANCE

Monastiraki is a vast collecting center of the Old Palace period on the low hill of Charakas in the Amari valley west of Psiloriti. On the top of the hill, walls were visible before the start of the new excavations, and the whole area was littered with small cairns of stones created by local farmers who gradually dismantled the Minoan walls to improve cultivation. The aerial photographs were taken before work began on the hilltop and before these cairns were removed.

The new excavations have revealed a large area of the site with extensive storerooms, two archives of clay sealings, and large habitation quarters. There is evidence of monumental architecture, whose construction would have involved a communal effort, and of a complicated system of account keeping: both features argue a palatial character for the site. The hill of Charakas controls a natural route from northern to southern Crete. Undoubtedly, much of the importance of Monastiraki is due to this location.

The storerooms were full of pithoi containing wine, olive oil, figs, and cereals together with household and fine (Kamares ware) pottery. The pottery is exactly like that of the Old Palace of Phaistos.

The trenches of a Greek-Italian exploratory survey in 1982 and 1984 revealed the first archive room at Monastiraki. A clay model of a shrine also found in these trenches suggests there may have been a religious center on the hill.

II. USE

MM settlement; H reoccupation; R building near Monastiraki village spring.

III. SITUATION

In the rich and well-watered Amari valley, southeast of Rethymno, west of Psiloriti, and northwest of the Mesara plain, a few minutes east of Monastiraki village.

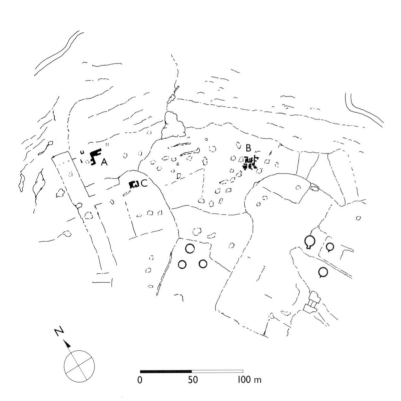

0   50   100 m

A   Original excavation site (Grundmann; and Kanta 1980)
B   New excavations (Kanta 1981–)
C   New excavations (Tzedakis and Godart; and Kanta 1984–)

Figure 26.1   Plan of Monastiraki

Figure 26.2   Higher aerial view

IV. GEOMORPHOLOGY

The modern village of Monastiraki is on the north slopes of Mt. Samitos. This mountain, along with Mt. Kedros, is composed of the lower Pindos-Ethia nappe (cherts, radiolarites, and massive pelagic limestones), which here overthrusts flysch rocks of the Tripolitza zone. The village overlooks a wide basin, elongated northwest–southeast and floored by Miocene conglomerates and sandstones. This basin, with its internal drainage, is rich agricultural land.

Downslope of the village, but still overlooking the cultivated basin, is a geologically exotic rock mass—a small klippe of limestone "floating" on the underlying flysch sequence. In Middle Minoan times a settlement was constructed on this elongate limestone klippe, similar in siting to that at Gournia far to the east. Minoan Monastiraki could avail itself of both the excellent massive Pindos limestone a few hundred meters upslope to the south and a spring located at the contact between this limestone and the underlying flysch unit. The more fractured limestone bedrock of the klippe itself was easily cleared and leveled for building, and the plain to the north must have been farmed. The new excavations show that Minoan walls lie just below the ridge surface, whereas more extensive sedimentation has deeply covered the walls on the slope to the north. Some of this sediment appears to be redeposited mud brick.

V. EXCAVATION HISTORY

K. Grundmann, 1942; A. Kanta, 1980–, for the University of Crete; Y. Tzedakis and L. Godart, 1982 and 1984, for the Archaeological Service and the University of Naples.

VI. BUILDINGS

MM (Old Palace period) Two phases revealed to date in main living quarters on northwest part of hill. Traces of first phase also on east side of hill. Most rooms excavated are of second phase, including more than sixty intercommunicating storerooms belonging to the same building complex. Clear evidence for an upper storey: for instance, more than five hundred clay sealings fallen from second archive room into storeroom below. Destruction by earthquake and fire at end of Old Palace period.

H Part of east side of Charakas hill reoccupied; also H occupation on southeast slopes (H wall founded on M remains visible in aerial photographs).

Figure 26.3 Monastiraki from the southeast

VIII. BIBLIOGRAPHY

General

1951 Kirsten, E., and K. Grundmann. "Die Grabung auf der Charakeshöhe bei Monastiraki I, II," in *Forschungen auf Kreta 1942*, ed. F. Matz (Berlin) 27–71.

1982 Sanders, I. F. *Roman Crete* (Warminster) 161.

Forthcoming Kanta, A., L. Godart, and A. Tzigounaki. *Monastiraki* (Rome).

Seals

1975 *CMS* 5.1:227–34 nos. 286–96 (I. Pini).

IX. FINDS

Chania Museum; Rethymno Museum.

X. DATE OF PHOTOGRAPHY

June 8, 1983.

Figure 26.4   Lower aerial view

PETER WARREN

35°00′ N, 25°36′ E

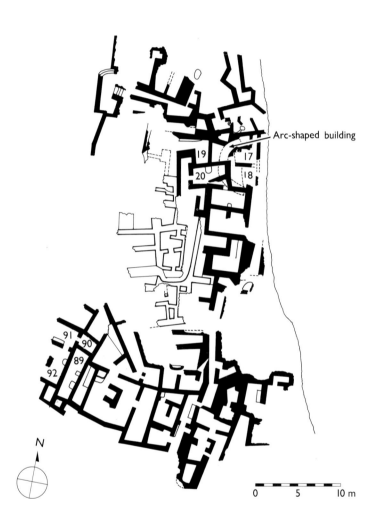

Figure 27.1   Myrtos–Phournou Koryphi

Figure 27.2   Phournou Koryphi

I. IMPORTANCE

Phournou Koryphi is the only completely excavated village of Minoan Crete. Built and destroyed by fire in Early Minoan II, it belongs to the middle of the 3rd millennium B.C. Although its ninety-odd small rooms and passages may be divided into at least six individual family units, it seems to have been a densely packed community, the houses joined to each other in a cellular structure. The shrine rooms at the southwest corner would have served the whole village; and the terracotta statuette of a goddess found in one of the rooms holds a miniature of the jugs typical of the village. Water was most likely a problem, as was security, if a circuit wall around the village was defensive, as seems probable.

Phournou Koryphi has yielded evidence for the farming of cereals, olives, and vines and for the herding of sheep, goats, cattle, and pigs as well as equipment for weaving, potting, and making wine and olive oil in the village. Its seals and sealing are the earliest in Crete that are securely dated.

The storage vessels show a minimum capacity of 7,125 liters at the time of the destruction. If one-third of that was for keeping oil and if the rate of consumption and the storage capacity resemble those of modern Crete, the population can be estimated at between 35 and 70, probably nearer the first figure.

The only post–Early Minoan II occupation was a substantial arc-shaped building on the summit. Its function is not known, though it had a floor on which were a pithos and a quernstone. There is no evidence that it was a hill shrine or a tomb. The absence of later pottery suggests a date soon after the Early Minoan II destruction, when wall stones and pottery of Early Minoan II were reused.

II. USE

EM II settlement; post–EM II building.

III. SITUATION

The settlement of Myrtos–Phournou Koryphi sits on a hill 66 m high, rising directly above the south shore of Crete about 2.3 km east of Myrtos village and 1.7 km east of Myrtos-Pyrgos. The fertile

Figure 27.3   Phournou Koryphi

Troulli and Sarikampos valleys lie to the east and the west; they were probably farmed and used as sources of water in the Bronze Age. The small plateau west of the settlement was probably also farmed. There are no wells or cisterns in the settlement, which extended about 50 m north–south and 25 m east–west, with a cliff on the east and a surrounding wall, probably defensive, on the other sides. Traces of occupation appear at the base of the next hillock on a ridge to the northwest, 128 m from settlement.

IV. GEOMORPHOLOGY

Wagstaff (1972) explains the site's geomorphological setting, on a high point of a Pliocene marl ridge overlooking the present shoreline. Besides his geological sketch map of the Viannos-Ierapetra region, see also Fortuin's 1:76,000 Geological Map (1977) covering the isthmus of Ierapetra region. Fortuin maps the bedrock of Phournou Koryphi as the Myrtos formation: gypsum, white and gray marls, and marl breccias overlain by fossiliferous marls, all deposited during Early to Middle Pliocene time (c. 5–3 million years ago). His type section for illustrating the formation is the cliff exposure immediately below the site.

A discontinuous stratum of beach rock capping the marl at the site represents a raised marine terrace deposited during the last glaciation, when the sea level was high. Fortuin designates the terrace as "Quaternary Terrigenous-Clastic," a type of terrace common in the Ierapetra region.

The stratigraphical sections of the site indicate that the marl bedrock dips south toward the shore at a low angle. Natural slope breaks, due to the detachment of bedrock blocks along bedding planes, were exploited by the Early Minoan builders as the upslope walls of several rooms in the settlement. Also visible in the sections and in the walls on the site is a tilt downslope: evidence of the gradual gravitational creep of the archaeological strata.

V. EXCAVATION HISTORY

P. M. Warren, 1967–68, for the British School.

VI. BUILDINGS

EM II Two phases, the earlier confined to the summit and west central part, the later built over the earlier on the summit and extending over the whole area within the wall. Shrine rooms (89–92) at the southwest corner carry back to the Prepalatial period essential elements of Minoan religion (cult statuette on bench; storerooms for vessels associated with the shrine) and add others (skull beside a hearth). Individual family units usually include a workroom, kitchen, and storeroom. All constructions in the village were of undressed stone, with or without mud bricks as superstructure. Some walls and a passage bore on discovery remains of white lime plaster painted red. Buildings were of one storey, with a flat roof of timbers overlaid with reeds and coarse plaster. Larger stones were used for rising passage steps and door sills. The main entrance, on the south, was protected by a small bastion and closed by a door whose post turned in a stone socket. A clay sealing near an internal door suggests the room may have been sealed.

Post–EM II Arc-shaped building over rooms 17–20, with internal platform and bench.

VII. RADIOCARBON DATES

	B.P.	1σ cal. B.C.	2σ cal. B.C.
EM II destruction			
Q-952	4172 ± 70	2894–2619	2920–2509
Q-953	4142 ± 80	2886–2588	2920–2491
Q-1004	3986 ± 80	2591–2458	2867–2290
Q-1002	3965 ± 80	2582–2401	2861–2280
Q-1003	3907 ± 80	2557–2294	2590–2143

	B.P.	1σ cal. B.C.	2σ cal. B.C.
Q-951	3835 ± 80	2461–2146	2562–2040
Q-950	3805 ± 85	2455–2137	2552–1989

Thermoluminescence dates of seven sherds from pottery in use at time of EM II destruction (the preferred dates carry an error of not less than 8 percent, about ± 350 years B.C. with these dates).

Oxford Lab. ref.	Preferred age	Oxford Lab. ref.	Preferred age
107 a 5	2580 B.C.	107 a 4	2330 B.C.
107 a 2	2430 B.C.	107 a 6	2290 B.C.
107 a 7	2430 B.C.	107 a 3	2170 B.C.
107 a 1	2380 B.C.		

Figure 27.4   Phournou Koryphi and Libyan Sea

VIII. BIBLIOGRAPHY

General

1964   Hood, M. S. F., P. M. Warren, and G. Cadogan. "Travels in Crete, 1962," *BSA* 59:95–96, 99.

1969   Warren, P. M. "An Early Bronze Age Potter's Workshop in Crete," *Antiquity* 43:224–27.

1971   Branigan, K. "An Early Bronze Age Metal Source in Crete," *SMEA* 13:10–14.

1972   Warren, P. M. *Myrtos: An Early Bronze Age Settlement in Crete,* British School at Athens Supplementary Paper 7 (London).

1977   ———. "Restoration Work and New Architectural Observations at Myrtos, Phournou Koryphi, in 1976," *AAA* 10: 188–97.

1979   Whitelaw, T. M. *Community Structure and Social Organization at Fournou Korifi, Myrtos,* Master's thesis, University of Southampton.

1983   Warren, P. M. "The Settlement at Phournou Koryphi, Myrtos and Its Place within the Evolution of the Rural Community in Bronze Age Crete," in *Les communautés rurales* 2. Recueils de la Société Jean Bodin pour l'histoire comparative des institutions (Paris), 41:239–71.

Whitelaw, T. M. "The Settlement at Phournou Koryphi, Myrtos and Aspects of Early Minoan Social Organization," in *Minoan Society* 323–45.

Seals

1970   Warren, P. M. "The Primary Dating Evidence for Early Minoan Seals," *Kadmos* 9:29–37.

1975   *CMS* 5.1:12–17 nos. 14–20 (I. Pini).

Radiocarbon and Thermoluminescence Dates

1970   Switsur, V. R., M. A. Hall, and R. G. West. "University of Cambridge Natural Radiocarbon Measurements IX," *Radiocarbon* 12:597.

1972   Fleming, S. "Appendix XIV: Thermoluminescent Dating of Sherds," in P. M. Warren, *Myrtos* (London) 343.

Switsur, V. R., and R. G. West. "University of Cambridge Natural Radiocarbon Measurements X," *Radiocarbon* 14: 245–46.

Warren, P. M. *Myrtos* (London) 344–45.

Geomorphology

1972   Wagstaff, J. M. "The Physical Geography of the Myrtos Region: A Preliminary Appraisal," Appendix 2 in P. M. Warren, *Myrtos: An Early Bronze Age Settlement in Crete.* British School at Athens Supplementary Paper 7 (London) 273–82.

1974   Angelier, J., and M. Gigout. "Sur les platesformes marines et néotectoniques de la région d'Ierapetra," *Comptes Rendus, Académie des Sciences* (Paris), 278:2103–6.

1977   Fortuin, A. R. "Stratigraphy and Sedimentary History of the Neogene Deposits in the Irapetra Region, Eastern Crete," *Geologische Uitgaven.* Amsterdam Papers of Geology series 1, 8.

IX. FINDS

Ayios Nikolaos Museum.

X. DATE OF PHOTOGRAPHY

May 21, 1981.

GERALD CADOGAN

35°00′ N, 25°35′ E

I. IMPORTANCE

Pyrgos exemplifies how long-lived and how prosperous a small provincial settlement of the Minoans could be. It has major monuments from three of its four principal periods of use by the Minoans (Pyrgos I–IV), plentiful evidence of crafts, and a rich and copious collection of pottery.

Chosen probably as a defensible site as well as a good one for agriculture, with the water supply in the valley of the river Myrtos, Pyrgos was settled in the same phase (Early Minoan IIA) as nearby Myrtos–Phournou Koryphi and likewise suffered a destruction by fire in Early Minoan IIB. Later building removed most of this first settlement (Pyrgos I), but Phournou Koryphi shows how life would have been there.

After the Early Minoan II destruction Pyrgos, unlike Phournou Koryphi, was resettled (Pyrgos II), probably after an intervening period of desertion. (No buildings or deposits have been found that can be assigned to Early Minoan III alone, by contrast with Gournia and Vasiliki.) Pyrgos II probably began in Middle Minoan IA—although the Early Minoan III style pottery of eastern Crete was still in use—and probably continued into the Old Palace period.

The principal monument of Pyrgos II, the two-storey house-tomb at the southwest corner of the village, continued in use, if intermittently, till Late Minoan I. A well-made paved road led to a small courtyard in front of the tomb, and steps came down the hillside to the start of the road. There are two ossuaries, one on either side of the tomb. Road, courtyard, tomb, and ossuaries are on a terrace formed from the Early Minoan II destruction debris.

The tomb and ossuaries contained about sixty-five dead, nine of them (all male) in extended burials in the tomb chamber that were datable to the principal Old Palace phase of Pyrgos (Pyrgos III) or to Late Minoan I (Pyrgos IV). Over the last burials a mass of Late Minoan I pottery, both fine and plain, and an assortment of stone vases had cascaded down from the upper floor, together with bronze daggers and triton shells. Study of these bones shows that the inhabitants were generally in good health, and the animal bones from the settlement reveal that they ate a surprisingly large amount of pork.

The road leading to the tomb went out of use in the later phases of Pyrgos II. The principal buildings of Pyrgos III are a tower and a large cistern near it on the north slope of the hill and a second, smaller, cistern on the hilltop. It is likely that there was a major building at the top of the hill, later incorporated into the Late Minoan I country house. From it could have come the vast quantities of pottery found fallen, or dumped, down the northwest slopes. The pottery and other finds of Pyrgos III date closely resemble what was found in Old Palace period Mallia, suggesting a cultural (and perhaps political) unit stretching around and across the Lasithi massif. Pyrgos III ended with another destruction by fire.

During Pyrgos IV (Late Minoan I, with no separate Middle Minoan III phase yet identified) a grand country house was built at the top of the hill; it must have been the ruling building of the Myrtos valley. Its architecture is of palatial quality. The finds include two Linear A tablets, clay sealings, a red faience triton shell, and clay tubular stands for offerings, all part of the contents of a shrine—and epitomizing the complete mingling of religion, administration, the economy, and the arts in Crete at the time.

That this house burnt down in Late Minoan IB although houses in the village around apparently did not suggests human agency. The short-lived barley and vetch kept in pithoi in the building's storerooms give important radiocarbon dates (P-2113 and P-2114).

In Hellenistic times (Pyrgos V) a shrine was built over the ruins of the country house. An inscription shows that it belonged to Hermes and Aphrodite, who were also being worshiped in the mountain shrine at Syme, a few hours' walk away.

In probably the 17th century A.D. a watchtower or beacon tower (Pyrgos VI) was put at the very top of the hill as a lookout against pirates. It has two phases, the later probably of the early 19th century, and gave the hill the name Pyrgos, "tower."

II. USE

EM II–LM I village; LM IIIC chance find; H shrine; V and Ott tower.

III. SITUATION

On a steep, flat-topped hill, 77.63 m high on the east side of the mouth of the river Myrtos on the south coast, south-southeast of the Lasithi mountains near the point where the old route around the south side of the mountains descends to cross the Myrtos river. On the west side of the mouth of the river is Myrtos village, and Myrtos–Phournou Koryphi is 1.7 km to the east. Rich farming in the river valley. Likely water sources: river and wells in the valley; also Middle Minoan cisterns in the settlement, which extended about 90 m east–west and 65 m north–south.

IV. GEOMORPHOLOGY

The hill is composed predominantly of poorly cemented fossiliferous marl strata interbedded with laminated sands, collectively named the Makrilia formation by Fortuin (1977). Its shape is controlled on the west by the lower channel of the Myrtos river valley, just at its embouchure, and on the east by a northeast–southwest trending normal fault that has dropped and steeply tilted the sediment layers immediately to the east.

Fortuin's definitive field study of the Neogene deposits around Ierapetra includes the coast in the vicinity of Myrtos. The Makrilia sediments were deposited in late Miocene time (c. 10–6 million years ago), in a deep low-energy shelf environment possibly analogous to the present bottom of the Bay of Mirabello on the north side of the island. The Makrilia formation was found to contain the highest percentage of homogeneous marls suitable for pottery making of any of the nine Neogene units mapped by Fortuin in the isthmus of Ierapetra.

Stratigraphically overlying the Makrilia formation in the Ierapetra region is Fortuin's Ammoudares formation, a rock unit of carbonate- and fossil-rich sandstones and marls deposited—also during late Miocene time—in very shallow marine waters. The presence of carbonate-rich sandstone and beach-rock strata in situ at certain points below the foundation walls at Pyrgos suggests that a thin stratum of Ammoudares capped the hill prior to the Minoan occupation.

It is unlikely that the reason for locating the settlement at the mouth of Myrtos river was that it could make a natural harbor. Proximity to the narrow strip of alluvium on both sides of the lower river valley is a more probable explanation.

V. EXCAVATION HISTORY

G. Cadogan, 1970–73, 1975–76, 1980, 1982, for the British School.

VI. BUILDINGS

EM II (Pyrgos I) Scanty traces. Destruction by fire.

EM III–MM IA (and probably MM IB) (Pyrgos II) Two-storey tomb on west slope, used—probably intermittently—through Pyrgos III and IV, with two ossuaries, and yard outside, approached by road. Steps down hill to this road. Road apparently out of use before end of Pyrgos II.

MM IB–II (and probably MM IIIA) (Pyrgos III) Terrace walls on north slope with tower (4.38 by 3+ m) and cistern (d about 5 m, and 3+ m deep); on top of hill a smaller cistern, later filled with river pebbles, and possibly a large house. Other scanty traces. Destruction by fire.

LM I (and MM III?) (Pyrgos IV) Grand country house on top of hill facing south across courtyard and north with view up valley (19.68 by 14+ m). Two building phases (earlier Pyrgos III?): later with ashlar, gypsum, and purple limestone and some fresco traces. Freestanding two-storey building on east side of courtyard.

Other houses around upper slopes of hill and street system on east slope; entrance system at southwest corner of top of hill and outbuildings to west of country house. LM IB destruction by fire, apparently of country house alone. Abandonment.

LM IIIC Chance find.

H (late 2nd or early 1st century B.C.) (Pyrgos V) Circular shrine of Hermes and Aphrodite built over light well and staircase of country house. Other traces.

V and Ott (Pyrgos VI) Beacon tower with two phases (V and Ott).

VII. RADIOCARBON DATES

The sequence of periods at Pyrgos is explained above.

	B.P.	1σ cal. B.C.	2σ cal. B.C.
Pyrgos I/IIa (pottery EM II)			
P-2349	3990 ± 70	2588–2461	2863–2330
P-2348	3700 ± 230	—	—
Pyrgos IIb?			
P-2353	4390 ± 280	—	—
Pyrgos IIc			
P-2339	5590 ± 350	—	—
Pyrgos IIb–d			
P-2350	3770 ± 370	—	—

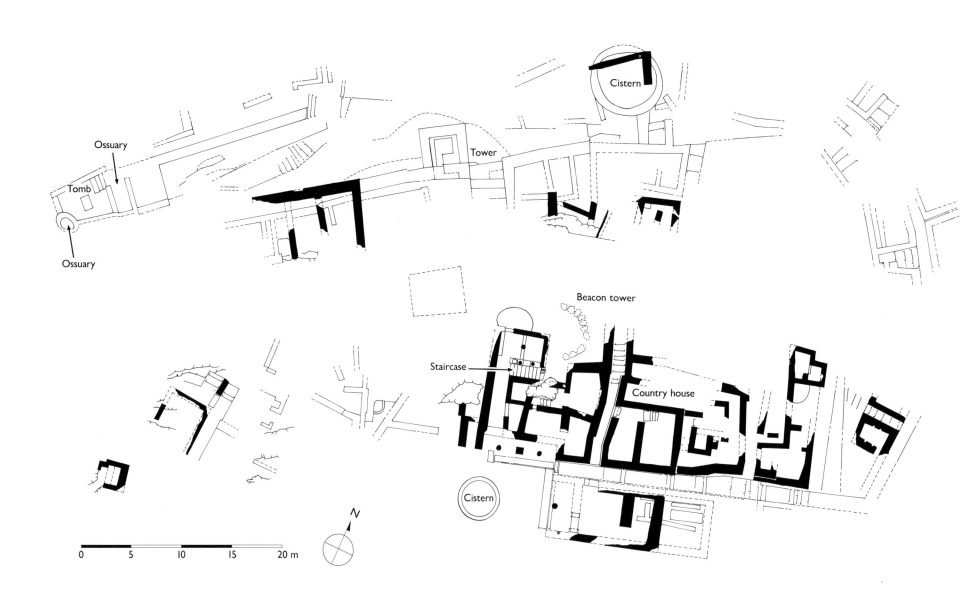

Ossuary

Tomb

Ossuary

Cistern

Tower

Beacon tower

Staircase

Country house

Cistern

N

0   5   10   15   20 m

Figure 28.1 Plan of Myrtos-Pyrgos

Figure 28.2 Pyrgos, with Venetian-Turkish beacon tower

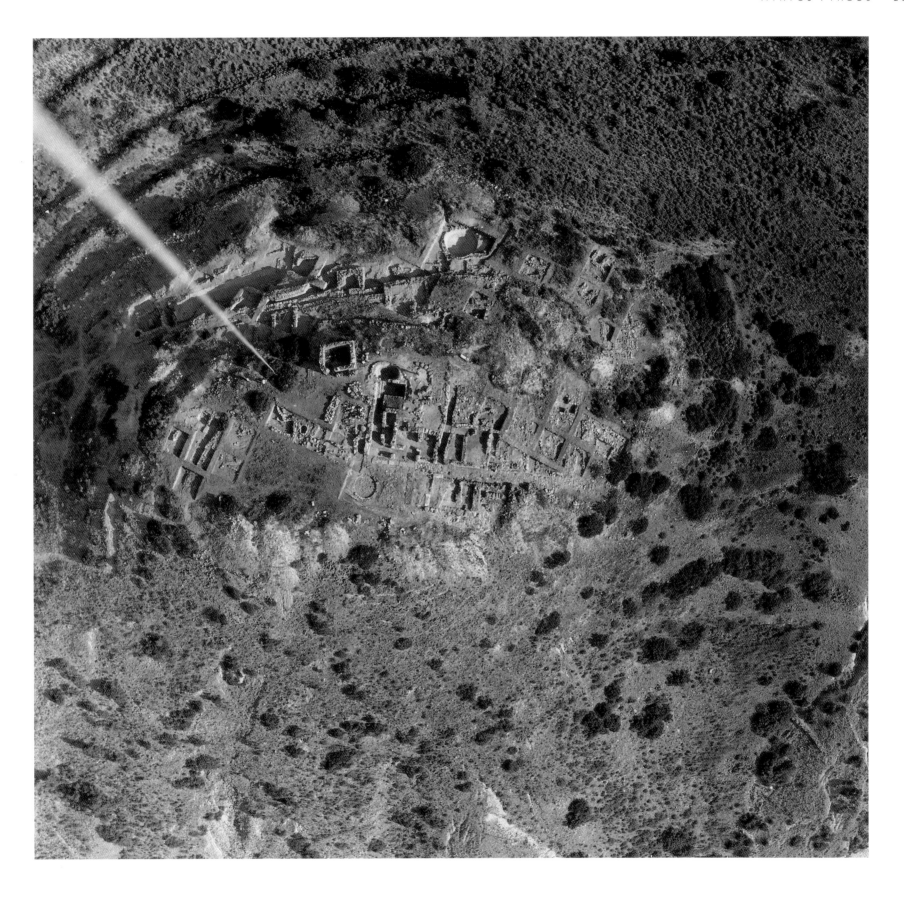

Figure 28.3   Tomb

Figure 28.4   Middle Minoan cistern and tower

RADIOCARBON DATES (continued)

	B.P.	1σ cal. B.C.	2σ cal. B.C.
Pyrgos IIc–d			
P-2351	3790 ± 300	—	—
Pyrgos IId/III			
P-2347	3430 ± 70	1878–1677	1930–1530
Pyrgos III			
P-2341	3670 ± 230	—	—
P-2340	3560 ± 200	2195–1680	2470–1430
Pyrgos IV			
P-2343	3560 ± 60	2020–1787	2125–1750
P-2116	3440 ± 60	1878–1685	1910–1620
P-2344A	3410 ± 70	1872–1640	1900–1530
P-2115	3350 ± 60	1737–1530	1870–1520
P-2114	3320 ± 60	1685–1523	1750–1641
P-2113	3320 ± 60	1685–1523	1750–1641

VIII. BIBLIOGRAPHY

General

1964   Hood, M. S. F., P. M. Warren, and G. Cadogan. "Travels in Crete, 1962," *BSA* 59:93–95.

1972   Cadogan, G., R. K. Harrison, and G. E. Strong. "Volcanic Glass Shards in Late Minoan I Crete," *Antiquity* 46:310–13.

1973   Cadogan, G. "Clay Tubes in Minoan Religion," in *3 Cretological* 1:34–38.

1977–78 ———. "Pyrgos, Crete, 1970–77," *AR* 70–84.

1978   Andreou, S. *Pottery Groups of the Old Palace Period in Crete,* Ph.D. diss., University of Cincinnati 75–92, 142–63, 172.

         Cadogan, G., and R. K. Harrison. "Evidence of Tephra in Soil Samples from Pyrgos, Crete," in *2 Thera* 1:235–55.

1979   Gamble, C. S. "Surplus and Self-Sufficiency in the Cycladic Subsistence Economy," in *Papers in Cycladic Prehistory*, Institute of Archaeology, University of California, Los Angeles, Monograph 14, ed. J. L. Davis and J. F. Cherry (Los Angeles) 122–34.

1980   Cadogan, G. "Minoan Pyrgos," in *4 Cretological* 1:57–61.

         Hankey, V. "Stone Vessels at Myrtos Pyrgos," in *4 Cretological* 1:210–15.

1981   Cadogan, G. "A Probable Shrine in the Country House at Pyrgos," in *Sanctuaries and Cults in the Aegean Bronze Age* 169–71.

Figure 28.5 Country house

Figure 28.6   Country house and small cistern

1985   Gesell, G. C. *Town, Palace, and House Cult in Minoan Crete, SIMA* 67 (Gothenburg) 35, 51, 134.

1986   Hankey, V. "Pyrgos: The Communal Tomb in Pyrgos IV (Late Minoan I)," *BICS* 33:135–37.

Scripts

1976   *GORILA* 1:321–22.

1985   *GORILA* 5:58–80.

Radiocarbon Dates

1978   Fishman, B., and B. Lawn. "University of Pennsylvania Radiocarbon Dates XX," *Radiocarbon* 20:213–15.

Geomorphology

1977   Fortuin, A. R. "Stratigraphy and Sedimentary History of the Neogene Deposits in the Irapetra Region, Eastern Crete," *Geologische Uitgaven*. Amsterdam Papers of Geology, series 1, 8.

1984   Gifford, J. A., and G. H. Myer. "Clay Sources in the Isthmus of Irapetra," in *East Cretan White-on-Dark Ware*, ed. P. P. Betancourt (Philadelphia) 118–25.

IX. FINDS

Ayios Nikolaos Museum; Herakleion Museum.

X. DATE OF PHOTOGRAPHY

May 30, 1976.

YANNIS TZEDAKIS

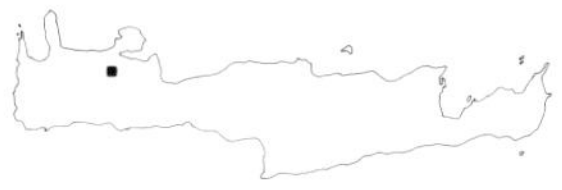

35°29′ N, 24°03′ E

I. IMPORTANCE

The country house at Nerokourou is one of the rare examples of fine New Palace period architecture to be found in western Crete. Its large hall with pier-and-door partitions and the paved floors of its rooms suggest a building of the highest quality in the style of contemporary town houses at Knossos.

Because a bulldozer destroyed the north and west sides of the building, only about one-third of it is preserved. (The walls on the north side are restored.)

II. USE

N; MM IIIB–LM I country house.

III. SITUATION

On the southern edge of the flat country by Souda Bay about 3 km southeast of Chania.

IV. GEOMORPHOLOGY

The site is located on a thin stratum of Miocene-age marly limestone, a few hundred meters from where an ephemeral stream channel has eroded through the Miocene limestone to the more resistant Triassic limestone underlying it.

V. EXCAVATION HISTORY

Y. Tzedakis and A. Sacconi, 1977–80, for the Archaeological Service and the Institute for Mycenaean and Aegean-Anatolian Studies, Rome.

VI. BUILDINGS

N Traces of occupation about 300 m away to northwest. Walls of a trapezoidal building (but-and-ben architecture?).

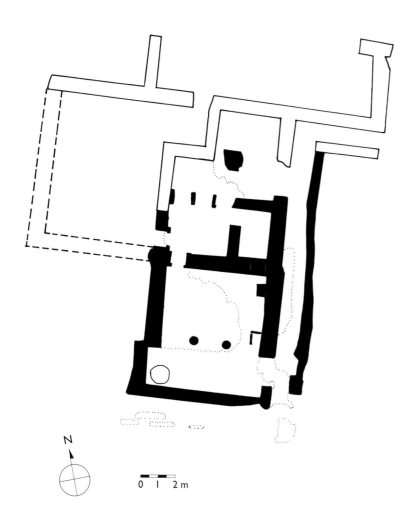

0 1 2 m

Figure 29.1   Nerokourou country house

Figure 29.2   Country house

MM IIIB–LM I Grand country house, with walls of roughly faced limestone blocks and colored limestone slabs for the paving. Doorjambs and column bases of light-colored limestone, carefully dressed. Some conglomerate used to support a possible staircase at north end of the hall.

Three phases identified: first, an open area with a stone-lined and paved cistern and a hall with two column bases and two large pillar bases (supports for a balcony?) and at least one pier-and-door partition; in the second phase (LM IA), the open area was walled in and became a light well for the hall; in the third (LM IB), the access to the building was blocked and the access area used for storage. Destruction in LM IB.

VIII. BIBLIOGRAPHY

1977 Tzedakis, Y. "Archaiotites kai mnimeia dytikis Kritis," *ArchDelt* 32, pt. 2: 329–30.

1978 ———. "Ephoreia proistorikon kai klasikon archaiotiton Chanion," *ArchDelt* 33, pt. 2: 369–70.

——. "L'insediamento urbano medio-minoico di Nerokourou," *SMEA* 19: 7–10.

1979 ———. "Ephoreia proistorikon kai klasikon archaiotiton Chanion," *ArchDelt* 34, pt. 2: 392–93.

1980 Rocchetti, L. "Relazione preliminare sulle campagne di scavo della Missione Greco-Italiana a Nerokourou," *SMEA* 21: 381–84.

1984 *Creta antica* 264 (L. Rocchetti).

Vagnetti, L. "Testimonianze di metallurgia minoica dalla zona di Nerokourou (Kydonias)," *SMEA* 25: 155–71.

1985 *Ancient Crete* 174 (L. Rocchetti).

1987 Tzedakis, Y., and S. Chrysoulaki. "Neopalatial Architectural Elements in the Area of Khania," in *The Function of the Minoan Palaces* 111–15.

1989 Tzedakis, Y., and A. Sacconi, ed. *Scavi a Nerokourou, Kydonias* I. Ricerche Greco-Italiane in Creta occidentale 1 (Rome).

IX. FINDS

Chania Museum.

X. DATE OF PHOTOGRAPHY

June 27, 1984.

ANTONIS VASILAKIS

34°58′ N, 24°49′ E

I. IMPORTANCE

The recently excavated tholos tombs of Odigitria are comparable in wealth to those of Platanos. Although both tombs were looted, some 52 seals have been found, as well as 275 pots, 20 stone vases, 12 amulets, 11 necklaces with 600 beads, 3 gold diadems and a gold bracelet, 5 small objects of copper or bronze, 2 stone axes, and 30 obsidian blades—accompanying an estimated 150 burials. The two separate burial layers in the rooms outside the tholoi had not been disturbed. An Early Minoan III–Middle Minoan IA closed deposit in the ossuary contained, among various finds, 22 of the 52 seals.

II. USE

EM I–MM IA cemetery; some LM I use.

III. SITUATION

At the west end of the Asterousia range of mountains, on the flat hilltop of Chatzinas Liophyto, with steep sides to the east and south, 150 m north of the monastery of Odigitria. Marl (*kouskouras*) to the south of the small tholos tomb (Tomb A). Olives, carobs, thyme, and scrub. Area excavated: 25 by 20 m.

IV. GEOMORPHOLOGY

The site appears to be located at the contact near the head of the Ayiopharango valley between flysch deposits of the Pindos-Ethia nappe and the overlying upper Miocene marine and brackish-water marls.

The tholos tombs were built on a small east–west ridge of Mio-Pliocene limestone, buried by 20–40 cm of slopewash prior to excavation. Most of the tholos wall foundation blocks are small boulder-sized pieces of the local limestone bedrock, with occasional fragments of fine-grained reddish sandstone also used.

Bedrock dips to the northeast at approximately 10 degrees, which explains the infilled area in that direction from the tholoi. The filling appears to represent a soil that was available to the builders but has since been eroded away from the vicinity. The paved surface laid over the fill consists of fine-grained sandstone and mudstone flags, obtained from outcrops of flysch just a few hundred meters down the valley from the site.

V. EXCAVATION HISTORY

N. Dimopoulou, 1979, and A. Vasilakis, 1980, for the Archaeological Service.

VI. BUILDINGS

EM I–II   Small tholos tomb (Tomb A: d 4 m) and yard; large tholos tomb (Tomb B: d 6–6.1 m) with two rectangular rooms on the east side. Of roughly worked stones and mud.

EM III–MM IA   Three rooms (a, b, c) to east of Tomb B; ossuary (d) between tholos tombs. Yard paved. Circuit wall to north and east.

LM I   Probable pit burial.

VIII. BIBLIOGRAPHY

1982   Touchais, G. "Chronique des fouilles en 1981," *BCH* 106:625.

1986   Spanakis, S. G. *I Kriti*, 3rd ed. (Herakleion) 1:421–23.

1989–90   Vasilakis, A. "Proistorikes theseis sti Moni Odigitrias," *Kritiki Estia* 3:64–65.

IX. FINDS

Herakleion Museum.

X. DATE OF PHOTOGRAPHY

May 31, 1983.

Figure 30.1   Tombs and monastery

Figure 30.2   Tombs and monastery

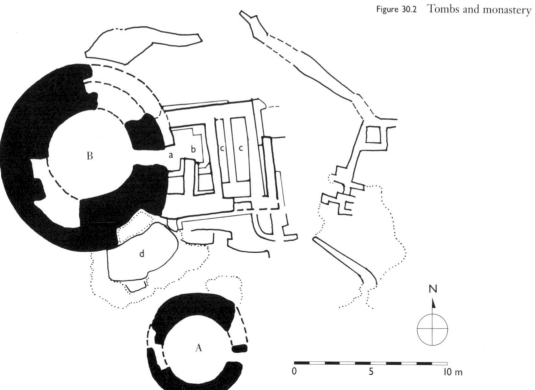

Figure 30.3   Odigitria tholos tombs

Figure 30.4   Tombs

HENRI VAN EFFENTERRE

35°15′ N, 25°45′ E

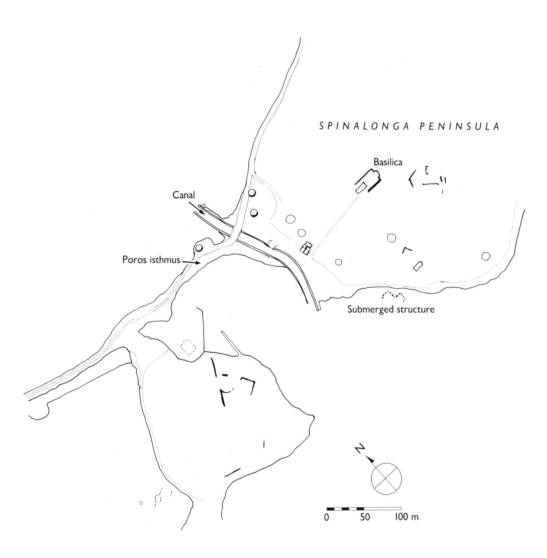

Figure 31.1   Plan of Olous

Figure 31.2   East side of isthmus

I. IMPORTANCE

Olous is an important harbor city on the west coast of the Bay of Mirabello, with the advantage of a double natural harbor on the north and south sides of the isthmus of Poros. Because sea level has risen, the main part of the isthmus now lies underwater. Some ancient walls and structures are visible underwater; others were reused in salt pans. The French navy, when in charge of this part of Crete in 1898, dug a canal through the isthmus and discovered a large stone stele inscribed with proxeny decrees confirming the name of the Greek city. The navy also cleared the mosaic pavement of a nearby Early Byzantine basilica.

The Greek and Roman city, now submerged, had its center on the isthmus, though there are many ruins and other traces of occupation, from Early Minoan II to late in Roman times, scattered over a large area of about 25 sq km.

Several inscriptions inform us about the history, institutions, and cults of the city. A long contest with Lato about the possession both of the sanctuary of Ares and Aphrodite (called the old Aphrodision), on the border between the two territories, and of the cargo of a vessel that had sunk near the coast has left us a detailed account of the place-names on the mountainous range between the two cities. It also provides valuable evidence for arbitration by Knossos and border demarcation by Miletus at the end of the 2nd century B.C. Other inscriptions record sailors giving thanks to Zeus Meilichios, and Christians to God (on a rock table on the islet of Kolokythia). And there was a temple with a *xoanon*, or wooden image of Britomartis, that has not been found but was probably on the Spinalonga peninsula.

II. USE

EM II chance finds; MM III settlement; LM III cemetery; G temple; A–R city; EByz basilicas.

III. SITUATION

On the sea on the west side of the Bay of Mirabello, at the foot of the Oxa, a rock ridge. North of Lato pros Kamara (modern Ayios

Figure 31.3 Basilica

Figure 31.4 View from the east

Nikolaos) and in the lee of Cape Ayios Ioannis, sheltered by the island and peninsula of Spinalonga.

IV. GEOMORPHOLOGY

Spinalonga and the adjacent Cretan mainland are composed of the Plattenkalk series of limestones (Crete's basement rocks), which forms the bedrock of the Ayios Ioannis peninsula as well as the islets of Pseira and Mochlos to the east on the other side of the Bay of Mirabello. This is a coarsely crystalline gray to black-gray limestone with intercalations of chert. The 1:50,000 Geological Map of Crete (Ayios Nikolaos region) shows Spinalonga and the adjacent mainland to be crisscrossed with numerous high-angle normal faults, suggesting the possibility that Spinalonga, like Pseira and Mochlos, is a horst separated from the adjacent mainland by the water-filled graben (the Bay of Spinalonga).

The low and narrow isthmus of Poros at one time must have connected Spinalonga to Crete, and the Greco-Roman town of Olous was built on it. The submerged foundations visible in the shallow water on the north and south sides of the isthmus may represent buildings of Olous, but no systematic underwater excavation has been attempted here. Around Spinalonga itself, solution notches in the limestone bedrock submerged some 0.5–1.0 m below present sea level lend further support to the idea of a relative rise in sea level around the Bay of Mirabello in the past 2,000 years.

V. EXCAVATION HISTORY

H. Van Effenterre and J. Bousquet, 1937–38, for the French School; A. K. Orlandos, 1955, for the Archaeological Society; N. Platon, 1960, and C. Davaras, 1972, for the Archaeological Service.

VI. BUILDINGS

EM II   Chance finds.

MM III   Poor settlement at Mavrikyano on west beach of north harbor, now covered.

LM IIIA1–IIIC   Cemeteries on promontories south of Poros isthmus, with larnax and pithos burials (some pithoi [LM IIIC and/or SM?] with cremations). Now destroyed.

G   Ruined temple with square hearth (*eschara*) and one base for wooden column (probably originally like the Delphinion of Dreros) below H temple of Ares and Aphrodite.

Figure 31.5   Mosaic pavement in basilica

A–R *Favissa*, "votive pit," on isthmus, east of canal, with A and C terracotta offerings; traces of C city west of canal beneath H and R walls. Many H inscriptions around site. H forts near city boundary on mountains; at Pinies (or Stis Pines), north of harbor, and on the Oxa southwest of isthmus; probably others as well.

H Temple of Ares and Aphrodite at city boundary near the Oxa and Sta Lenika hamlet (double shrine with portico [*pastas*]).

EByz East of isthmus and 100 m from canal, basilica with mosaic pavement and 7th-century dedicatory inscriptions. Another basilica probably at same distance to the southwest, under a small chapel(?).

VIII. BIBLIOGRAPHY

1890   Svoronos 248–50.

1935   *IC* 1:243–67 (= *IC* I. XXII. 1–65). Also *IC* 1:112–16 (= *IC* I. XVI. 3–4).

1937   Bousquet, J. "Le temple d'Arès et Aphrodite à Sta Lénikà," *BCH* 61:473–75.

       RE 17:2504–8 (E. Kirsten).

1941   Van Effenterre, H. "La basilique paléochrétienne de Poros," *L'architecture française* March: 31–34.

1942   ———. "Querelles crétoises," *REA* 31–51.

1948   ———. *Nécropoles du Mirabello*, *EtCr* 8 (Paris) 1–13, 23–59.

       ———. *La Crète et le monde grec de Platon à Polybe*, 2nd ed. 1968 (Paris) 221–34.

1949   ———. "Fortins crétois," in *Mélanges Charles Picard*, *RA* 31–32:1035–46.

       ———. "Pieux flâneurs ou rescapés?" *REA* 53–59.

1955   Orlandos, A. K. "Exerevnisis tis vasilikis tou Olountos," *PAE* 336–37.

       Van Effenterre, H. "Cupules et naumachies," *BCH* 79: 541–48.

1960   Platon, N. "Anatoliki Kriti," *ArchDelt* 16, pt. 2:259–60.

1963   Orlandos, A. K. "Neon temachion tis synthikis Olountion kai Rodion," *KrChron* 15:230–40.

1964   Desborough, V. R. d'A. *The Last Mycenaeans and Their Successors: An Archaeological Survey c. 1200–c. 1000 B.C.* (Oxford) 188.

1968   Andronikos, M. *Totenkult*, Archaeologia Homerica (Göttingen) 3, pt. W:55.

       Pini, I. *Beiträge zur minoischen Gräberkunde* (Wiesbaden) 60, 78.

1971   Davaras, C. "Perisyllogi archaion anatolikis Kritis," *PAE* 301–2.

       Snodgrass, A. M. *The Dark Age of Greece* (Edinburgh) 43, 168, 189, 210.

1972   Davaras, C. "Archaiotites kai mnimeia anatolikis Kritis," *ArchDelt* 27, pt. 2:645–46.

1973   ———. "Archaiotites kai mnimeia anatolikis Kritis," *ArchDelt* 28, pt. 2:593–94.

       ———. "Cremations in Minoan and Sub-Minoan Crete," in *Antichità cretesi* 1:163–64.

1973–74 ———. "Archaiotites kai mnimeia anatolikis Kritis," *ArchDelt* 29, pt. 2:932–33.

1974   ———. "Archaiotites kai mnimeia anatolikis Kritis 1972," *Amaltheia* 4:46–47.

1976   ———. *Guide to Cretan Antiquities* (Park Ridge, N.J.) 213–14.

       PECS 645–46 (D. J. Blackman).

1980   Davaras, C. "Kritikes epigraphes III," *ArchEph* 37–38.

       Kanta, A. *The Late Minoan III Period in Crete: A Survey of Sites, Pottery, and Their Distribution*, *SIMA* 58 (Gothenburg) 129–33.

1982   Sanders, I. F. *Roman Crete* (Warminster) 91–92, 143.

1983   Tiré, C., and H. Van Effenterre. *Guide des fouilles françaises en Crète*, 3rd ed. (Paris) 96–97.

IX. FINDS

Ayios Nikolaos Museum; Louvre, Paris.

X. DATE OF PHOTOGRAPHY

April 30, 1982.

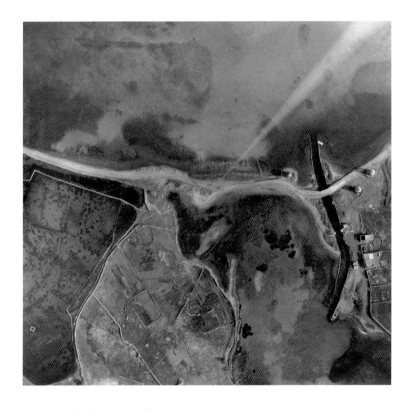

Figure 31.7   Underwater structure

Figure 31.6   Underwater walls

Figure 31.8   West side of isthmus

J. ALEXANDER MACGILLIVRAY AND L. HUGH SACKETT

35°12′ N, 26°16′ E

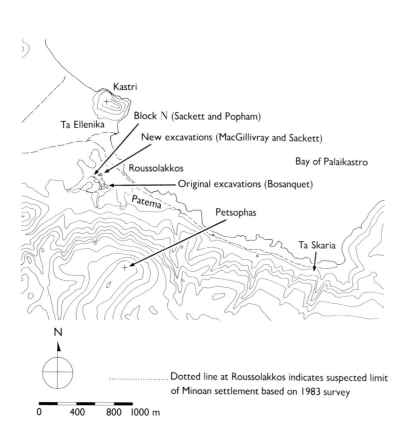

Figure 32.1   Palaikastro area

Figure 32.2   Roussolakkos

I. IMPORTANCE

The principal monument at Palaikastro is a long-lived Minoan town in a plain by the sea at Roussolakkos. Large and prosperous in Late Minoan I, it was carefully laid out with substantial houses and streets forming blocks. Its wealth may have come from olives and/or sheep and maritime trade. It was destroyed by a severe fire in Late Minoan I but resettled in Late Minoan II, continuing till Late Minoan IIIB.

In Late Minoan IIIC, settlement moved to the bleak and windy hill of Kastri, which had also been occupied in Early Minoan IB/IIA (at the time that Roussolakkos was settled) and in Early Minoan III. All three periods were probably times of trouble.

There are several Early Minoan and Middle Minoan ossuaries in the country around Roussolakkos, and an important Middle Minoan II–Late Minoan I mountain shrine above the sites at Petsophas, which has produced many votive figurines of people and animals and stone offerings with Linear A inscriptions.

The discovery in 1987–88 of a chryselephantine statuette of a male with a serpentine head and rock-crystal eyes may indicate a temple or town shrine at the north end of the Late Minoan I town. It was associated with buildings of regular rectangular plan, one of which was adorned with horns of consecration on a balcony at the northeast corner.

In Greco-Roman times there was a temple of Dictaean Zeus at Roussolakkos and Hellenistic and Roman buildings at Ta Ellenika at the foot of Kastri. The site may well have been called Dikta.

II. USE

EM IB/IIA–LM I and LM II–IIIB settlement and G, A, and R temple(s) at Roussolakkos; EM and LM IIIC settlement on hill of Kastri, with H–R buildings at Ta Ellenika at the foot of Kastri; MM II–LM I mountain shrine at Petsophas; M sandstone quarries at Ta Skaria (to the southeast of Roussolakkos); M kiln 300 m southeast of Roussolakkos.

Figure 32.3   Roussolakkos, excavation plan through 1906, with blocks

Figure 32.4   Block N (1962–63 excavation)

III. SITUATION

Settlement at Roussolakkos on low gravel and conglomerate ridges in a plain about 200 m west of the sea; originally on the beach but now separated from it by recent alluvial deposits. Isolated hill of Kastri to the north, 89.79 m high, and Petsophas to the south, 254.75 m high. Grazing land around but also cultivation of olives and vines. Present water sources: a few wells with brackish water around Roussolakkos. Settlement about 600 by 600 m: about 10,000 sq m excavated, but much subsequently filled in.

IV. GEOMORPHOLOGY

In a setting similar to that of Zakro to the south, Palaikastro lies at the edge of a triangular alluvial plain formed by the ephemeral stream draining the hills of northeastern Crete. Dominating the plain at the shoreline is the flat-topped bedrock promontory of Kastri.

The bedrock of Kastri is marly limestone of Miocene age; on the N. Kreutzberg et al. (1977) 1:200,000 Geological Map of Greece, Crete Island (East sheet), however, this bedrock is more precisely characterized as Upper Miocene–Lower Pliocene bioclastic and reef-derived limestones alternating with white and yellow laminated or homogeneous marls. Its flat top represents a stratum of dense massive limestone less prone to erosion than the other units in the vicinity.

Kastri serves to anchor a 1.5-km-long curving beach to its north and a small beach to its south, with rocky coast beyond the sand beaches.

The Minoan site at Roussolakkos is located on a bedrock surface of "yellowish marly sandstone" (1:50,000 Geological Map of Crete, Siteia region) that forms the southern border of the alluvial plain (it also crops out at the base of Kastri). All the major structures appear to have been founded directly on the shallow bedrock surface. In at least one location, in Block Γ, the pebbly sandstone bedrock is exposed where a basin was cut into it; two flat slabs of "skidproof" eolianite sandstone were installed as steps down into the basin.

A dense gray dolomite makes up the ashlar blocks of the 40-m-long facade fronting the main street; apparently it was quarried from the extensive exposures of Triassic-age bedrock immediately southeast of the site. Quarries exist at Ta Skaria along the shore to the southeast; Bosanquet (1901–2) mentioned that the ashlar blocks of "yellow freestone" (eolianite) came from them. These were further studied by Driessen in 1983 (MacGillivray et al. 1984).

In addition to this building stone, a wide range of ornamental rocks was used in floor construction, including red and green slabs of phyllite, most easily obtained from coastal bedrock exposures just north of Palaikastro.

Bosanquet (1902–3) remarks on the relatively high water table around the site; the well excavated by him in 1902 to a depth of 4.5 m suggests that the water table may not have been as high in Minoan times.

A major fault trending east–west, inferred to exist immediately north of the town site, would explain the different bedrock units exposed to the north and south of the alluvial plain. Although no Minoan site is far from such faults, Palaikastro's close proximity would have guaranteed some deleterious effect from any motion along this fault.

V. EXCAVATION HISTORY

R. C. Bosanquet, 1902–6; L. H. Sackett and M. R. Popham, 1962–63, for the British School; C. Davaras, 1972 and 1978, for the Archaeological Service; and J. A. MacGillivray and L. H. Sackett, 1986–, for the British School.

VI. BUILDINGS

EM IB/IIA   Small deposits of pottery below Block Δ and on Kastri. Ossuaries at Ta Ellenika and Tou Galeti I Kephala.

EM IIB   Large and well-made building below Block X; ossuary at Ta Ellenika.

EM III/MM IA   Deposits of pottery from Blocks Δ and X, from Kastri, from one of the ossuaries at Ta Ellenika and the Patema ossuary; no buildings at Roussolakkos assignable with certainty to this phase.

MM IB/IIA   Walls and pottery deposits below Blocks Γ, E, O, and X suggest the emergence of a town. Large ossuary at Tou Galeti I Kephala. Peak sanctuary on Petsophas founded.

MM IIB/IIIA   Traces of large buildings in Block X above the EM II building: many deposits of fine pottery from Roussolakkos and from the ossuary at Tou Galeti I Kephala. There seems to have been a widespread destruction of the settlement at the end of MM IIIA, after which the ossuaries went out of use.

MM IIIB–LM IB   Date of most houses in the town blocks of Roussolakkos. Walls most often of local *sideropetra* and conglomerate, but also sandstone ashlar facades; gray limestone for thresholds and poros limestone for doorjambs and some ashlar masonry; purple and green-blue schist for paving in houses and streets. LM IB destruction by fire and abandonment.

Figure 32.5 Buildings 1–5 (1986–87 excavation)

LM II–IIIB   Resettlement at Roussolakkos in LM II continued into LM IIIB; then abandonment. Burials at several sites around.

LM IIIC   Settlement at Kastri.

G–A (LG–   Temple of Dictaean Zeus and its temenos over Blocks P and X.
5th century B.C.)

H–R   H and R pottery and traces of buildings at Ta Ellenika and fragment of large marble statue of seated figure (Ptolemy VI Philometor?).

VII. RADIOCARBON DATES

	B.P.	1σ cal. B.C.	2σ cal. B.C.
MM III			
St-1265	3450 ± 75	1885–1683	1960–1541
LM IB			
St-1263	3535 ± 70	1970–1767	2120–1690
St-1264	3510 ± 120	2020–1689	2192–1530

VIII. BIBLIOGRAPHY

General

1901–2   Bosanquet, R. C. "Excavations at Palaikastro. I," *BSA* 8:286–316.

1902–3   Bosanquet, R. C., R. M. Dawkins, M. N. Tod, W. L. H. Duckworth, and J. L. Myres. "Excavations at Palaikastro. II," *BSA* 9:274–387, including: Myres. "The Sanctuary-Site of Petsophas," 356–87.

1903–4   Dawkins, R. M., and C. T. Currelly. "Excavations at Palaikastro. III," *BSA* 10:192–231.

1904–5   Dawkins, R. M., C. H. Hawes, and R. C. Bosanquet. "Excavations at Palaikastro. IV," *BSA* 11:258–308.

1905–6   Dawkins, R. M. "Excavations at Palaikastro. V," *BSA* 12:1–8.

1923   Bosanquet, R. C., and R. M. Dawkins. *The Unpublished Objects from Palaikastro Excavations, 1902–1906*, British School at Athens Supplementary Paper 1 (London).

1939–40   Bosanquet, R. C. "Dicte and the Temples of Dictaean Zeus," *BSA* 40:60–77.

Hutchinson, R. W., E. Eccles, and S. Benton. "Unpublished Objects from Palaikastro and Praisos. II," *BSA* 40:38–59.

1942   *IC* 3:5–17 (= *IC* III. II. 1–5).

1965   Sackett, L. H., M. R. Popham, and P. M. Warren. "Excavations at Palaikastro. VI," *BSA* 60:248–315.

1968   Pini, I. *Beiträge zur minoischen Gräberkunde* (Wiesbaden) 89.

1970   Sackett, L. H., and M. R. Popham. "Excavations at Palaikastro. VII," *BSA* 65:203–42.

1972   Davaras, C. "Archaiotites kai mnimeia anatolikis Kritis," *ArchDelt* 27, pt. 2:652–53.

1980   ———. "A Minoan Pottery Kiln at Palaikastro," *BSA* 75:115–26.

———. "Syntheta iera kerata apo to iero koryphis tou Petsopha," in *4 Cretological* 1:88–93.

Kanta, A. *The Late Minoan III Period in Crete: A Survey of Sites, Pottery, and Their Distribution*, SIMA 58 (Gothenburg) 189–93.

1984   MacGillivray, J. A., L. H. Sackett, et al. "An Archaeological Survey of the Roussolakkos Area at Palaikastro," *BSA* 79:129–59, including: Driessen, J. "II. Notes on Building Materials and Quarries," 143–49.

1987   MacGillivray, J. A., L. H. Sackett, J. Driessen, and D. Smyth. "Excavations at Palaikastro, 1986," *BSA* 82:135–54.

1988   Crowther, C. "A Note on Minoan Dikta," *BSA* 83:37–44.

MacGillivray, J. A., L. H. Sackett, J. Driessen, C. Macdonald, and D. Smyth. "Excavations at Palaikastro, 1987," *BSA* 83:259–82.

1989   Driessen, J., and J. A. MacGillivray. "The Neopalatial Period in East Crete," *Aegaeum* 3:99–111.

MacGillivray, J. A., L. H. Sackett, J. Driessen, R. Bridges, and D. Smyth. "Excavations at Palaikastro, 1988," *BSA* 84:416–45.

1990   MacGillivray, J. A., and J. Driessen. "Minoan Settlement at Palaikastro," in *L'habitat égéen préhistorique*, BCH Supplement 19, ed. P. Darcque and R. Treuil (Athens) 395–412.

Frescoes

1976   Cameron, M. A. S., and R. E. Jones. "A Note on the Identification of Fresco Material from the British Campaigns at Palaikastro, 1902–1906," *BSA* 71:15–19.

Figure 32.6–8   Promontory with Minoan houses eroding into the sea

1990   Immerwahr, S. A. *Aegean Painting in the Bronze Age* (University Park, Pa.) 182–83.

Scripts and Seals

1969   *CMS* 2.1:571–75 nos. 479–82 (N. Platon).

1976   *GORILA* 1:279–81.

1977   *CMS* 2.2:369–80 nos. 257–62 (N. Platon, I. Pini, and G. Salies).

Davaras, C. "Perisyllogi archaion anatolikis Kritis," *PAE* 492–95.

1982   *GORILA* 4:22–44, 126–27.

1984   *CMS* 2.3:329–38 nos. 277–85 (N. Platon and I. Pini).

1985   *CMS* 2.4:87–89 nos. 64–65, 263–65 nos. 209–10 (N. Platon and I. Pini).

GORILA 5:110.

1987   MacGillivray, J. A., et al. "Excavations at Palaikastro, 1986," *BSA* 82:153.

1989   Olivier, J.-P. "Le sceau hiéroglyphique SM 8254," in J. A. MacGillivray et al. "Excavations at Palaikastro, 1988," *BSA* 84:437–38.

Weingarten, J. "The Noduli, a Sealing, and a Seal," in J. A. MacGillivray et al. "Excavations at Palaikastro, 1988," *BSA* 84:438–44.

Radiocarbon Dates

1965   Engstrand, L. G. "Appendix," in L. H. Sackett and M. R. Popham, "Excavations at Palaikastro. VI," *BSA* 60:314–15.

————. "Stockholm Natural Radiocarbon Measurements VI," *Radiocarbon* 7:286.

IX. FINDS

Herakleion Museum; Siteia Museum; Fitzwilliam Museum, Cambridge; University of Liverpool Art Gallery, Liverpool; British Museum, London; Ashmolean Museum, Oxford.

X. DATES OF PHOTOGRAPHY

May 29, 1981 (Block N); October 8–13, 1987 (all others).

Figure 32.9   Ta Skaria quarry

Figure 32.10   Kastri

Figure 32.11   Kastri and Roussolakkos from Petsophas

Figure 32.12   View from the top of Kastri

VINCENZO LA ROSA

35°03' N, 24°49' E

I. IMPORTANCE

Second only to Knossos in the literary tradition, Phaistos was the home of the mythical Rhadamanthys, brother of Minos. It was the capital of south central Crete in the Old Palace period and had the best-known palace of that time on the island. It sits on an acropolis formed from three low hills and overlooks the Mesara plain and Yeropotamos river, with views to Psiloriti (Mt. Ida) and the sacred cave of Kamares as well as the Asterousia mountains to the south.

Phaistos, whose long life is exceeded only by that of Knossos, began in Final Neolithic at the end of the 4th and the beginning of the 3rd millennium B.C., when settlers made huts with fixed hearths and with plenty of household pottery. These huts may be contemporary with the last phase of the longer and more complicated Neolithic sequence of Knossos. The round hut at the southwest corner of the Central Court has a unique plan and is important evidence for discussions of how the round plan of the Mesara tholos tombs (such as those at Lebena, Odigitria, and Platanos) developed. Final Neolithic pottery painted with red ocher marks a gradual transition to that of Early Minoan.

Early Minoan sherds are found scattered throughout the excavations, but building remains are few—and concentrated beneath the palace. It is likely that the settlement was in disparate, small nuclei, with perhaps a concentration on the west hill, which was to become the site of the palace. One such nucleated settlement, down below on the Mesara plain, may have been the source of the burial deposit found in 1894 near Ayios Onouphrios. The pottery found in the Prepalatial strata at Phaistos is predominantly Early Minoan dark-on-light painted wares (like those from Ayios Onouphrios); there are also fragments of dark burnished wares. None of the Early Minoan II mottled Vasiliki ware has been found at Phaistos. The Prepalatial levels lie immediately beneath the surrounds of the first palace. No closed deposits of Middle Minoan IA pottery have been found beneath the palace (though they are abundant in the workshop settlement at Patrikies between Phaistos and Ayia Triada). The stratification of Phaistos and the homogeneity of its pottery have led Levi (1981)—against current opinion—to limit the whole Prepalatial era of Crete to 150–200 years.

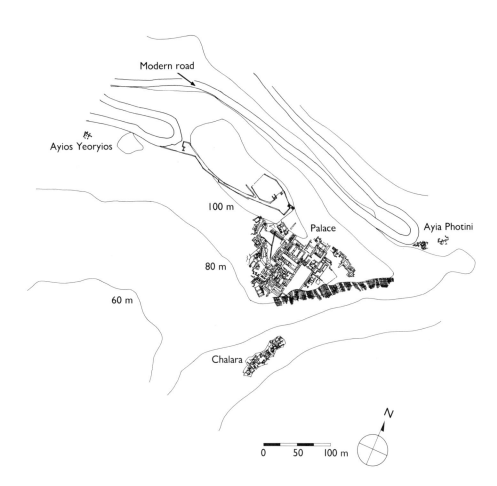

Figure 33.1   Phaistos area

Figure 33.2   High aerial view

The building of the first palace, the Old Palace, aligned on Psiloriti and the Kamares cave, was a leap forward in the life of Phaistos and the result, probably, of an aggregation of territory and a rapid economic growth that was essentially agricultural. Living quarters scattered around the palace, with no apparent ranking or order, stretched south as far as the modern village of Ayios Ioannis and west to the slopes of Christos Ephendis. The best known are those at Chalara to the southeast and Ayia Photini to the northeast, near the small church of that name. Cemeteries have not yet been identified, either for the Old or the New Palace period.

With five paved courts, Phaistos is unique among the Cretan palaces for its remains of the Old Palace period, which are especially well preserved on its west side. Levi (1976) was fortunate to distinguish three different levels resulting, according to him, from three distinct building phases—his I (divided into Ia and Ib), II, and III, which correspond to the four building phases of Fiandra (1961–62), lying one on top of the other with accumulations of destruction debris in between. Carinci (1989) has recently proposed a revision of phase III.

The pottery from the oldest destruction level corresponds to that of Middle Minoan IB in Evans's Knossian system, but there is also much pottery of Middle Minoan II, in the context of a partial rebuilding (Levi's phase Ib). (For a recent discussion of the problems of the Old Palace of Phaistos, with ample references, see Warren and Hankey 1989.) The pottery of Levi's phase II is very scarce, as is that of his phase III (it was taken away, with the building remains, by the builders of the New Palace).

The imbalance between the architectural data and the pottery, the difficulty of making stylistic observations on the changes and development of Middle Minoan pottery to coincide with the upheavals and destructions caused by earthquakes, and the discovery in two rooms, in different disaster levels, of pieces of one vase have led some scholars to group the buildings of the southwest part of the Old Palace as three (contemporary) floors in one building. One should keep in mind, however, that rich and homogeneous groups of Middle Minoan pottery that complement the stratigraphy of the southwest part have been found in houses south and west of the Theater Court; moreover, the three paved streets that connect the Lower Court and the Theater Court, assigned by Levi to his phases Ia, Ib, and II–III, confirm in his view the validity of the three Old Palace phases.

The Old Palace developed around its Central Court. West of the Palace was the important Theater Court (or West Court) with terracing and two raised walks. Various uses for it have been suggested: bull games, games, performances, and religious rites. The latest suggestion, that it was an agora, or market place, has been based more on the strength of similar possibilities at Mallia than on secure argu-ments. It is certain, however, that this was a place of assembly outside the palace—but closely linked to it—where it was intended that people stand in rows, as the low height of the terraces makes clear.

Levi has looked tentatively toward Mallia to explain room CVII, paved with gypsum slabs and having a bench and no pottery, at the foot of the middle hill. He suggests that it may be a public building, a large hall for meetings.

Levi assigns the Old Palace a life of about three hundred years (1800–1500 B.C.), including all of Middle Minoan III and allowing that the last phase at Phaistos may overlap the first phase of the New Palace at Knossos. To judge from the finds, Phaistos was probably destroyed at the end of Middle Minoan II.

The most impressive of all the Old Palace period finds from Phaistos is the vast quantity of Middle Minoan pottery (or Kamares ware), whose astonishing delicacy shows craftsmanship of the highest quality. Among the formal motifs of the pottery are a few figured designs such as a snake goddess and a lily goddess.

The most famous object, without doubt, is the clay Phaistos Disc (d about 16 cm) found in a layer of collapse in the northeast part (room 101) and dating to Middle Minoan III; stamped on each face is a series of signs and ideograms in a syllabic script, arranged in a spiral, that probably forms a ritual text.

The most valuable find for Minoan history, however, is the archive of clay sealings (*cretule*) in the lower levels of room 25. It has more than 7,500 sealings and also tablets in Linear A, the earliest occurrence of this script. Its date is Middle Minoan II (Levi's phase Ib). The seal impressions allow the reconstruction of about three hundred seal designs with stylistic similarities that seem to confirm the low chronology that Levi has proposed. Fiandra (1968, 1975) derived from Oriental analogies her view that the sealings sealed principally round wooden door handles, thus suggesting how the centralized system of accounting and control was organized. If her view is correct, the score of Linear A tablets found already in the Old Palace of Phaistos, from room 25 and elsewhere, assume a major importance in explaining the rise of the Linear A-based palatial organization of Crete in New Palace times.

The New Palace, completed perhaps only at the beginning of Late Minoan times, was built over the Old Palace and reused the Central Court (except that the west colonnade was covered). It was less spread out than the Old Palace, with its west front pulled in 7–8 m. The principal entrance (the monumental Propylaea 67–69) opens onto the west side rather than the south, as at Knossos and Mallia. The paving of the Theater Court was covered over by destruction debris and a "concrete" leveling, and the number of the terraces was reduced to four. The palace certainly had an intermediate phase (Late Minoan IA–IB), as is shown by levels principally in the southwest sector (room 25, passage 7, rooms 8, 17, 18, etc.). The pottery of the end of the New Palace of Phaistos is, as at Ayia Triada, Late Minoan IB.

The complex plan and monumentality of the palace are not borne out by rich and numerous finds. Portable objects of value may have been removed by people who did not soon reinhabit the place, but such a theory does not explain the almost total absence of fixtures such as frescoes in the New Palace or of movable items such as sealings and tablets, which would certainly have been found in excavation (even if not in their original positions). The chance find of two Linear A tablets is not enough to suggest that the flourishing Old Palace archive continued into New Palace times.

This state of affairs at Phaistos was completely different from that at Ayia Triada. The differences are equally clear in the settlement patterns. At Ayia Triada in the New Palace period we see a continuous urban setting without gaps. But at Phaistos there were only isolated houses in the old quarters of the settlement (Chalara and Ayia Photini) and a remarkable lack of buildings west of the palace where a potter's kiln was built. (There were other Late Minoan craft shops between Christos Ephendis and the small church of Ayios Yeoryios at Phalandra.)

Though this paucity of evidence does not have a definite significance on its own, it cannot be the result entirely of subsequent changes in the settlement pattern that affected the archaeological record. Rather, it seems probable that the relative "isolation" of the palace confirms that there was a progressive lessening of the political role of Phaistos while that of Ayia Triada grew, the one settlement complementing the other in a way not yet completely clear.

Late Minoan II is documented, at Phaistos as at Ayia Triada, only by pottery. Of Late Minoan III there are house remains in different parts of the excavation, including in Late Minoan IIIA1 at Chalara. The reference in the Knossos Linear B tablets to *pa-i-to* is clear enough and may mean the whole territory of Phaistos and Ayia Triada.

Late Minoan IIIB–IIIC remains have been found west of the Theater Court (with some of the walls reused in Hellenistic times). There were also dwellings southwest of the palace, where part of a ramp is preserved.

The curious stepped structure in the northwest corner of the Central Court, comparable to the altar shown on the painted Ayia Triada sarcophagus, and a pithos found near it, belong to Late Minoan III. The middle hill was also occupied. There is no evidence, however, of any Postpalatial monumental or "public" building as at Ayia Triada.

Cemeteries were found and dug on the low hills north of the palace in 1901–2: they may not have belonged to the main settlement. The group of fourteen chamber tombs at Kalyvia is older (Late Mi-

noan IIIA1–IIIA2) than that at Liliana, part of which is probably to be classed as already Sub-Minoan—with eight rock-cut tombs of irregular plan containing clay larnakes, or coffins. The different state of affairs at Ayia Triada leads to the supposition that the lessening of Phaistos' power that had begun in Late Minoan I was continuing in Late Minoan III and that in effect the center of power had moved from Phaistos.

The most significant part of the Protogeometric and Geometric city—the "Phaistos fair to dwell in" of the *Iliad* (2.64)—is to the west and southwest of the palace and has a paved ramp running north–south. There are many house remains also at Chalara and Ayia Photini, and it is easy to imagine inhabitation in the area of the palace. The first excavators found Geometric houses on the west slope of Christos Ephendis. It is possible that toward the end of the period the first temple was founded south of the palace (attributed to the Magna Mater on the basis of an inscription found near the village of Ayios Ioannis). Fragments of 8th-century tripods and shields thrown into pits or found beneath the pavement support the date.

Study of the pottery in the settlement deposits at Phaistos shows a continuity from the end of Late Minoan III. Pots with decorative schemes attributable to late in Geometric times, the likely date of most of the buildings, are more frequent than those with Protogeometric shapes. A graffito of the owner's name on a pithos (found reused in a Hellenistic room west of the Theater Court) is thought to date to the end of the 8th century B.C. and to be the oldest graffito in the Greek script from Crete.

Remains of Orientalizing and Archaic date are rare, though Phaistos was the home of Epimenides, the renowned priest who was called to Athens, according to Aristotle, to perform the purification after the killing of the Cylonian conspirators. Along with a fine relief pithos with a cock from Ayios Ioannis, female statues of Ionian type, and fragments of Corinthian and Attic pottery, some architectural fragments—in particular a pair of palmette antefixes—show that there were sacred buildings at Phaistos at the time. Pernier (1902) placed one of them on the middle hill.

An interesting Doric capital with an Ionic kymation molding probably belonged to a votive column (first half of the 6th century B.C., from the south slopes of the middle hill). A legal inscription, found by chance in the bed of an irrigation channel near Chalara in 1978, is of the end of the 6th century and older than the Gortyn Code. It deals with mothers' property and mentions an agora, or marketplace. That the inscription had probably been in a public building near where it was found is valuable evidence for the topography of Archaic Phaistos.

The dating sequence of the so-called Magna Mater temple at the southern end of the west side of the palace is uncertain. Its plan,

Figure 33.3 Palace

Figure 33.4 Palace

which recalls that of the megaron at Ayia Triada, is what the first excavators assigned in general to "Hellenic."

Classical remains are few: pottery and perhaps some terracottas, principally from the early excavations. Coins are the best evidence. The oldest series of silver staters with the legend *Paistion to paima* belongs to the second half of the 5th century B.C.

The Hellenistic settlement experienced a remarkable expansion, becoming almost as large as the Minoan town. The area of the palace was entirely covered with houses (removed during excavation). Pernier put a temple or precinct of Asklepios or Apollo north of court 48, on the evidence of an inscription and a small marble head. Chalara had a truly urban settlement with paved roads, and so did the area west and north of the Theater Court, with rooms with an *eschara*, "hearth," set between column bases—a scheme typical in Geometric times, several centuries earlier, and seen at Dreros and Prinias. The so-called Magna Mater temple seems to have had a Hellenistic phase.

Near the church of Ayia Photini were rooms with an olive press, and near that of Ayios Pavlos a wine cellar. East of Ayios Yeoryios in Phalandra were houses, and near the village of Ayios Ioannis part of a magnificent street was found in 1986. The Hellenistic city was surrounded by a defense wall.

Phaistos became subject to Gortyn in the second half of the 3rd century B.C. but was still formally independent in 183, the date of the treaty of Eumenes (of Pergamon) with the cities of the Cretan Koinon, or league. Gortyn destroyed Phaistos, probably in the middle of the 2nd century B.C. The city was not rebuilt. Destruction levels in some houses (with finds including locally made Hadra ware) may belong to the period before the destruction by Gortyn. These disaster levels document the progressive decline of the settlement.

In Roman times Phaistos was nothing more than an isolated *chora*, "estate," with some farms. A few tombs on the eastern edge of court 94 may be Byzantine, but they had no grave goods. The foundations of a Byzantine chapel on the summit of Christos Ephendis and of the Venetian monastery of Ayios Yeoryios in Phalandra (14th century?) are the last evidence of a sporadic settlement.

Eventually all that was left of Phaistos' past glory and ancient age was the place-name of the palace site, Kastro.

II. USE

FN–EM II settlement; MM IB–G town (MM IB–LM IB palace); H city; R farms; Byz(?) tombs and chapel; V monastery.

III. SITUATION

The main Minoan settlement area is on three low hills: (from west to east) Christos Ephendis, the middle hill, and the palace hill; it slopes from west to east and is 700 m long, above the Mesara plain and Yeropotamos river (to the north). The Central Court, 90 m above sea level, is aligned on the Kamares cave, which is below the right peak of a pair of prominent peaks that form a saddle in the Psiloriti massif, visible as well from Ayia Triada.

The principal sites with settlements around Phaistos are Chalara, below the south end and southeast corner of the palace hill; Ayia Photini, northeast of the palace hill; Ayios Yeoryios, at Phalandra on Christos Ephendis (the west hill); Patrikies on the west slope of the hills midway between Phaistos and Ayia Triada; and Ayios Ioannis village, 1 km to the south. The cemetery sites are probably Ayios Onouphrios, Kalyvia, and Liliana, all north of the palace.

IV. GEOMORPHOLOGY

Phaistos, on a ridge crest overlooking the alluvial plain of the Yeropotamos river, has a remarkably appealing site. Its main drawback from a geological viewpoint is that the ridge containing both Phaistos and Ayia Triada is part of a horst that in the geologic past has been uplifted relative to the surrounding modern and ancient floodplain of the Yeropotamos. During and after the uplift, the Yeropotamos river eroded its channel through this fault block just south of the village of Vori.

Phaistos and Ayia Triada share a common geology not only in tectonism but also in bedrock types; the same types are present at both sites: limestones, soft marls, and gypsum. The builders at Phaistos removed a bedrock protrusion in the southeast sector of the site and also used the more resistant limestone for their ashlar masonry. A gypsum deposit within the marine sedimentary rock sequence immediately east of the palace could have supplied this building stone even more conveniently than the deposit 0.5 km to the west toward Ayia Triada.

Between 1902 and 1976, a total of 126 earthquakes with Richter magnitudes between 5.5 and 7.5 had epicenters between 34 and 37 degrees north and 23.5 and 26.5 degrees east (which area contains all of Crete). Of this total, 5 shallow-focus earthquakes, having magnitudes from 6.0 to 6.9, occurred within a 50-km radius of Phaistos–Ayia Triada. The probability that an earthquake of Richter magnitude >7 affected the western Mesara plain sometime during the past four thousand years is very high. The intensities associated with such large-magnitude earthquakes would destroy most masonry and wooden frame structures and severely damage stone foundations.

Although a large-magnitude earthquake is unlikely to have had its epicenter precisely on the faults just north and south of Phaistos, earth motions generated nearby would be concentrated there because of the established plane of weakness in the bedrock stratigra-

Figure 33.5   Central Court and north end of palace, looking north toward Kamares
cave (below twin peaks of Psiloriti)

phy. Thus the location of Phaistos cannot have improved chances that the Old Palace would survive a major earthquake in central Crete during the 17th century B.C.

V. EXCAVATION HISTORY

L. Pernier, 1900–1909, for the Italian Archaeological Mission; D. Levi, 1950–66, 1969, 1971, for the Italian School.

VI. BUILDINGS

N.B. In general, roman numerals are used for rooms and spaces in the Old Palace and arabic numerals for those in the New Palace. Some arabic numerals also refer to rooms and spaces of the last phase of the Old Palace; and some rooms or spaces numbered in both systems were in use in both the Old Palace and the New Palace.

FN   Round hut (d about 2.5 m) at the southwest corner of the Central Court; other huts under the west side of the Central Court.

EM I–II   Buildings inside peristyle 74, beneath Theater Court and Lower Court, and in the area west of these two courts. Chance finds of pottery. Burials at Ayios Onouphrios.

MM IA   Chance finds of pottery; small craftsmen's(?) settlement at Patrikies.

MM IB–IIB   Old Palace (with Levi's three principal building phases: I [Ia, Ib], II, III); houses in town south as far as Ayios Ioannis village and west to slopes of Christos Ephendis; also Chalara and Ayia Photini to the northeast.

MM IB   Destruction (Levi's phase Ia).

MM IIA   Partial rebuilding (Levi's phase Ib).

MM IIB   Partial rebuilding and destruction (Levi's phases II–III).
      Old Palace (about 120 by 120 m, its southeast part lost), around Central Court of 46.5 by 22.3 m. Storerooms on the west (including room XXXIV beneath the monumental west entrance of New Palace). Small room VIII/2 at northwest corner a shrine, linked to V, VI, and VII, which interrupt the west orthostat facade. Theater Court has eight rows of terracing (steps), 22 m long, and two raised walks. Residential quarter on the south slope of the middle hill.

MM IIIA   House to the south of the ramp and rooms on the northeast edge of palace.

LM IA(?)–IB   New Palace. Central Court still in use, but west colonnade covered. Principal entrance through Propylaea 67–69 opening to the west. Paving of Theater Court covered (with Old Palace destruction debris) and only top four terraces in use. At northeast corner of buildings only pillared room 103 (of rooms 101–104) reused. Upper Court 94 still in use and East Court 90 (with a kiln or furnace in both Old and New Palaces). Storerooms 27–37 on the west. Residential quarter at the north, probably on three floors.
      Rebuilding in LM IB, observable especially in the southwest part (room 25; passage 7; rooms 8, 17, 18, etc). Destruction by fire in LM IB.
      Isolated houses in old settlements of Chalara and Ayia Photini. Potter's kiln (and little else) to the west of palace. Other LM I workshops at Christos Ephendis and Ayios Yeoryios.

LM II   Chance finds of pottery.

LM IIIA1   Buildings in Chalara; tombs at Kalyvia.

LM IIIB–IIIC   Buildings west of Theater Court (some walls reused in H times) and southwest of palace (where there was also a ramp); in the palace area LM IIIB stepped altar and pithos in northwest corner of Central Court. Also occupation on the middle hill and at Patrikies.

LM IIIC (SM)   Liliana cemetery (eight tombs). Also tomb near old mill on Yeropotamos river; pottery deposit nearby.

PG–G   Settlement to the west and southwest of palace, with paved north–south ramp. Many house remains at Chalara and Ayia Photini. Possible occupation of palace area; G houses on west slopes of Christos Ephendis. Possible first phase of temple of "Magna Mater" southwest of palace.

A   Chance finds and probable sacred buildings in area of palace; probable public building near Chalara. "Magna Mater" temple likely to have been still in use. Sacred(?) building on the middle hill.

C   Chance finds.

H   Revival of settlement until conquest and destruction by Gortyn. Area of palace covered by houses (still visible: some cisterns, and buildings above room 21). Precinct or small shrine of Asklepios or Apollo north of court 48. Many houses and paved roads at Chalara; houses also west and north of Theater Court, and *eschara*, "hearth." "Magna Mater" temple: some rebuilding. Also buildings at Ayia Photini and near Ayios Pavlos (wine cellar), and houses east of Ayios

Figure 33.6   Old and New Palaces from the west

Figure 33.7   Mesara plain from Phaistos

Yeoryios at Phalandra. Road near Ayios Ioannis. H city defended by walls (preserved on north side of middle hill, near Ayios Yeoryios, and on Christos Ephendis: with rectangular towers). Destruction by Gortyn around middle of 2nd century B.C.

R   Farm at Chalara.

Byz   Tombs(?) near east edge of Court 94; chapel on summit of Christos Ephendis.

V   Ayios Yeoryios at Phalandra (14th century?).

VII. RADIOCARBON DATES

	B.P.	1σ cal. B.C.	2σ cal. B.C.
Old Palace			
Pi-15B	3480 ± 120	1960–1680	2140–1520
Pi-15A	3470 ± 120	1950–1670	2140–1520

VIII. BIBLIOGRAPHY

NEOLITHIC

1972–73   Vagnetti, L. "L'insediamento neolitico di Festòs," *ASAtene* 50–51:7–138.

MINOAN

General

1935, 1951   Pernier, L., and L. Banti. *Il palazzo minoico di Festòs* 1–2 (Rome).

1939–40   Banti, L. "Cronologia e ceramica del palazzo minoico di Festòs," *ASAtene* n.s. 1–2:9–39.

1961–62   Fiandra, E. "I periodi struttivi del primo palazzo di Festòs," in *1 Cretological* 1:112–26.

Pelagatti, P. "Osservazioni sui ceramisti del I palazzo di Festòs," in *1 Cretological* 1:99–111.

1965   Zois, A. A. "Phaistiaka," *ArchEph* 27–109.

1965–66   Levi, D. "Bolli d'anfore e pesi fitili da Festòs," *ASAtene* 43–44:569–88.

———. "La conclusione degli scavi a Festòs," *ASAtene* 43–44:313–99.

1967–68   Levi, D. "L'abitato di Festòs in località Chalara," *ASAtene* 45–46:55–166.

1968   Fiandra, E. "A che cosa servivano le cretule di Festòs?" in *2 Cretological* 1:383–97.

1972–73   Vagnetti, L. "L'insediamento neolitico di Festòs," *ASAtene* 50–51:7–138.

1973   Fiandra, E. "Skoutelia MM a Festòs," in *3 Cretological* 1:84–91.

           Laviosa, C. "La casa TM III a Festòs: Osservazioni sull'architettura cretese in età micenea," in *Antichità cretesi* 1:79–88.

1974–75   Mercando, L. "Lampade, lucerne, bracieri di Festòs (scavi 1950–1970)," *ASAtene* 52–53:15–167.

1975   Fiandra, E. "Ancora a proposito delle cretule di Festòs: Connessione fra sistemi amministrativi centralizzati e l'uso delle cretule nell'età di bronzo," *BdA* 1–25.

1976   Levi, D. *Festòs e la civiltà minoica* I, *Incunabula Graeca* 60 (Rome).

1979–80   Follieri, M., and G. Coccolini. "Travi carbonizzate del palazzo minoico di Festòs (Creta)," *ASAtene* 57–58:173–85.

1980   Fiandra, E. "Precisazioni sul MM IIA a Festòs," in *4 Cretological* 1.1:169–96.

           Kanta, A. *The Late Minoan III Period in Crete: A Survey of Sites, Pottery, and Their Distribution*, *SIMA* 58 (Gothenburg) 96–98.

           Popham, M. R. "Cretan Sites Occupied between c. 1450 and 1400 B.C.," *BSA* 75:164–67.

1981   Coccolini, G., and E. Corona. "Nota dendrocronologica sulle travi del palazzo minoico di Festòs (Creta)," *Bolletino del Museo Civile di Storia Naturale Verona* 8:427–34.

           Hayden, B. J. *The Development of Cretan Architecture from the LM IIIA through the Geometric Periods*, Ph.D. diss., University of Pennsylvania 89–91.

           Levi, D. *Festòs e la civiltà minoica* II.1. *La civiltà minoico-micenea a un secolo dalla sua scoperta*, *Incunabula Graeca* 77 (Rome).

1982   Damiani Indelicato, S. *Piazza publica e palazzo nella Creta minoica* (Rome) 85–120.

           Fiandra, E. "L'archeologia dei sistemi economici," *Le Scienze* 169 (September):102–13.

1983   ———. "Cultura e scambi commerciali nella civiltà minoica," *Le Scienze* 176 (April):30–43.

1984   *Creta antica* 121–60 (V. La Rosa with A. L. D'Agata).

           La Rosa, V. "Gli scavi e le ricerche di età minoica," in *Creta antica* 35–42.

           Liritzis, Y. "Reappraisal of Minoan Kilns by Thermoluminescence and Neutron Activation/XRF Analyses," *RdArchéom* 8:7–20.

1985   *Ancient Crete* 75–107 (V. La Rosa with A. L. D'Agata).

           La Rosa, V. "Preliminary Considerations on the Problem of the Relationship between Phaistos and Hagia Triada," *Scripta Mediterranea* 6:45–54.

1987   Branigan, K. "The Economic Role of the First Palaces," in *The Function of the Minoan Palaces* 245–49.

           Kopaka, K. "Pilino omioma anaklintrou apo ti Phaisto," in *Eilapini* 93–100.

1988   Levi, D., and F. Carinci. *Festòs e la civiltà minoica* II.2. *L'arte festia nell'età protopalaziale: Ceramica ed altri materiali*, *Incunabula Graeca* 77 (Rome).

1989   Carinci, F. "The 'III fase protopalaziale' at Phaestos: Some Observations," *Aegaeum* 3:73–80.

           Warren, P. M., and V. Hankey. *Aegean Bronze Age Chronology* (Bristol).

Patrikies

1967–68   Bonacasa, N. "Patrikiès. Una stazione medio-minoica fra Haghia Triada e Festòs," *ASAtene* 45–46:7–54.

1984   *Creta antica* 195 (V. La Rosa).

1985   *Ancient Crete* 137 (V. La Rosa).

Frescoes

1990   Immerwahr, S. A. *Aegean Painting in the Bronze Age* (University Park, Pa.) 22–23, 183.

Cemeteries

1895   Evans, A. J. "The Sepulchral Deposit of Hagios Onuphrios near Phaestos in Its Relation to the Primitive Cretan and Aegean Culture," in his *Cretan Pictographs and Prae-Phoenician Script* (London and New York) 105–36.

1904   Savignoni, L. "Scavi e scoperte nella necropoli di Phaestos," *MonAnt* 14:501–666.

1980 Kanta, A. *The Late Minoan III Period in Crete: A Survey of Sites, Pottery, and Their Distribution*, SIMA 58 (Gothenburg) 99–101.

1984 *Creta antica* 136–37 (V. La Rosa).

1985 *Ancient Crete* 85–86 (V. La Rosa).

Scripts and Seals

1957–58 Levi, D. "L'archivio di cretule a Festòs," *ASAtene* 35–36:7–192.

Pugliese Carratelli, G. "Nuove epigrafi minoiche di Festo," *ASAtene* 35–36:363–88.

1969 *CMS* 2.1:118–39 nos. 104–22, 501–5 nos. 423–26 (N. Platon).

1970 *CMS* 2.5: nos. 1–327 (I. Pini).

1976 *GORILA* 1:285–319.

1977 *CMS* 2.2:23–28 nos. 20–24 (N. Platon, I. Pini, and G. Salies).

Duhoux, Y. *Le Disque de Phaestos* (Louvain).

1979 *GORILA* 2:89–96.

1982 *GORILA* 4:92–95.

1983 Duhoux, Y. "Les langues du Linéaire A et du Disque de Phaestos," *Minos* 18:33–68.

1984 *CMS* 2.3:113–33 nos. 99–115 (N. Platon and I. Pini).

Creta antica 47–49 (G. Pugliese Carratelli).

1985 *CMS* 2.4:23–25 nos. 16–17, 191–94 nos. 150–52 (N. Platon and I. Pini).

POST-MINOAN

1890 Svoronos 253–65.

1902 Pernier, L. "Scavi della Missione Italiana a Phaestos 1900–1901: Rapporto preliminare," *MonAnt* 12:14–22.

1935 *IC* 1. 226–78 (= *IC* I. XXIII. 1–31) (including Ayia Triada and surroundings).

1943 Guarducci, M. "I rapporti fra Gortyna e Phaistos nel III secolo e i decreti delle città cretesi per la ἀσυλία di Tenos," *RivFil* n.s. 21:66–73.

1966 Le Rider, G. *Monnaies crétoises du Ve au Ier siècle av. J.C.*, *EtCr* 15 (Paris) 84–98, 131–32.

Manganaro, G. "Iscrizione opistographa di Axos con prescrizioni sacrali e con un trattato di *symmachia*," *Historia* 15:20–22.

1969 Levi, D. "Un pithos iscritto da Festòs," *KrChron* 21:153–76.

1969–70 Rocchetti, L. "Depositi sub-micenei e protogeometrici nei dintorni di Festòs," *ASAtene* 47–48:41–70.

1974 La Rosa, V. "Capitello arcaico da Festòs," in *Antichità cretesi* 2:136–48.

Rocchetti, L. "Materiali ceramici a Festòs fra il XIII e il X sec. a.C.," in *Antichità cretesi* 2:59–74.

1974–75 ———. "La ceramica dell'abitato geometrico di Festòs a occidente del palazzo minoico," *ASAtene* 52–53:169–300.

1976 *PECS* 696 (K. Branigan).

1978 Di Vita, A., and E. Cantarella. "Iscrizione arcaica giuridica da Festòs," *ASAtene* 56:429–35.

Manganaro, G. "Fiscalismo monetale nelle città cretesi," in *Scritti storico-epigrafici in memoria di M. Zambelli*, ed. L. Gasperini (Rome) 221–40.

1979–80 Privitera, F. "Frammenti di pithoi a decorazione impressa da Festòs," *ASAtene* 57–58:173–85.

1982 Sanders, I. F. *Roman Crete* (Warminster) 161.

1984 La Rosa, V. "Ceramiche del tipo Hadra a Festòs," in *Alessandria e il mondo ellenistico-romano. Studi in onore di A. Adriani*, ed. N. Bonacasa and A. Di Vita (Rome) 3:804–18.

1990 ———. "Ceramiche ellenistiche di Festòs: Per il problema della distruzione finale della città," in *Praktika tis Defteris Synantisis yia tin ellenistiki kerameiki* (Athens) 159–66.

Radiocarbon Dates

1959 Ferrara, G., M. Reinharz, and E. Tongiorgi. "Carbon-14 Dating in Pisa," *Radiocarbon* 1:107.

IX. FINDS

Herakleion Museum; Pigorini Museum, Rome; Archaeological Museum, Florence.

X. DATE OF PHOTOGRAPHY

April 21, 1984.

ELPIDA HADJIDAKI

35°31′ N, 23°34′ E

I. IMPORTANCE

Phalasarna is a Classical-Hellenistic port town on the remote and beautiful west coast of Crete. It has an artificial harbor (*kleistos limin*), dominated by the acropolis of Cape Koutri, whose temple would have been a mark for returning vessels. In 172 B.C. Phalasarna was large enough to send, together with Knossos, three thousand men to Perseus against the Romans; and it minted its own coins. In 1987 a trench in the harbor entrance revealed an artificial blockage, probably to be connected with Metellus Creticus's campaign against Cretan piracy in 68–66 B.C.

The harbor is now 100 m inland and quite dry, not as the result of silting but from the tectonic uplift of western Crete that has been tentatively linked to one or several large earthquakes that struck the southern Aegean, and particularly Crete, in the 4th and 5th centuries A.D. Spratt, when surveying Crete in 1851–53 for the Royal Navy's charts, was the first to realize that the present sea level is about 6.5 m below the easily identifiable ancient sea level. Recent excavations show that the local regression of sea level did not occur while the harbor was in use, from about 600 to 66 B.C. (The change can be seen at many other places in western Crete.)

II. USE

A burials; C–H city.

III. SITUATION

At the northwest extremity of Crete at the neck of the Gramvousa peninsula (ancient Korykos), on the Bay of Livadi. On the rocky promontory of Cape Koutri, 90 m high, running northeast–southwest and forming the town's acropolis. The rest of the town is situated along the slopes and on the rich plain. Likely water sources: a spring near Platanos, 7 km to the south; cisterns and wells in the town, which covers an area about 1,000 by 600 m.

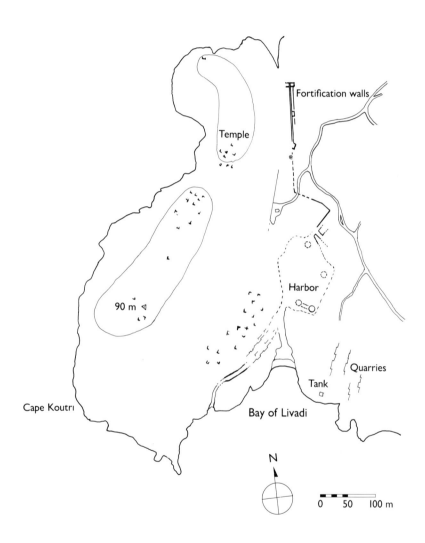

Figure 34.1   Plan of Phalasarna

Figure 34.2   High aerial view

Figure 34.3 Harbor

periods of the last two million years (when the sea level was much lower than it is now), and later lithified. This stone is fairly common around the coasts of Crete and was used for ashlar buildings in Minoan and later times, as shown by quarries here and, for instance, near Chania and in eastern Crete near Mallia and Zakro.

V. EXCAVATION HISTORY

Y. Tzedakis, 1968; V. Niniou-Kindeli, 1981, 1984–85; and E. Hadjidaki, 1986–87, for the Archaeological Service; E. Hadjidaki and F. J. Frost, 1988–, for the Archaeological Service and the American School.

VI. BUILDINGS

A 6th-century pithos burials 100 m south and 300 m east of fortification walls.

C (5th– Long fortification walls with four square towers of pseudo-isodomic
4th century) dressed sandstone blocks. Four-sided artificial harbor, 100 by 75 m, with four towers, quays, and channels to the sea. The round tower excavated in 1986 is preserved to a height of 4.5 m and is 9 m in diameter, built of large sandstone blocks in isodomic style.

Possible temple to east of harbor, with fragments of two Doric columns. Another temple on summit of acropolis. Other buildings on summit and slopes include a tower and possible public buildings, houses, and cisterns. Large rock-cut tank (5 by 5 by 3 m) near town quarries and ancient shoreline. Quarries to southwest of town. Cemetery with more than thirty-two 4th-century cist graves to the southeast; and huge (2 by 0.95 m) rock-cut "throne."

H Cist graves and inscriptions.

VIII. BIBLIOGRAPHY

General

1837   Pashley, R. *Travels in Crete* (London) 2:61–79.

1865   Spratt, T. A. B. *Travels and Researches in Crete* (London) 2: 227–35.

1890   Stavrakis, N. *Statistiki tou plithysmou tis Kritis* (Athens) 32, 104. Svoronos 268–71.

1901   Savignoni, L., and G. De Sanctis. "Esplorazione archeologica delle provincie occidentali di Creta," *MonAnt* 11:348–86.

1938   *RE* 19:1653–58 (E. Kirsten).

1939   *IC* 2:218–25 (= *IC* II. XIX. 1–7).

IV. GEOMORPHOLOGY

Cape Koutri is composed of the massive microcrystalline limestone that forms the Gramvousa, Rodopou, and (most of the) Akrotiri peninsulas. They are all structural elements of the calcareous series of the Tripolitza nappe, emplaced 60–10 million years ago (early–mid Cenozoic time). The harbor, however, and many other buildings were cut into or built on a rock of very recent geologic age: Quaternary eolianite. This quartz-rich sandstone, cemented by calcium carbonate, represents coastal sand dunes deposited during recent glacial

Figure 34.4   Fortification wall across Cape Koutri

1969   Tzedakis, Y. "Archaiotites kai mnimeia tis dytikis Kritis," *ArchDelt* 24, pt. 2:433–34.

1976   *PECS* 697–98 (D. J. Blackman).

1984   *Creta antica* 60 (M. A. Rizzo).

1985   *Ancient Crete* 32 (M. A. Rizzo).

1988   Gondicas, D. *Recherches sur la Crète occidentale* (Amsterdam) 85–142.

Hadjidaki, E. "Preliminary Report of Excavations at the Harbor of Phalasarna in West Crete," *AJA* 92: 463–79.

1989   Frost, F. J. "The Last Days of Phalasarna," *Ancient History Bulletin* 3:15–17.

1990   Frost, F. J., and E. Hadjidaki. "Excavations at the Harbor of Phalasarna in Crete: The 1988 Season," *Hesperia* 59: 513–27.

Geomorphology

1973   Flemming, N., N. M. G. Czartoryska, and P. M. Hunter. "Archaeological Evidence for Vertical Earth Movements in the Region of the Aegean Island Arc," *Science Diving International* 46–65.

1981   Flemming, N., and P. A. Pirazzoli. "Archéologie des côtes de la Crète," *Histoire et Archéologie* 50:71–78.

Thommeret, J., et al. "Late Holocene Shoreline Changes and Seismo-tectonic Displacements in Western Crete," *Zeitschrift für Geomorphologie* Supplement 40: 127–49.

Figure 34.5   Cliffs at Phalasarna, showing raised ancient sea level

1982   Pirazzoli, P. A., J. Thommeret, Y. Thommeret, J. Laborel, and L. Montagnoni. "Crustal Block Movements from Holocene Shorelines: Crete and Antikythira (Greece)," *Tectonophysics* 86:27–43.

IX. FINDS

Chania Museum.

X. DATE OF PHOTOGRAPHY

June 12, 1984.

ANTONIS VASILAKIS

35°02' N, 24°55' E

I. IMPORTANCE

The tholos tombs of Platanos show the remarkable prosperity of the inhabitants of the Mesara plain in Prepalatial and Old Palace times. Tomb A is exceptionally large; and Tombs A and B have produced many seals, stone vases, gold jewelry, and bronze or copper tools or weapons, as well as imported goods such as three Egyptian scarabs and an Old Babylonian cylinder seal (from Tomb B). Of the many attempts made to use these finds in the framework of Minoan chronology, none has been successful.

II. USE

EM II–MM II cemetery; some LM I use.

III. SITUATION

On flat ground at the southern edge of the Mesara plain at Stavros, 150 m west of Platanos village beside road to Pobia. Arable land and olives around. Area excavated: about 20 by 50 m.

IV. GEOMORPHOLOGY

The site is on a low swale of a Pleistocene alluvial fan and thus was not deeply buried by more recent sediment deposition. A wide range of rock types, derived from the bedrock units west and south of the site, was used in the construction of the tomb foundations and the paved yard: calcareous sandstone from the Neogene marine strata; marble, gneiss, and amphibolite from the Asterousia nappe fragment; calcareous sandstone from the flysch; and graywacke from the Vatos schist.

The paving between the two circular tomb foundations gives an indication of the immediate source of many of the rocks: their degree of rounding suggests that they were collected from alluvium of the Yeropotamos river to the north.

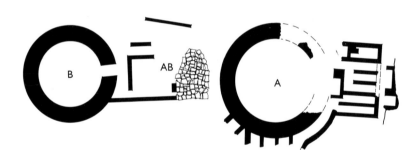

0   5 m

Figure 35.1   Platanos, tholos tombs A and B

Figure 35.2   Tombs

V. EXCAVATION HISTORY

S. Xanthoudides, 1914–15, for the Archaeological Service.

VI. BUILDINGS

EM II–MM II Three tholos tombs (Tomb A, Tomb B, and half-destroyed Tomb Γ, 5 m north of Tomb B). Annexes to the east of Tomb A and Tomb B. Groups of rectangular buildings (house-tombs) northeast of Tomb Γ; ossuaries; and yard (area AB). Internal d: Tomb A, 13.1 m; Tomb B, 10.23 m; Tomb Γ, 7.3 m.

LM I Final use of house-tombs.

VIII. BIBLIOGRAPHY

General

1924   Xanthoudides, S. *The Vaulted Tombs of Mesará* (London) 88–125.

1970   Branigan, K. *The Tombs of Mesara* (London).

1976   Pelon, O. *Tholoi, tumuli et cercles funéraires* (Athens) 32–33.

Scripts and Seals

1969   *CMS* 2.1:272–405 nos. 241–349 (N. Platon).

1977   *CMS* 2.2:29–30 no. 25 (N. Platon, I. Pini, and G. Salies).

1982   *GORILA* 4:160–61.

1984   *CMS* 2.3:141–43 nos. 120–21 (N. Platon and I. Pini).

IX. FINDS

Herakleion Museum.

X. DATE OF PHOTOGRAPHY

May 11, 1983.

VANNA NINIOU-KINDELI

35°27′ N, 23°39′ E

I. IMPORTANCE

Polyrrhenia is the most important Classical city of western Crete after Kydonia (Chania). Founded in Archaic times and colonized from Laconia, it flourished especially in Hellenistic times and during the Roman Empire. It was a traditional enemy of Knossos and of Kydonia and also of the neighboring harbor town of Phalasarna. It took part in the Lyttian War (221–219 B.C.). It welcomed the Roman conquerors, as an inscription datable to 68–66 B.C. on the base of a statue shows. The Polyrrhenians dedicated the statue to Quintus Caecilius Metellus (Creticus); the inscription refers to him as a "savior and benefactor of the city."

II. USE

A–R city.

III. SITUATION

In western Crete, 7 km south–southwest of Kisamos, Polyrrhenia is on the summit of a high and sheer hill in the mountain range of Prophitis Ilias, from which it is separated by gorges and ravines. The formation of the hill provides a natural stronghold for the acropolis, and the slopes and fertile valleys around are good for farming. The acropolis obtained its water principally from rainwater cisterns (compare Lato and Dreros), but the rest of the city in Roman times took water by aqueduct from two copious springs still in use in the modern village of Polyrrhenia.

Because there have been no extended excavations, it is difficult to measure the area of the city. To judge from visible remains, an area of 30 ha is likely (including the cemetery). Many tombs are fairly low down on the west slope of the hill; others, mostly chamber tombs with one or several chambers, are on nearby hills to the southwest.

IV. GEOMORPHOLOGY

The geological setting of Polyrrhenia, an isolated pinnacle of massive limestone rising above later deposits of soft marly limestones and conglomerates, resembles that of Early Minoan Debla, some 30 km to the east. Both sites are built on nappe fragments, though that of Polyrrhenia is considerably smaller than that of Debla and represents a later nappe emplacement, of the Pindos series. Rocks of this nappe sequence, though found across the island, are both much less common and more tectonically deformed than the underlying Tripolitza series over which they were carried some 50 million years ago. Zones of chert breccias are to be seen in the limestone bedrock underlying Polyrrhenia.

Polyrrhenia is built on the westernmost of three massive eminences, the other two having slopes too steep for construction. Abutting the acropolis to the west is a somewhat lower, flat-topped, ridge of Miocene conglomerates (see Fig. 36.3), where it would have been possible to dig wells down to the water table. On the acropolis, cisterns for rainwater were the only source of drinking water.

Structures at Polyrrhenia were built of both limestone and sandstone angular boulders collected or shallowly excavated from the surrounding hillslopes. There appears to have been little quarrying of limestone bedrock for ashlar boulders, perhaps because of its relatively fractured nature.

V. EXCAVATION HISTORY

F. Halbherr, 1893, for the Archaeological Institute of America; V. D. Theophaneidis, 1938, and S. Markoulaki, 1987, for the Archaeological Service.

VI. BUILDINGS

A, C, and later   Fortification walls around summit and low slopes, surviving chiefly to the north, northwest, and southeast. Different styles of building (Cyclopean, pseudo-isodomic, etc.) show that walls were used for many centuries, till V times, and often repaired and altered. Large cisterns. Building remains. Outside the walls: house remains, some dug into rock, on the south and southeast slopes of hill and in village.

H On west slope of hill outside the walls and next to the church of Ninety-nine Holy Fathers, a wall 30 m long of the end of the 4th century, probably the peribolos enclosure wall of a sanctuary (see Fig. 36.3). Of the same date an adjacent building, 60.65 by 6.73 m, facing south and entered from the east; built in pseudo-isodomic style (Theophaneidis 1942–44: colossal altar).

R The rock-cut tunnels, 1.35 m wide and 2.30 m high, of the Hadrianic aqueduct end at the springs in the two squares of the village: length not known because not fully explored.

Byz and V Last use of fortifications.

VIII. BIBLIOGRAPHY

1837 Pashley, R. *Travels in Crete* (London) 1:48–49, 53–56, and 2:46–50.

1865 Spratt, T. A. B. *Travels and Researches in Crete* (London) 2:211–15.

1867 Thenon, L. "Fragments d'une description de l'île de Crète, III: Polyrrhénie," *RA* n.s. 15:416–27.

1890 Svoronos 274–84.

1901 Savignoni, L., and G. De Sanctis, "Esplorazione archeologica delle provincie occidentali di Creta," *MonAnt* 11: 364–80.

1905 Gerola, G. *Monumenti veneti dell'isola di Creta* (Venice) 1: 72–80.

1939 *IC* 2:237–66 (= *IC* II. XXIII. 1–66).

1942–44 Theophaneidis, V. D. "Anaskaphikai erevnai kai tychaia evrimata ana tin dytikin Kritin," *ArchEph* Chronika 17–31.

1951 Kirsten, E. "Siedlungsgeschichtliche Forschungen in West-Kreta," in F. Matz, ed., *Forschungen auf Kreta 1942* (Berlin) 119–52.

Welter, G., and U. Jantzen. "Das Diktynnaion," in F. Matz, ed., *Forschungen auf Kreta 1942* (Berlin) 106–17.

1952 *RE* 21:2530–48 (E. Kirsten).

1956 Alexiou, S. "Epitymvion epigramma ek Polyrrhineias," *KrChron* 10:237–40.

1976 *PECS* 722–23 (D. J. Blackman).

1982 Sanders, I. F. *Roman Crete* (Warminster) 172–73.

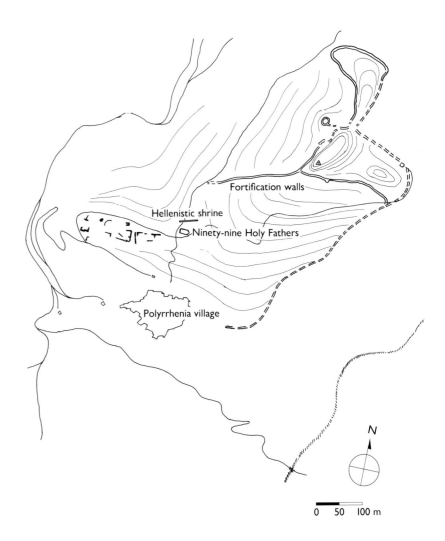

Figure 36.1 Plan of Polyrrhenia

Figure 36.2 High aerial view

Figure 36.3   Site (at churchyard) of temple

1984   *Creta antica* 60 (M. A. Rizzo).

1985   *Ancient Crete* 32 (M. A. Rizzo).

1988   Gondicas, D. *Recherches sur la Crète occidentale* (Amster-
         dam) 173–257.

IX. FINDS

Chania Museum; Kisamos Museum; inscriptions built into Church
of the Ninety-nine Holy Fathers.

X. DATE OF PHOTOGRAPHY

June 30, 1984.

Figure 36.4   Looking northeast toward acropolis

JAMES WHITLEY

35°07′ N, 26°05′ E

I. IMPORTANCE

Praisos is an Archaic-Classical-Hellenistic city in the far eastern end of Crete. It was known to ancient authors (Herodotus 7.170–71; Strabo, *Geography* 10.4.6–12) as the city of the Eteocretans (*eteo*, "true" or "aboriginal"), one of the five peoples of ancient Crete listed in the *Odyssey* (19.172–77). The Eteocretans spoke a non-Greek language, which is known from five inscriptions from Praisos (found with terracotta and bronze figurines at the shrine on the so-called Third Acropolis). This language may be related to the language(s) of the Linear A script.

Praisos, although an inland city, had territory extending to the north and south coasts of the Siteia peninsula and may even have included the small island of Leuke (Kouphonisi), off southeast Crete, and the temple of Dictaean Zeus at Palaikastro. Praisos had its own coinage. It was in constant rivalry with its neighbors, Hierapytna (Ierapetra) to the west and Itanos (Erimoupoli) to the east; but unlike its coastal neighbors, it was unable to interest either the Romans or the Ptolemies in its continuing existence. In about 145–140 B.C. Hierapytna destroyed Praisos, which ceased to be occupied thereafter.

II. USE

N–G cave deposits (Skales); LM IIIB and G–A tombs; A–H city.

III. SITUATION

Inland in the Siteia peninsula, in the valley that runs between Siteia and Lithines, and directly north of the village of Nea Praisos (Vavelli). Area of about 500 by 350 m includes the so-called First and Second Acropoleis. To the south, outside the circuit of the city, is the Third Acropolis or Altar Hill. Also in the region: quarries and Skales cave to the north; tholos tombs; shrines at Vavelli and Mesamvrysis; and "Megalithic House" at Ayios Konstantinos to the south.

IV. GEOMORPHOLOGY

Bedrock in the region of Praisos consists of middle to late Miocene conglomerates interbedded with sandy and marly strata and fossiliferous marine marls interbedded with laminated sands. These two units were deposited in a downfaulted trough, or graben, between the higher (and harder) limestone uplands of extreme eastern Crete and the east flank of the Ornon mountains. The main route today and in the past from Siteia to the south coast winds along this graben.

Two different bedrock types form the First and Second Acropoleis. The Second Acropolis, which is lower, has a cream-colored fossiliferous limestone; the First Acropolis is made of the more common sandstone-pebble conglomerate.

The whole top of the First Acropolis is terraced. The builders combined artificial terracing and the cutting of terraces into the relatively soft conglomerate bedrock, so that the original slopes are completely modified. The artificial terrace walls were built of small roughly dressed limestone blocks derived from the bedrock of the Second Acropolis. The general construction technique is strongly reminiscent of that at Dreros.

V. EXCAVATION HISTORY

F. Halbherr, 1884, for the Italian Archaeological Mission, and 1894 for the Archaeological Institute of America; R. C. Bosanquet, 1901–2, for the British School; M. Mavroeidis, 1935, for the Archaeological Service; N. Platon, 1953 and 1960, for the Archaeological Society; C. Davaras, 1978, for the Archaeological Service, and 1980, for the Archaeological Society; N. Papadakis and B. Rutkowski, 1983, for the Archaeological Service and the Polish Academy of Sciences.

VI. BUILDINGS

N, MM, LM, and G   Deposits in Skales cave, 500 m north of Second Acropolis.

MIII–LMI "Megalithic House" at Ayios Konstantinos 800 m southeast of First Acropolis; chance finds on First and Third Acropoleis.

IIIB, G–A Tholos Tombs A–E to south and east of First and Third Acropoleis. Tomb A 200 m south-southeast of Third Acropolis still visible.

G–H Shrine on Third Acropolis, or Altar Hill, with rock-cut steps and ashlar masonry.

A–H Shrines at Vavelli 600 m southwest of Third Acropolis on path to village and at Mesamvrysis by a spring 900 m southeast of Third Acropolis; votive deposit on First Acropolis; more than fifty-three tombs to the south and east of First and Third Acropoleis.

C–H Temple foundations on summit of First Acropolis.

H "Almond Tree House," or Andreion, in saddle between First and Second Acropoleis, with ashlar masonry, steps, and olive press; rock-cut houses, with shelves and alcoves in walls, on lower west slopes of First Acropolis and south slopes of Second Acropolis. One rock-cut house preserved to a height of several meters on the northeast slope of Second Acropolis. Quarries and rock-cut houses on slope 250 m north of Second Acropolis.

VIII. BIBLIOGRAPHY

General

1865 Spratt, T. A. B. *Travels and Researches in Crete* (London) 1:163–70.

1888 Comparetti, D. "Iscrizioni di varie città cretesi," *Museo Italiano di Antichità Classica* (Florence) 2:669–86.

1890 Svoronos 285–92.

1895 Mariani, L. "Antichità cretesi," *MonAnt* 6:283–311.

1901 Halbherr, F. "Report on the Researches at Praesos," *AJA* 5:371–92.

1901–2 Bosanquet, R. C. "Excavations at Praesos. I," *BSA* 8: 231–70.

Conway, R. S. "The Pre-Hellenic Inscriptions of Praesos," *BSA* 8:125–56.

Forster, E. S. "Praesos: The Terracottas," *BSA* 8: 271–81.

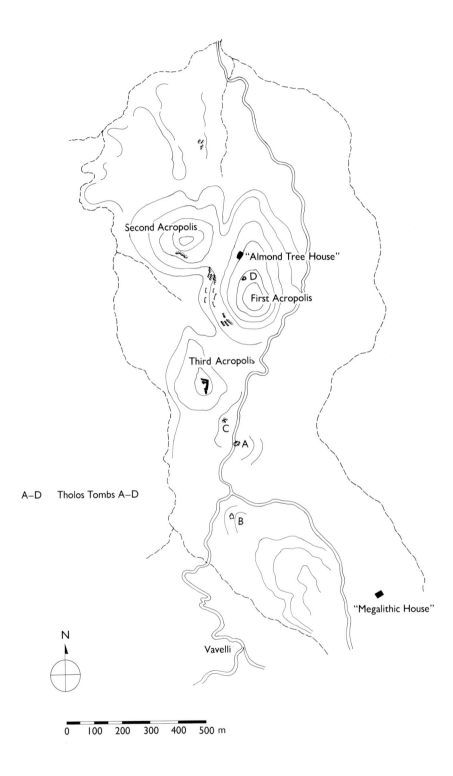

A–D Tholos Tombs A–D

N

Figure 37.1 Plan of Praisos

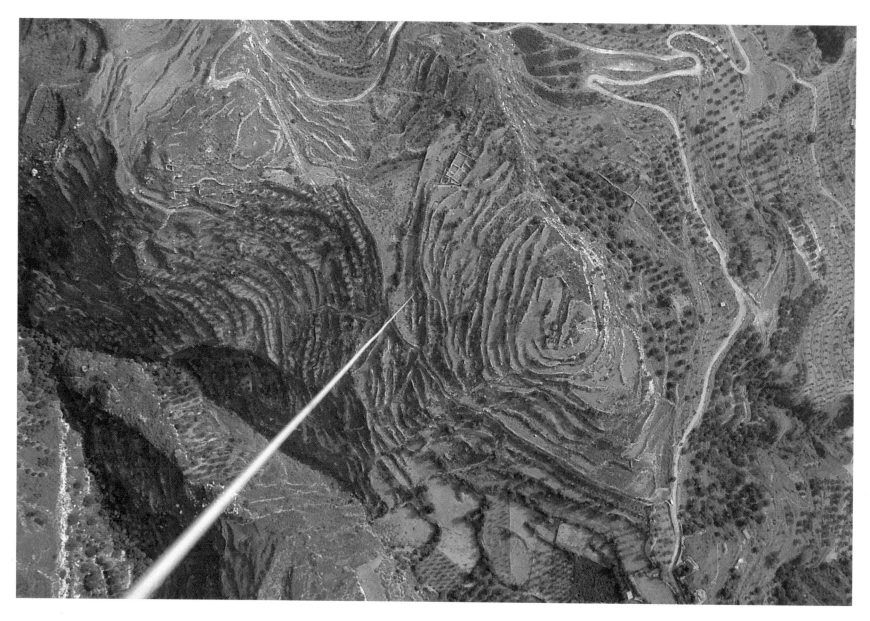

Figure 37.2 First (in center) and Second Acropoleis

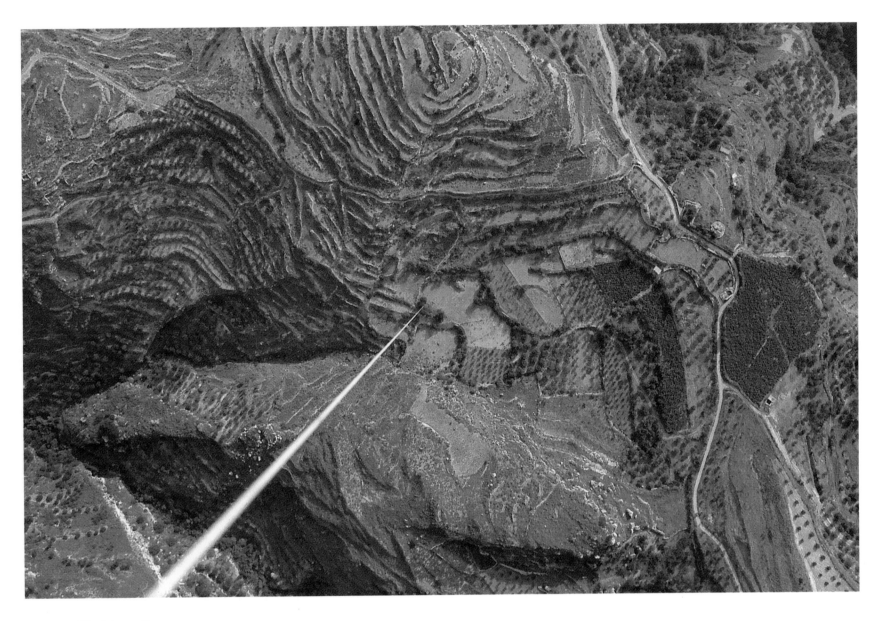

Figure 37.3 Third Acropolis

Figure 37.4   "Almond Tree House"

Figure 37.5 "Almond Tree House"

1904–5   ———. "Terracotta Plaques from Praesos," *BSA* 11: 243–57.

1905–6   Droop, J. P. "Some Geometric Pottery from Crete," *BSA* 12:24–62.

Marshall, F. H. "Tombs of Hellenic Date at Praisos," *BSA* 12:63–70.

1937   Mavroeidis, M. "O taphos tou athliti tis Praisou: Archaiologikes erevnes Siteias," *Driros* (Neapolis, Crete) 1:140–42, 172–74.

1939–40   Bosanquet, R. C. "Dicte and the Temples of Dictaean Zeus," *BSA* 40:60–77.

Hutchinson, R. W., E. Eccles, and S. Benton. "Unpublished Objects from Palaikastro and Praisos. II," *BSA* 40:38–59.

1942   *IC* 3:134–55 (= *IC* III. VI. 1–34).

1953   Platon, N. "Anaskaphai eis tin periochin Siteias," *PAE* 295–96.

———. "I archaiologiki kinisis en Kriti kata to etos 1953," *KrChron* 7:485.

1959   ———. "I archaiologiki kinisis en Kriti kata to etos 1959," *KrChron* 13:389–90.

1960   ———. "Anaskaphai periochis Praisou," *PAE* 294–307.

1976   *PECS* 737 (K. Branigan).

1978   Davaras, C. "Archaiotites kai mnimeia anatolikis Kritis," *ArchDelt* 33, pt. 2:392–93.

1980   ———. "Perisyllogi archaiotiton stin Praiso," *PAE* 408–11.

1982   Duhoux, Y. *Les Etéocrétois. Les textes—la langue* (Amsterdam) 55–85, 119–24.

1984   *Creta antica* 59 (M. A. Rizzo).

1985   *Ancient Crete* 31 (M. A. Rizzo).

Papadakis, N., and B. Rutkowski. "New Research at Skales Cave near Praisos," *BSA* 80:129–37.

Seals

1984   *CMS* 2.3:321–26 nos. 271–75 (N. Platon and I. Pini).

IX. FINDS

Herakleion Museum; Siteia Museum; Louvre, Paris; Ashmolean Museum, Oxford; Fitzwilliam Museum, Cambridge; Metropolitan Museum of Art, New York.

X. DATE OF PHOTOGRAPHY

June 6, 1981.

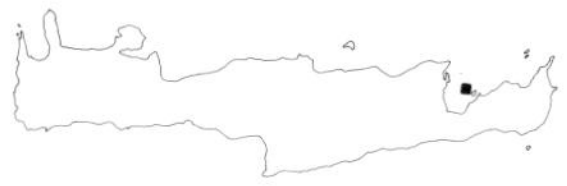

COSTIS DAVARAS, PHILIP P. BETANCOURT,

AND WILLIAM R. FARRAND

35°12′ N, 25°52′ E

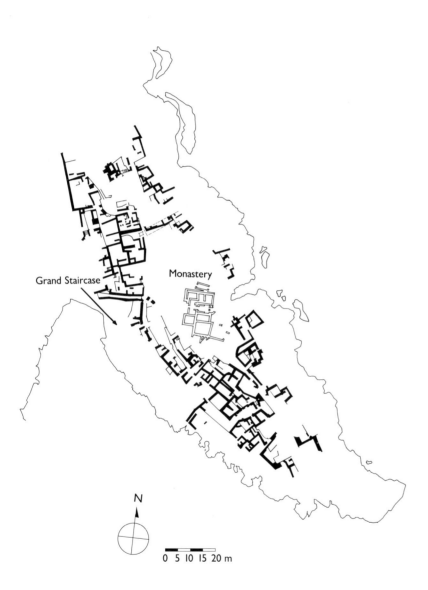

Grand Staircase

Monastery

N

0 5 10 15 20 m

Figure 38.1   Plan of Pseira

Figure 38.2   High aerial view

I. IMPORTANCE

Pseira is a small island at the eastern end of the Bay of Mirabello with an excellent harbor facing south-southeast, away from the prevailing winds in late summer, making it a strategic port during much of the year and a necessary one when northern winds blew. In Late Minoan IB, at the height of the settlement's prosperity, the town boasted a shrine with fine frescoes, imported pottery of high quality, and comfortable residences.

II. USE

FN/EM I–LM I town; FN/EM I–MM II cemetery; LM IIIA2 settlement; EByz monastery and farmsteads.

III. SITUATION

The settlement, on the terraced slopes of a peninsula and the hill opposite, overlooks a harbor on the small island of Pseira in the Bay of Mirabello, 2.5 km from the north coast of Crete. The island is barren and eroded, with no modern source of water. Ancient water source: wells and cisterns. Minoan settlement over 200 m east–west by over 100 m north–south.

IV. GEOMORPHOLOGY

Pseira is related to the bedrock of the eastern shore of the Bay of Mirabello, being part of a series of nappes in which quartzites and phyllites have been thrust over younger limestones (Plattenkalk). Long after the overthrusting event, the floor of the Bay of Mirabello subsided, leaving the islet standing high, separated by deep water from the main Cretan shore. A small but conspicuous peninsula projecting from the southeast shore affords some natural protection; it is composed mostly of carbonate rocks—Plattenkalk and somewhat metamorphosed (foliated) limestone—that dip generally to the east at relatively low angles (10–16 degrees).

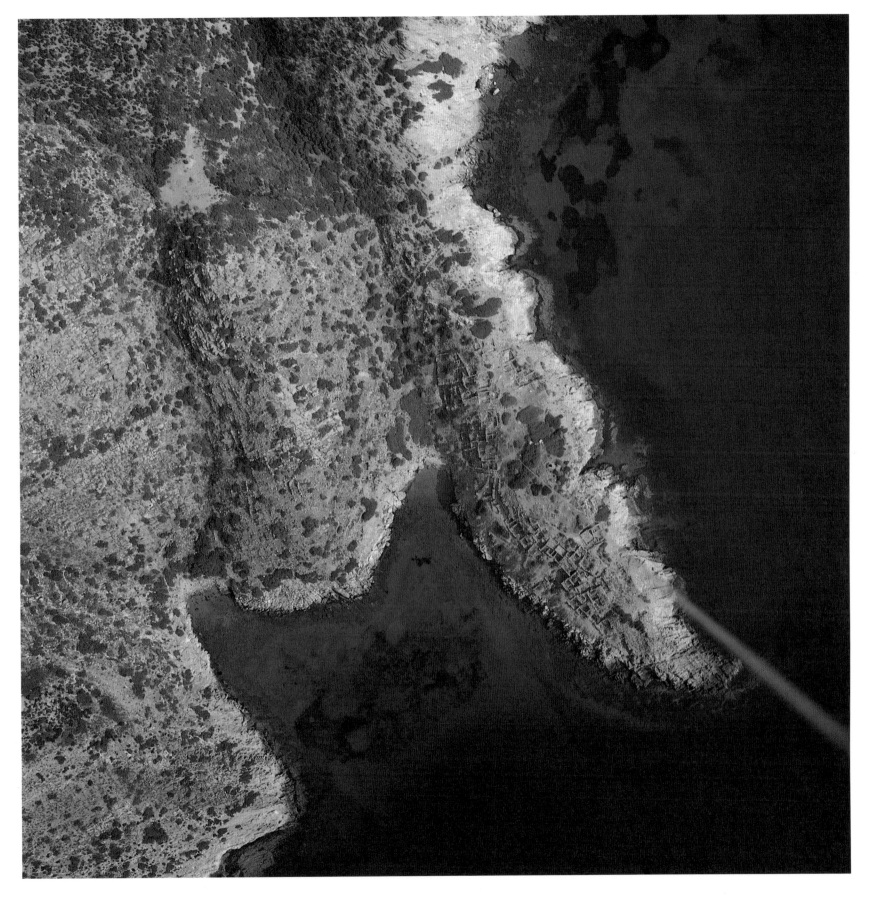

Figure 38.3 Town, with stairs from harbor

The settlement was built along the crest and southwest side of this peninsula in terraced fashion to accommodate the steep slopes to the northeast and southwest. The wall foundations are of gray-veined Plattenkalk limestone common in the vicinity. Structures were built on leveled areas of the naturally curving ridge crest. Unlimited quantities of phyllite flagstones, derived from adjacent outcrops of the Phyllite-Quartzite series, were at hand to use as flooring material.

V. EXCAVATION HISTORY

R. B. Seager, 1906–7, for the American Exploration Society; C. Davaras and P. P. Betancourt for the Archaeological Institute of Crete and the American School, 1985–.

VI. BUILDINGS

I–MM II	Cemetery (various tomb types).
–EM IIA	Scattered traces.
EM IIB	Scattered traces.
III–MM I	Extensive traces on entire hill northeast of harbor.
MM IB–II	House remains.
MM III	Extensive dumps from LM I leveling and building.
LM I	Large town with streets and stairs forming blocks of buildings. Long stairs (Grand Staircase) up from harbor. Over sixty houses identified, including some with many rooms on several terrace levels. Court near top of Grand Staircase. LM IB destruction. Abandonment.
M IIIA2	Limited reoccupation.
EByz	Monastery with chapel, cistern, and associated rooms; farmsteads.

VIII. BIBLIOGRAPHY

General

1910   Seager, R. B. *Excavations on the Island of Pseira, Crete* (Philadelphia).

Figure 38.4   Approaching Pseira from the mainland

1958–59   Leatham, J., and M. S. F. Hood. "Sub-Marine Exploration in Crete, 1955," *BSA* 53–54:275–78.

1976   Davaras, C. "Archaiotites kai mnimeia anatolikis Kritis," *ArchDelt* 31, pt. 2:375–76.

1977   ———. "Archaiotites kai mnimeia anatolikis Kritis," *ArchDelt* 32, pt. 2:340.

1983   Betancourt, P. P. *Minoan Objects Excavated from Vasilike, Pseira, Sphoungaras, Priniatikos Pyrgos, and Other Sites* (Philadelphia) 22–40.

1986   Betancourt, P. P., and C. Davaras. "Anaskaphiki erevna Pseiras: Periodi 1985 and 1986," *Amaltheia* 68–69: 183–200.

1988   ———. "Excavations at Pseira," *CrSt* 1:35–38.

———. "Excavations at Pseira, 1985 and 1986," *Hesperia* 57:207–26.

1990   Betancourt, P. P., P. Goldberg, R. Hope Simpson, and C. J. Vitaliano. "Excavations at Pseira: The Evidence for the Theran Eruption," in *3 Thera* 3:96–99.

Figure 38.5   Town peninsula

Frescoes

1990 Immerwahr, S. A. *Aegean Painting in the Bronze Age* (University Park, Pa.) 58, 62, 161–62, 184.

Seals

1969 *CMS* 2.1 : 576–77 no. 483 (N. Platon).

IX. FINDS

Herakleion Museum; Siteia Museum; University Museum, University of Pennsylvania, Philadelphia.

X. DATE OF PHOTOGRAPHY

June 5, 1981.

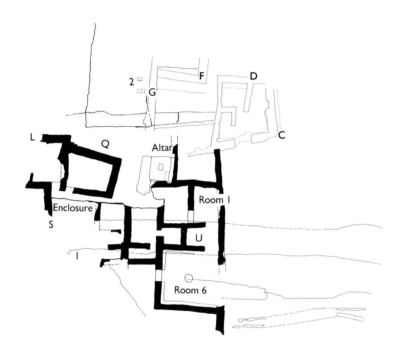

ANGELIKI LEBESSI

35°03′ N, 25°30′ E

N

I Protogeometric hearth
■ Middle Minoan II–Geometric
■ Late Geometric–Archaic
▨ Classical–Roman
2 Archaic hearth

0 2 4 6 m

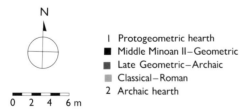

Figure 39.1   Syme sanctuary

Figure 39.2   Sanctuary

I. IMPORTANCE

Syme is the only Cretan cult site that has produced evidence of continuous occupation and ritual activity from the Minoan to the Roman period. Continuity is attested in architectural remains and in sacrificial deposits containing material from New Palace times to the 5th century B.C. Epigraphical evidence suggests that the sanctuary was widely known in Crete in Hellenistic and Roman times.

II. USE

MM II–R sanctuary.

III. SITUATION

On the south flank of the Lasithi mountains in a natural amphitheater, separated at the north and east from the Viannos plateau by steep slopes and open to the west and south with a clear view of the Libyan Sea. At Krya Vrysi, "cold spring," a copious spring uphill from the village of Kato Syme (20 minutes' walk for the athletic; 45–60 minutes' for those less so) and 1,130 m high. Pine and scrub oak cover the slopes. Grazing for flocks of feral goats.

Estimated area of sanctuary: 9,350 sq m; excavated area: about 1,250 sq m.

IV. GEOMORPHOLOGY

The south flank of the Lasithi mountains is one of the most highly faulted areas of Crete, a condition reflected both in the local topography, which is dominated by limestone blocks several square kilometers in area (horsts) that have been uplifted relative to the surrounding terrain, and in the concentration of large springs around the modern village of Pefkos greater than that in any other part of the island.

The Krya Vrysi is noted on the Kreutzberg et al. (1977) 1:200,000 Geological Map of Greece, Crete Island (East sheet). The spring issues from the fault contact between highly deformed rocks (phyllonites) of the Phyllite-Quartzite (or Phyllitic) series and over-

lying Upper Jurassic age massive gray limestones of the Gavrovo-Tripolitza series. The flow has been measured at more than 200 cu m per hour.

Most building foundations appear to be composed of cut blocks of Tripolitza limestone and to be built on the underlying phyllonite bedrock that forms the lower slope of the natural amphitheater containing the site. Some foundations are on sedimentary deposits.

Since the site's abandonment, the sediments covering it have included both fine-grained slopewash from the decomposition of the phyllonite and limestone boulders (up to car-sized) that have been mechanically weathered from the vertical cliff rising above the site to the north.

V. EXCAVATION HISTORY

A. Lebessi, 1972–, for the Archaeological Society.

VI. BUILDINGS

MM II   Sherds from various contexts.

MM III–LM I   *Phase A:* Building U, of which many rooms and paved courtyard have been excavated. Of small roughly worked limestone and some serpentinite (reused from earlier structure?). Largest room, room 6, has a bench. Destroyed by rock slide.

Phase B: Partly excavated Sacred Enclosure, built of large limestone blocks (excavated length of west wall 12.5 m; south wall 13 m) that together with an associated paved road encompassed a sacrificial area with a monumental podium (12.5 by 7 m) in the center.

Phase C: Building S (not on plan) of which four rooms have been excavated.

LM II–IIIA   Building S continues in use; pottery and three bronze swords.

LM IIIA   Pottery from sacrificial deposits.

LM IIIB   Storeroom R with pithoi accommodated in reused area of Building S.

LM IIIC   Building Q (6.6 by 6.4 m).

SM–PG   Partly excavated Building L.

PG–G   First phase of altar (wide wall 4 by 1.4 m); π-shaped hearth to the southwest, made of rough fieldstones set on edge; bench for offerings in room 1 of Building U, the walls of which must have been visible.

LG–EA   Second phase of altar; rectangular addition with *bothros* in center and step on east side (2.3 by 2.6 m). Two terraces east, south, and west of altar; third terrace added 700–650 B.C., bordered on the south by a purification channel; north of altar wall a roofed building (Building J), partly excavated, and a hearth.

A   Partly excavated 6th-century B.C. roofed building to the north of altar (Building G).

C   Retaining wall facing south over A buildings north of altar (length preserved 11.6 m). Partly excavated Building F, which extends into unexcavated part to the north.

H   One room and annex excavated of house-shrine (Building D), with high bench in room, dedicated to Hermes Kedrites and Aphrodite (votives and graffiti on roof tiles).

R   Part of massive building over southeast corner of H shrine may belong with temple mentioned in stone inscription to Hermes Kedrites: Building C. Use of sanctuary till 3rd century.

VIII. BIBLIOGRAPHY

General

1972   Lebessi, A. "To iero tou Ermi kai tis Aphroditis sti Syme Viannou," *PAE* 193–203.

1973   ———. "To iero tou Ermi kai tis Aphroditis sti Syme Viannou," *PAE* 188–99.

1974   ———. "To iero tou Ermi kai tis Aphroditis sti Syme Viannou," *PAE* 222–27.

1975   ———. "To iero tou Ermi kai tis Aphroditis sti Syme Viannou," *PAE* 322–29.

1976   ———. "Sanctuary of Hermes and Aphrodite in Crete," *Expedition* 18.3:1–13.

———. "To iero tou Ermi kai tis Aphroditis sti Syme Viannou," *PAE* 400–407.

1977   ———. "To iero tou Ermi kai tis Aphroditis sti Syme Viannou," *PAE* 403–18.

1981   ———. "Iero tou Ermi kai tis Aphroditis sti Syme Viannou,"
       PAE 380–96.

       ———. "I synecheia tis kritomykinaikis latreias. Epivioseis
       kai anavioseis," *ArchEph* 1–24.

1983   ———. "Iero tou Ermi kai tis Aphroditis sti Syme Viannou,"
       PAE 348–66.

1985   ———. "Iero tou Ermi kai tis Aphroditis sti Syme Viannou,"
       PAE 263–85.

       ———. *To iero tou Ermi kai tis Aphroditis sti Syme Viannou* 1.1.
       Chalkina kritika torevmata (Athens).

1986   ———. "Iero tou Ermi kai tis Aphroditis sti Syme Viannou,"
       PAE 241–42.

       Lebessi, A., and D. S. Reese. "Recent and Fossil Shells from
       the Sanctuary of Hermes and Aphrodite, Syme Viannou,
       Crete," *ArchEph* 183–88.

1987   Lebessi, A., and P. M. Muhly. "The Sanctuary of Hermes and
       Aphrodite at Syme, Crete," *National Geographic Research*
       3:102–13.

1990   ———. "Aspects of Minoan Cult. Sacred Enclosures: The
       Evidence from the Syme Sanctuary (Crete)," *AA* 315–36.

Scripts

1984   Muhly, P. M. "Linear A Inscriptions from the Sanctuary of
       Hermes and Aphrodite at Kato Syme," *Kadmos* 23:124–35.

1985   *GORILA* 5:61–68.

1986   Muhly, P. M. "I enepigraphes trapezes prosphoron apo to
       iero tis Symes Viannou," in *Philia epi eis Yeoryion Mylonan*
       (Athens) 1:272–83.

Geomorphology

1979   Kourmoulis, N. E. *Inventory of Karstic Springs of Greece* II.
       Crete (Athens).

IX. FINDS

Herakleion Museum.

X. DATE OF PHOTOGRAPHY

April 29, 1983.

Figure 39.3   View to the southwest, with Mt. Keraton above the coast

ANTONIS VASILAKIS

35°18′ N, 25°01′ E

I. IMPORTANCE

The prosperous and long-lived Minoan settlement at Tylissos occupies a strategic position in the central area of the Malevisi district in the hinterland of Herakleion. Near Psiloriti, it lies on the principal road, originating in Minoan times or earlier, that linked Knossos and central Crete with western Crete.

Though only a little of the Minoan town has been excavated, two grand Late Minoan I houses (Houses A and Γ) have been discovered along with a third, less grand (House B), that is rectangular in plan and may have had some administrative or storage use. Finds from Tylissos include three huge bronze cauldrons, inscriptions in Linear A, frescoes, and a bronze statuette of an adorant. After a period of desertion, there seems to have been a Late Minoan III settlement of some size and, very much later, a Hellenistic settlement.

II. USE

EM II–LM I, LM III, and H settlement; PG burial; R and Byz chance finds.

III. SITUATION

On a high flat site surrounded by fertile country, at the north corner of the village of Tylissos, west–southwest of Herakleion. Cereals, olives, vines, pine trees. Excavated area: about 70 m north–south by 50 m east–west.

IV. GEOMORPHOLOGY

Both modern and Minoan Tylissos are located on a knoll or rise of geologically young (lower Pliocene) marine sedimentary marls and limestones that cap very similar but somewhat older rocks deposited in upper Miocene time, roughly 6 million years ago.

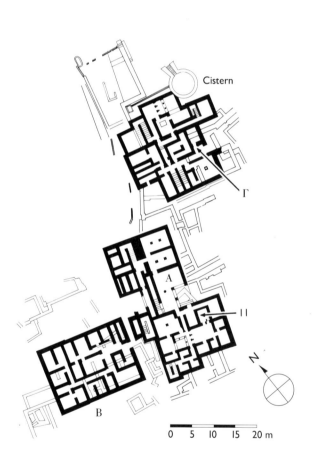

Figure 40.1   Plan of Tylissos

Figure 40.2   Houses A–Γ, with Late Minoan III house built over them

V. EXCAVATION HISTORY

J. Hazzidakis, 1909–13, for the Cretan government and the Archaeological Society; N. Platon, 1953–55, and A. Kanta, 1971, for the Archaeological Service.

VI. BUILDINGS

EM II–MM II   Scanty traces of houses in deeper levels throughout the excavation.

MM III–LM I   Three large houses—A, about 35 by 18 m; B, about 21.6 by 15.9 m; Γ, about 24 by 22.8 m—part of a town. Ashlar masonry. Houses A and Γ especially well appointed. House A includes a lustral basin (room 11). Paved road and court west of House Γ and aqueduct with clay pipes northwest of it.

LM IIIA–IIIB/C   Traces of considerable settlement; remains of megaron, with porch (and into SM?)   and anteroom, at about 1 m above ruins of House Γ; also circular cistern entered by steps, d 5 m (compare the cistern at Zakro and the spring chamber at Archanes-Tourkoyeitonia, both of the New Palace period). Houses east of House A. Channel (dump?) cut in rock northwest of modern guardhouse.

(PG   Cremation burial, southwest edge of modern village.)

H   Building remains above and to the north and northwest of House Γ include an altar. Three column bases may indicate a stoa.

R and Byz   Few chance finds.

VIII. BIBLIOGRAPHY

General

1890   Svoronos 328–30.

1931   Marinatos, S. "Mia ysterominoiki kavsis nekrou ek Tylisou," *AM* 56:112–18.

1934   J. Hazzidakis. *Les villas minoennes de Tylissos,* EtCr 3 (Paris).

1935   *IC* 1:306–10 (= *IC* I.XXX. 1–4).

1953   Platon, N. "I archaiologiki kinisis en Kriti kata to etos 1953," *KrChron* 7:481–82.

1954   ———. "I archaiologiki kinisis en Kriti kata to etos 1954," *KrChron* 8:508, 512.

     ———. "Ta minoika ikiaka iera," *KrChron* 8:450–52.

1955   ———. "I archaiologiki kinisis en Kriti kata to etos 1955," *KrChron* 9:562.

1969   Zois, A. A. *Provlimata chronologias tis minoikis kerameikis. Gournes—Tylisos—Malia* (Athens) 24–34.

1972   Alexiou, S. "Ai archaiotites tis Kritis kata to 1971," *KrChron* 24:491.

     Desborough, V. R. d'A. *The Greek Dark Ages* (London) 233.

1980   Kanta, A. *The Late Minoan III Period in Crete: A Survey of Sites, Pottery, and Their Distribution,* SIMA 58 (Gothenburg) 9–13.

1982   Sanders, I. F. *Roman Crete* (Warminster) 154.

1984   Hayden, B. J. "Late Bronze Age Tylissos: House Plans and Cult Center," *Expedition* 26.3:37–46.

1985   Gesell, G. C. *Town, Palace, and House Cult in Minoan Crete,* SIMA 67 (Gothenburg) 135–36.

Frescoes

1990   Immerwahr, S. A. *Aegean Painting in the Bronze Age* (University Park, Pa.) 66–67, 82, 184.

Scripts and Seals

1976   *GORILA* 1:323–29.

1977   *CMS* 2.2:33–34 no. 27 (N. Platon, I. Pini, and G. Salies).

1982   *GORILA* 4:108–9, 169–70.

1984   *CMS* 2.3:147–53 nos. 123–28 (N. Platon and I. Pini).

1985   *CMS* 2.4:3–5 nos. 1–2 (N. Platon and I. Pini).

IX. FINDS

Herakleion Museum.

X. DATE OF PHOTOGRAPHY

June 5, 1984.

Figure 40.3   House A

Figure 40.4   House B

Figure 40.5   House Γ

ANTONIS A. ZOIS

35°05′ N, 25°48′ E

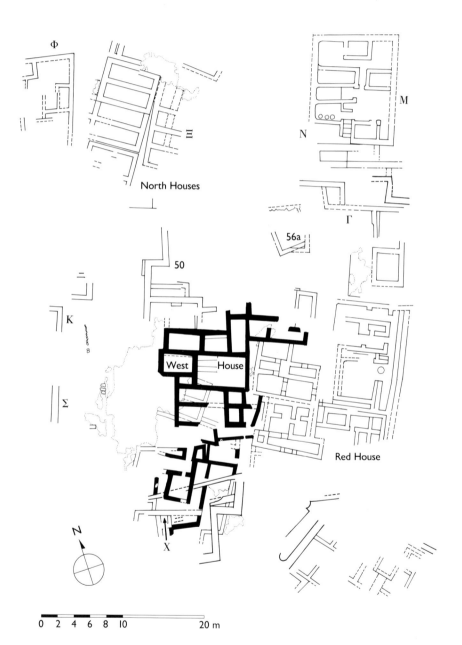

Figure 41.1   Plan of Vasiliki (black walls mark EM IIB, second phase)

Figure 41.2   Vasiliki village

I. IMPORTANCE

Vasiliki has been commonly known in Minoan studies as the site of the oldest, most primitive Minoan "palace," considered by many the prototype of the later palaces and thought to have served as the seat of some local "chieftain," and as the place that produced a peculiar type of pottery in Early Minoan II, abstractly decorated and modern looking, called Vasiliki or mottled ware. Recent research, however, shows that there is nothing like a primitive palace at Vasiliki, earlier workers having confused and misinterpreted the remains of different phases, and that Vasiliki ware was produced at several other sites and widely distributed in many more.

Vasiliki is interesting today mainly because it is the sole Minoan minor settlement with a long occupation that has been excavated, and is still being excavated, though some phases are represented by unimpressive or scanty remains. Vasiliki represents the typical Minoan village, one of the main constituents of Minoan society and the starting force for its evolution. It was largely self-sufficient in meeting its immediate needs. Its population may not have exceeded two hundred, but this is a highly hypothetical figure. Agriculture and stock raising were its main productive occupations. The remains at Vasiliki, set in one of the finest landscapes in Crete, offer first-rate material for studying settlement pattern as well as building techniques and their evolution.

In the oldest settlement of Early Minoan IIA the houses, architectonically equivalent, are placed side by side and touching each other. (Neolithic Çatal Hüyük in Anatolia is a well-known parallel for such a scheme.) This arrangement suggests a socially well-organized and efficiently integrated "egalitarian" community. In Early Minoan IIB the large paved yard in the center of the settlement was obviously a public square, the focal point of village life. (Mottled or Vasiliki ware is the hallmark of the phase, one of the great achievements of Minoan ceramics.)

The Early Minoan III houses found in the original excavations over a thick deposit of Early Minoan IIB are the best evidence at any site for identifying Early Minoan III as a distinct historical unit.

Figure 41.3 Village and surroundings

Sadly, they are not fully published. It is hoped that future excavations will relocate the remains.

Middle Minoan IA seems to have been the time when the settlement was largest. The houses of this phase found in the original excavations are not now visible, but the new excavations have added three more examples.

There is some evidence for at least two houses of the succeeding Middle Minoan II phase.

Late Minoan I was a time of continuing prosperity.

Late Minoan III is attested only by a nearby tomb (its location now unknown). In Protogeometric times there seems to have been a small sanctuary at the site. In Roman times there was considerable occupation as well as an aqueduct to bring water to the site from a distance of several kilometers. In view of the copious spring in the modern village of Vasiliki some 500 m away, how do we explain the bringing of more water during the Roman period? This is a difficult question that can be answered only after the further examination of geological data (to explain the appearance and disappearance of water resources over time) in conjunction with the settlement pattern and the economy of the Minoan and Roman periods. For the moment, we can hypothesize that the aqueduct carried water for olive pressing or making glass (many tiny glass fragments have been found at Vasiliki), whereas the spring water was for household use and irrigation.

Vasiliki suffered a destruction in Early Minoan IIA and destructions by fire in Early Minoan IIB and Middle Minoan IA. Unlike Myrtos–Phournou Koryphi, which was also destroyed by fire in Early Minoan IIB, it has important remains of Early Minoan III, and the settlement reached its greatest extent in Middle Minoan IA. In spite of the dramatic incidents of total or partial conflagration in the settlement—turning points in its history—and the equally dramatic change in some aspects of its material culture (for example, the shift from the mottled Vasiliki style of pottery to the white-on-dark style), there are no valid arguments for a cultural or historical break during the very long Minoan occupation of the site from Early Minoan IIA to Late Minoan I. Houses were rebuilt promptly after each catastrophe, using vast amounts of the debris in ever-improving techniques. Cultural traits could change quickly or slowly, but development almost always proceeded in step with that in other parts of Crete.

II. USE

EM IIA–LM I village; LM III tomb; probable PG sanctuary; R settlement; probable EByz basilica.

III. SITUATION

On a hill about 85 m high (and about 75 m above the plain below) in the isthmus of Ierapetra some 3 km from Pachyammos on the Bay of Mirabello, Vasiliki commands the north end of the isthmus, which is the only easy land route between the north and south coasts, linking such places as Gournia, Pseira, and Mochlos with Makryyialos, Myrtos–Phournou Koryphi, and Myrtos-Pyrgos.

The site lies about 500 m east of the village of Vasiliki, from which it took its name. The village has an abundant spring, used for irrigating the surrounding olive groves as well as for domestic purposes. Irrigation of the olive trees is indispensable here, as in the whole region of Ierapetra, which is the driest area in the Aegean, with summer weather from April till the end of October. The isthmus valleys, which form a depression between the mountains of central and eastern Crete, lack the much richer rainfall of the mountains. Both the excellent position of the site on the north–south route and the nearby spring may have attracted the first settlers.

The soil around the settlement is comparatively poor. The high quality of pottery and evidence of weaving may indicate that pots and textiles were exchanged for imported raw materials or prestige goods.

Much of the settlement is still to be excavated. Much was excavated in the original excavation and not recorded.

IV. GEOMORPHOLOGY

Vasiliki is built on a low north–south ridge of bioclastic limestone of Quaternary age. There are several outcrops of Neogene marine clays in the vicinity that could have served the potters making the Early Minoan III white-on-dark ware so common at the site.

To the east, the ridge top drops vertically 5–7 m down to new olive groves. The highest point on the site is a limestone knob. East–west walls along the east slope are sometimes set directly on limestone bedrock.

To the south-southeast, where new excavations have uncovered more of the settlement downslope, bedrock appears in a deep trench (below a carob tree). The walls probably continue 50–100 m downslope to a small north–south stream channel near the main road.

It is likely that the inhabitants of Vasiliki also took advantage of the small stream just east of their village.

V. EXCAVATION HISTORY

R. B. Seager, 1903, 1904, and 1906, for the American Exploration Society; N. Platon, 1953, for the Archaeological Service; A. A. Zois, 1970–82, 1990–, for the Archaeological Society.

VI. BUILDINGS

EM IIA Foundation fill of North Houses represents material from a temporary camp inhabited while settlers built the first houses. At least six houses identified; sophisticated construction in North Houses with filled-in cellular foundations in House Ξ and well-built walls of fieldstones. Destruction.

EM IIB Remains of about six houses identified, from two or more phases. In the center of the settlement a large (about 20 by 20 m) paved yard, bounded to the east by the first phase Red House (named after its red-painted plaster). West House second phase. Cellular foundations have open (not now filled-in) cells or small basement rooms. Double walls used (to give stronger support to upper floors and to help minimize damage from earthquakes). Violent destruction by fire of whole settlement probably caused by earthquake.

EM III Houses in southeast part of site (with EM IIB deposit 2 m deep below).

MM IA Apparently the time when the settlement was at its largest, with two or three phases, although the reports of the original excavations allow only two houses to be attested. Visible are three more houses found in the new excavations: Houses Γ, Φ, X. Note the sophisticated layout of the foundations of House Φ. Houses A and B not now visible. Violent destruction by fire, notably in House Γ.

MM II At least two houses, one on the east slope no longer visible, one on the south slope awaiting excavation.

LM I Foundations of House M well preserved; remains of others (Houses N, 50, K, Σ).

LM III Tholos tomb (LM IIIC), location now unknown.

PG Scanty remains of pavement at top of hill, with anthropomorphic statuettes and animal figurines, probably the remains of a sanctuary.

R Dense occupation shown by pottery and extensive fills of now-destroyed buildings. Surviving remains: part of a room (56α). Graves and a probable EByz basilica reported in neighborhood of settlement. Aqueduct (with open channel about 0.2 m wide) brought water to site from hills east of Episkopi, about 4 km to the south, after crossing the main stream running to the north coast on a partially surviving bridge about 500 m south of the settlement.

VIII. BIBLIOGRAPHY

General

1905   Seager, R. B. "Excavations at Vasiliki, 1904," *University of Pennsylvania, Transactions, Department of Archaeology* 1: 207–21.

1907   ———. "Report of Excavations at Vasiliki, Crete, in 1906," *University of Pennsylvania, Transactions, Department of Archaeology* 2: 111–32.

1908   ———. "Excavations at Vasiliki," in H. A. B. Hawes, B. E. Williams, R. B. Seager, and E. H. Hall. *Gournia, Vasiliki, and Other Prehistoric Sites on the Isthmus of Hierapetra* (Philadelphia) 49–50.

1968   Zois, A. A. *Der Kamares-Stil. Werden und Wesen*, Ph.D. diss., University of Tübingen 89–90, 97–115, 136–46, 254–55, 261, 382–84.

1972   ———. "Anaskaphi eis Vasilikin Ierapetras (1970 kai 1972)," *PAE* 274–309.

1973   ———. *Kriti, Epochi tou lithou*, Ancient Greek Cities 18 (Athens) 225.

1974   ———. "Anaskaphi eis Vasilikin Ierapetras," *PAE* 213–21.

1975   ———. "Anaskaphi eis Vasilikin Ierapetras," *PAE* 376–91.

1976   ———. "Anaskaphi eis Vasilikin Ierapetras," *PAE* 440–59.

———. *Vasiliki* I. *Nea archaiologiki erevna eis to Kephali plision tou choriou Vasiliki Ierapetras. Tomos protos* (Athens).

1977   ———. "Anaskaphi eis Vasilikin Ierapetras," *PAE* 447–54.

1978   ———. "Anaskaphi eis Vasilikin Ierapetras," *PAE* 300–308.

1979   Betancourt, P. P., et al. *Vasilike Ware: An Early Bronze Age Pottery Style in Crete*, SIMA 56 (Gothenburg).

Zois, A. A. "Anaskaphi eis Vasilikin Ierapetras," *PAE* 323–30.

1980   Kanta, A. *The Late Minoan III Period in Crete: A Survey of Sites, Pottery, and Their Distribution*, SIMA 58 (Gothenburg) 146.

Zois, A. A. "Anaskaphi eis Vasilikin Ierapetras," *PAE* 331–36.

1981   ———. "Anaskaphi Vasilikis Ierapetras," *PAE* 367–79.

1982   Sanders, I. F. *Roman Crete* (Warminster) 91, 140.

Zois, A. A. "Anaskaphi minoikou synikismou eis Vasilikin Ierapetras," *PAE* 307–11.

———. "Gibt es Vorläufer der minoischen Paläste auf Kreta? Ergebnisse neuer Untersuchungen," in *Palast und Hütte. Beiträge zum Bauen und Wohnen im Altertum* (Mainz) 207–15.

1983   Betancourt, P. P. *Minoan Objects Excavated from Vasilike, Pseira, Sphoungaras, Priniatikos Pyrgos, and Other Sites* (Philadelphia) 53–75.

1983–84   Mavriyannaki, K. "Minoiki metalliki mitra apo ti Vasiliki tis Ierapetras. I simasia tis metallotechnias sti diamorphosi tis protominoikis kinonias," *Kritologia* 16–19: 140–76.

1984   Betancourt, P. P., ed. *East Cretan White-on-Dark Ware: Studies on a Handmade Pottery of the Early to Middle Minoan Periods* (Philadelphia).

1989   Van Effenterre, H., and M. Van Effenterre. "Un obituaire crétois?" in *Aphieroma sto Styliano Alexiou, Ariadne* 5: 99–107.

1990   Zois, A. A. "Pour un schéma évolutif de l'architecture minoenne: A. Les fondations. Techniques et morphologie," in *L'habitat égéen préhistorique*, BCH Supplement 19, ed. P. Darcque and R. Treuil (Athens) 75–93.

Seals

1975   *CMS* 5.1: 24 no. 27 (I. Pini).

Geomorphology

1968   Dermitzakis, M. D. "Geologikai erevnai epi tou neogenous tis eparchias Ierapetras nisou Kritis," *Geologika Chronika ton Ellinikon Choron* 21: 349–488 (and separately, Athens 1969).

Figure 41.4   Early Minoan IIB paved yard

1977   Fortuin, A. R. "Stratigraphy and Sedimentary History of the Neogene Deposits of the Irapetra Region, Eastern Crete," *Geologische Uitgaven*. Amsterdam Papers of Geology, series 1, 8:123.

1984   Gifford, J. A., and G. H. Myer. "Clay Sources in the Isthmus of Irapetra," in *East Cretan White-on-Dark Ware*, ed. P. P. Betancourt (Philadelphia) 118–25.

IX. FINDS

Herakleion Museum; Ayios Nikolaos Museum; University Museum, University of Pennsylvania, Philadelphia.

X. DATE OF PHOTOGRAPHY

April 18, 1982.

42 VATHYPETRO

GERALD CADOGAN

35°13′ N, 25°09′ E

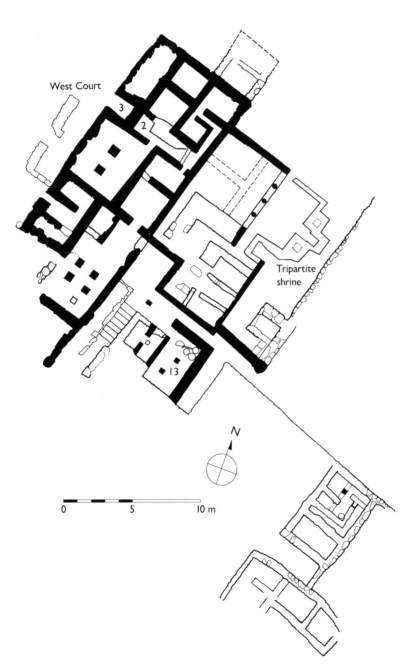

West Court

Tripartite shrine

0   5   10 m

Figure 42.1   Vathypetro country house

Figure 42.2   Vathypetro

I. IMPORTANCE

The Late Minoan I country house at Vathypetro was apparently not in a village or hamlet, although it has a few outbuildings, including a kiln. Its architecture is comparable to that of other grand country houses, such as those at Tylissos or Myrtos-Pyrgos. An unusual feature is its tripartite shrine, which faces the main entrance across a small courtyard. The structure has a central recess, which may have been for a seat or a statue, between two built squares with hollow centers. These could have held flagstaffs or masts, like those shown at the shrine on the stone-and-gold Mountain Shrine rhyton from Zakro.

The agricultural base of the house's wealth is clear. Its large views over rich country are matched by the large number of pithoi in the house to store what its olive oil press and wine press produced.

The house had at least two building phases. It awaits, and deserves, full publication.

II. USE

LM I country house and outbuildings.

III. SITUATION

About 5 km south of Epano Archanes and Archanes-Tourkoyeitonia, in a superb position on a bluff overlooking a large east–west valley typical of the country of inland central Crete, among vineyards in well-watered and fertile country. The wide view from the site stretches from Psiloriti on the west to the great double rock of Kanli Kastelli in the middle distance and the passes leading to the Mesara plain and Phaistos to the south. Dominating Vathypetro from the northwest is Mt. Juktas.

IV. GEOMORPHOLOGY

Vathypetro is sited just downslope of a geologic contact that follows the ridge north of the site. North of the contact, Mio-Pliocene marine limestones and marls make up the regional bedrock (as at Archanes-Phourni and Archanes-Tourkoyeitonia); south of the contact, a some-

Figure 42.3 Country house and outbuildings

what older (Middle Miocene) mixture of conglomerates, sandstones, and clays makes up the bedrock. The site is on a clay terrace of this latter bedrock, which drops away to the south several hundred meters into a broad valley of agricultural fields. The clay could have served Minoan potters, whose kiln was found in an outbuilding.

Most walls at Vathypetro, especially those of the room of the oil press, are made of roughly dressed blocks of the Mio-Pliocene limestone quarried from hillslopes to the north. No indurated bedrock appears on the site, and the oil press room extends at least 0.5 m below present ground level into the clay terrace. The pillar room has the remains of a gray phyllite paving, the stones of which would have come from the lower slopes of Mt. Juktas. Of the three column bases in the facade of the tripartite shrine, the southern two are gray limestone (probably from Mt. Juktas) whereas the northern one is a pebble conglomerate derived from the local bedrock.

It is not surprising that the lower walls of the country house are so thick, for the house was built on a clay bedrock terrace partway down a steep slope. Geologically the site is extremely unstable. It is likely that slope wash from above the site has buried surrounding buildings between the road and the excavated area.

V. EXCAVATION HISTORY

S. Marinatos, 1949–53, 1955–56, for the Archaeological Society.

VI. BUILDINGS

LM I Country house (over 20 by 20 m) of at least two building phases. Details include ashlar masonry, pillar basements, column bases of different stones, setbacks for windows, and a paved West Court. Rooms include wine press (13), shrine (2), another probable shrine outside facing onto the West Court (3), and a tripartite shrine on the east. Olive oil press in West Court. Outbuildings include kiln.

VIII. BIBLIOGRAPHY

General

1949 Marinatos, S. "Anaskaphi Vathypetrou Archanon Kritis," *PAE* 100–109.

1950 ———. "Megaron Vathypetrou," *PAE* 242–49.

1951 ———. "Anaskaphi megarou Vathypetrou Kritis," *PAE* 258–72.

1952 ———. "Anaskaphai en Vathypetro Kritis," *PAE* 592–610.

1953 ———. "Anaskaphai en Vathypetro Kritis," *PAE* 298.

1955 ———. "Anaskaphai en Lykasto kai Vathypetro Kritis," *PAE* 309–10.

Figure 42.4 Vathypetro from the north across a vineyard

1956 ———. "Ergasiai en Vathypetro, Archanais kai Idaio Antro," *PAE* 223.

1960 ———. *Crete and Mycenae* (London) 137, 140.

1978 Shaw, J. W. "Evidence for the Minoan Tripartite Shrine," *AJA* 82:442–46.

1985 Gesell, G. C. *Town, Palace, and House Cult in Minoan Crete*, *SIMA* 67 (Gothenburg) 20, 24–30, 136–37.

Frescoes

1990 Immerwahr, S. A. *Aegean Painting in the Bronze Age* (University Park, Pa.) 184.

Seals

1984 *CMS* 2.3:173–76 nos. 141–43 (N. Platon and I. Pini).

IX. FINDS

Herakleion Museum.

X. DATE OF PHOTOGRAPHY

June 6, 1982.

BARBARA J. HAYDEN

35°07' N, 25°45' E

I. IMPORTANCE

Vrokastro is a defensive or refuge settlement of the end of the Bronze Age and the Early Iron Age. Other such settlements include Karphi, Kavousi, and Kastri at Palaikastro. From the peak on which it sits Vrokastro overlooks a part of the island densely occupied since Early Minoan times along with the east–west route along the north coast of Crete; it has the advantages of difficult access and distant views.

Information about Vrokastro is incomplete because it was only partially excavated early in the century; but enough evidence was found to show its importance in several ways. It was inhabited for a long time, from the 12th (or possibly the 13th) century until the 7th century B.C., and it may have been defended by a town wall (the circuit wall on the north around the lower settlement). Its tombs show a surprising variety of burial habits, with pithoi, or storage jars; inhumations and cremations in rock-cut chamber tombs; and cremations in walled "bone enclosures." There are also different types of shrines and of figurines placed in them. The shrines include a domestic bench sanctuary in the town and a (possible) shrine—a one-roomed building—near the bone enclosures south of the site.

Metal was worked, including some of the earliest iron produced in Crete; and imported pottery, metal objects, and, perhaps, jewelry from the Cyclades, Dodecanese, and Athens may attest to direct links rather than links through central Crete.

II. USE

MM IA–III traces; LM IIIC–G/EO settlement.

III. SITUATION

On the peak of Vrokastro, 313.1 m high, east of the village of Kalo Chorio and overlooking the Bay of Mirabello. Tombs and possibly scattered houses extend west along the limestone ridges of Karako-vilia, Mazichortia, and Amigdali.

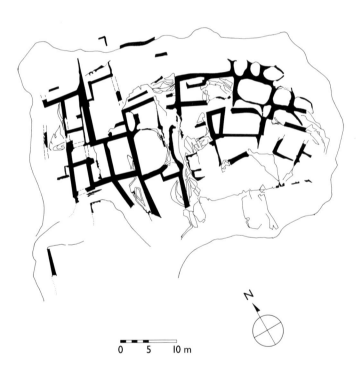

0   5   10 m

Figure 43.1   Vrokastro, upper settlement

Figure 43.2   Vrokastro, upper settlement

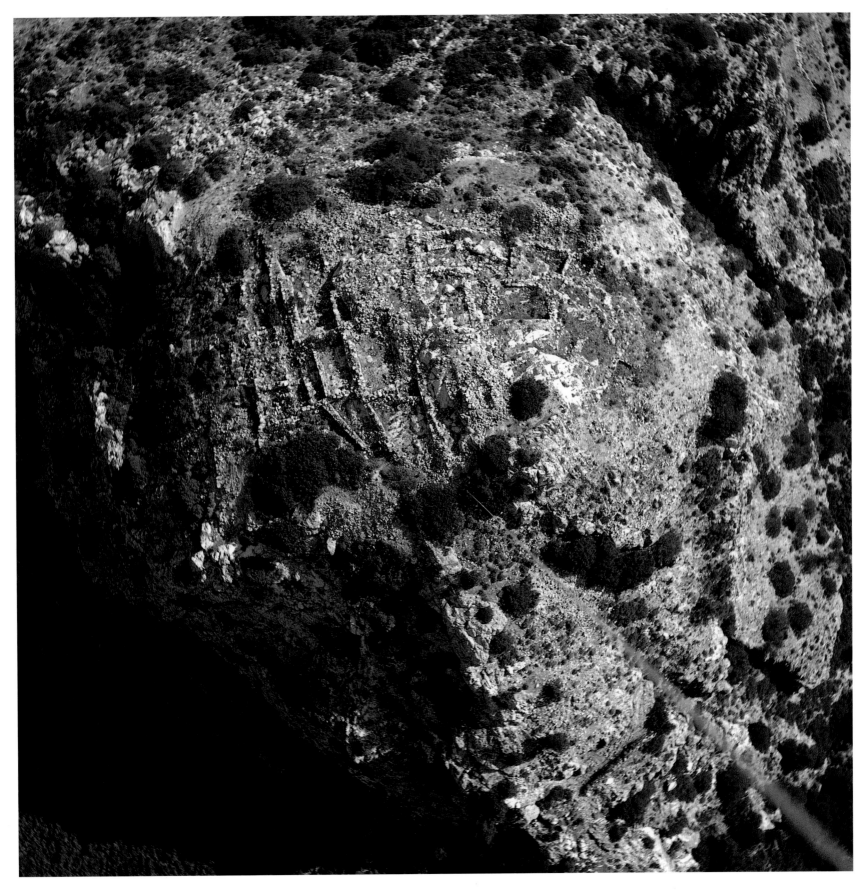

Figure 43.3   Vrokastro and Bay of Mirabello

IV. GEOMORPHOLOGY

The south and west shores of the Bay of Mirabello are mostly steep and rocky because of the white contact-metamorphosed Upper Cretaceous limestones and dolomites of the Gavrovo-Tripolitza series that crop out along the coast. Just east of the modern coastal village of Istro this rock unit curves inland from the present coastline, but a fault-bounded outlier rises some 300 m above the coastal road to a craggy peak that offers a nearly inaccessible location for the settlement. Vrokastro occupies the irregular top of this bedrock peak. Limestone flags form the walls of rooms built to conform to the uneven surface offered by bedrock outcrops.

As at Chamaizi and Karphi, the absence of groundwater suggests the use of cisterns, though none has been found. Springs 20 minutes' walk south of the summit and in the rich Kalo Chorio valley. Olives, almonds, and cereals grown in fields south of Vrokastro.

V. EXCAVATION HISTORY

E. H. Hall, 1910, 1912, for the University Museum, University of Pennsylvania.

VI. BUILDINGS

MM IA–III Sherds below later floors suggest possible small settlement on summit, or perhaps a shrine (though no figurines recovered).

M IIIC–SM Sherds (possibly back to late LM IIIB); no building remains.

G–LG/EO Houses excavated on summit and north slope (terraced) form part of settlement. Rubble masonry. Another sector partially excavated 50 m below on north slope, to the south of circuit wall: houses terraced into hill, of rubble masonry. Other walls scattered across limestone ridges and fields south and southwest of site; also chamber tombs and "bone enclosures." G floor reported on summit.

VIII. BIBLIOGRAPHY

General

1914 Hall, E. H. *Excavations in Eastern Crete, Vrokastro.* University of Pennsylvania, The Museum, Anthropological Publications 3.3 (Philadelphia) 39–185.

1983 Hayden, B. J. "New Plans of the Early Iron Age Settlement of Vrokastro," *Hesperia* 52:367–87.

————. "Work Continues at Vrokastro, 1910–12, 1979–82," *Expedition* 25.3:12–20.

1988 ————. "Fortifications of Postpalatial and Early Iron Age Crete," *AA* 1–21.

Seals

1969 *CMS* 2.1:578–79 no. 484 (N. Platon).

1984 *CMS* 2.3:265–68 nos. 228–30 (N. Platon and I. Pini).

IX. FINDS

Herakleion Museum.

X. DATE OF PHOTOGRAPHY

May 10, 1981.

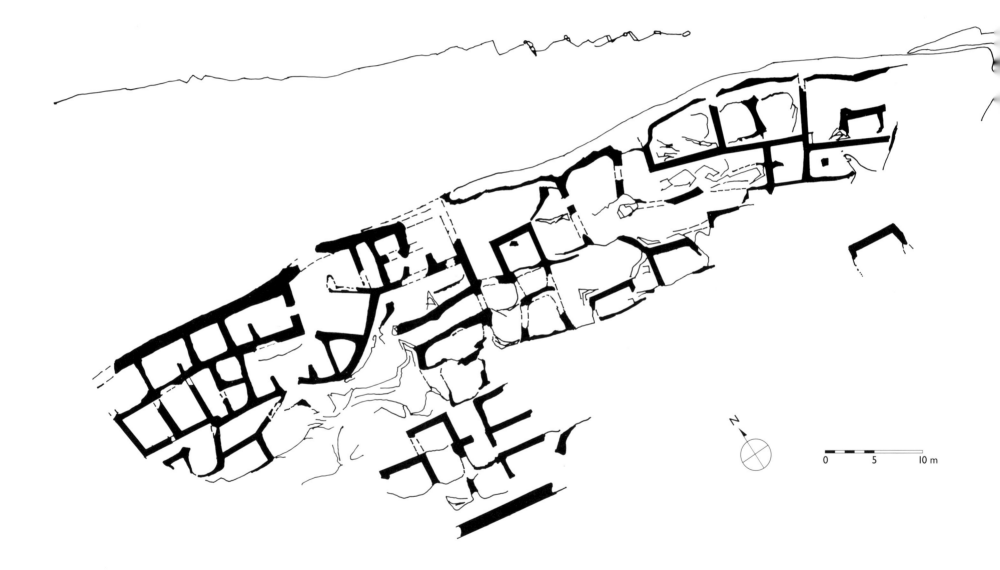

Figure 43.4   Vrokastro, lower settlement

Figure 43.5   Vrokastro, upper and lower settlements

NIKOLAOS PLATON

35°06′ N, 26°16′ E

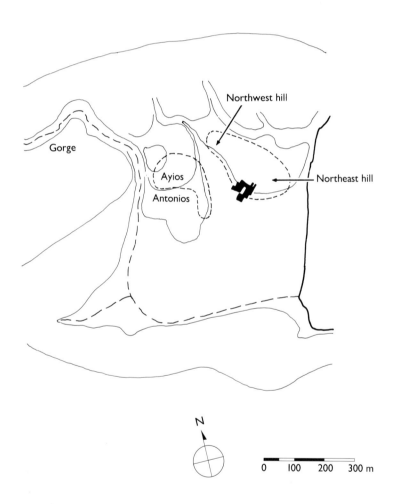

Figure 44.1 Zakro area (dotted line
shows limits of excavation)

I. IMPORTANCE

The excavation of the palace of Zakro has been among the most important for Minoan archaeology since World War II. Work began in 1961 and is still continuing in the town, of which a little had already been excavated at the beginning of the century.

Zakro owes its long Minoan life and importance to its unique position at the eastern end of Crete. Its bay provides natural shelter from the north winds near Cape Sidero, the northeast tip of Crete, where the winds are extremely strong and often veer to the west, making it impossible to round the cape. Zakro is thus ideally suited for trade and exchange with the Middle East, as the discovery of Syrian elephant tusks inside the palace shows, as well as with the neighboring Dodecanesian islands of Kasos and Karpathos. It may even be seen as a base for controlling the boats that entered the Aegean by the southeast channels. In any event, the siting of a palace at Zakro shows how important the eastern end of Crete was for the Minoans. In recent centuries the bay has often been used by sponge divers from the Dodecanese (especially those traveling from Symi to Libya) and by the sailors of other small boats to ride out storms. (Accounts of Zakro by Spratt [1865] and Hogarth [1910] are well worth reading.)

The evidence that led to the hardly expected discovery of the palace on low ground, whereas the Minoan town is on two hillslopes above it, included hints from Hogarth's excavations at the beginning of the century, particularly the sealings he found; the chance recovery of three gold objects of remarkable workmanship (now in the Herakleion Museum in the Yialamakis collection); and the blocks of dressed ashlar masonry in the fields (cut from stone quarried at Pelekita some 5 km to the north).

The palace at Zakro is the first Minoan palace to have been excavated completely after the pioneering excavations of the palaces at Knossos, Mallia, and Phaistos. Though destroyed in Late Minoan IB, the palace was found with many of its treasures and household objects intact. These have given a new understanding of the achievements of Minoan art and daily life in the New Palace period. Works such as the Mountain Shrine rhyton and other stone vases, including antique Egyptian pieces altered to make them appear Minoan,

Figure 44.2   Recent excavations of palace and town

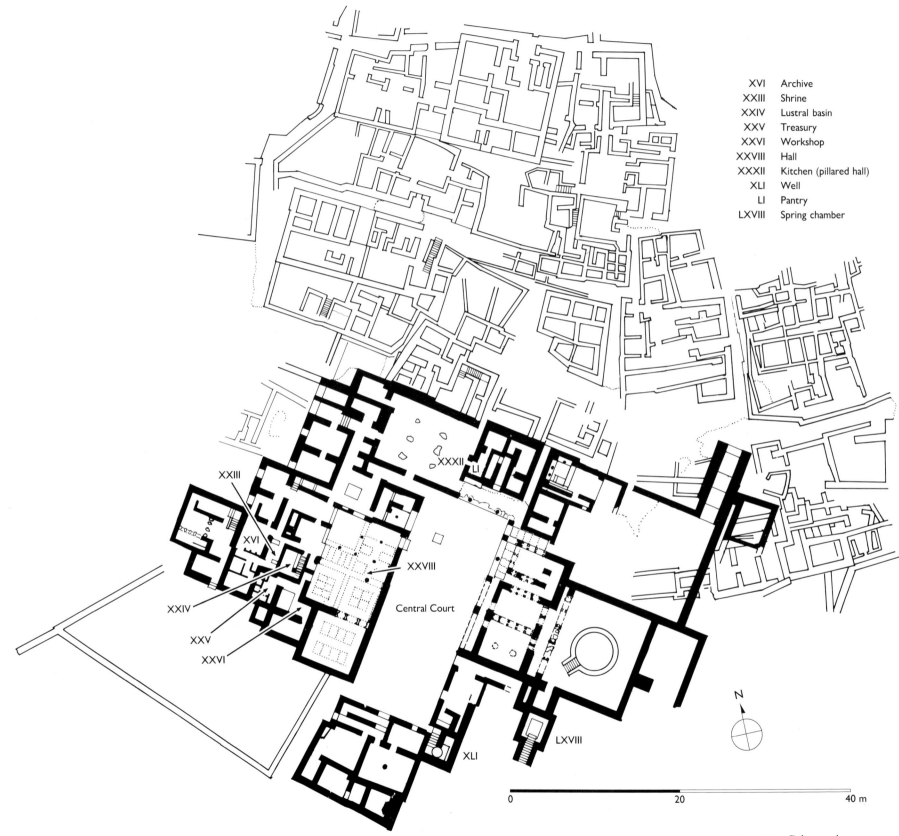

XVI   Archive
XXIII   Shrine
XXIV   Lustral basin
XXV   Treasury
XXVI   Workshop
XXVIII   Hall
XXXII   Kitchen (pillared hall)
XLI   Well
LI   Pantry
LXVIII   Spring chamber

XXIII

XVI

XXVIII

XXIV

XXV

XXVI

Central Court

XXXII

LXVIII

XLI

N

0   20   40 m

Figure 44.3 Palace and town

Figure 44.4   Palace

copper oxhide-shaped ingots, bronze saws and tools, an archive of Linear A tablets, and much fine pottery have all been found in the palace. The total of pots exceeds ten thousand.

The architecture of the palace gives clear evidence on the west side of the structure for the interconnection of religion, administration, the storage of agricultural wealth, and the arts and crafts that was such an important part of Minoan New Palace period society. On the east side the waterworks are an interesting feature. The building, carefully planned, is on a different axis from the town, which is aligned strictly north–south.

The relationship of the palace to the town and any changes from Old Palace times to New Palace times have yet to be fully explained. The town comes right up to the palace, even seeming to crowd it, suggesting that it was more a (preexisting) harbor town than one arranged around a palace.

Inhabitation at Zakro dates back to Early Minoan III at least. As at Mallia, traces of the Old Palace are discernible beneath the New Palace; the main axis of the town, the Harbor Road, dates to the Old Palace period, to which some of the houses in the town may also be assigned.

II. USE

EM II burials; EM III–LM I town (MM I/II–LM I palace); LM IIIA2 reoccupation.

III. SITUATION

At the eastern end of Crete, the palace of Zakro is on the northern edge of a small coastal valley, between the hills on which the Minoan town was built (one is to the southwest with the modern church of Ayios Antonios; those to the northeast, north, and northwest form an elongate east–west ridge). The soil around is fertile but liable to flooding; there have been severe flash floods in the great Gorge of Zakro, the Pharangi ton Nekron, "gorge of the dead," which brings water off the Siteia mountains to the sea. The rise in the water table since Minoan times has made it difficult at times to excavate the low-lying palace. In Minoan times drinking water may have been obtained from wells, which today produce a slightly saline water, and cisterns: the east wing of the palace contains a cistern, a spring chamber, and a well. There are also some indications of an aqueduct with clay pipes bringing water from the plentiful spring at Ano Zakro, where there was a New Palace period country house.

IV. GEOMORPHOLOGY

The bedrock of the east–west ridge of the Minoan town (at the foot of which is the palace) is a flysch, part of the Tripolitza series nappe, here composed of thinly bedded greenish sandstone and marl strata. The flysch is rather prone to disintegration into fist-sized or smaller fragments. The embayment of Zakro owes its existence to this and several other relatively soft rock units, which have been differentially eroded out of the harder dark gray dense limestone bedrock (also of the Tripolitza series) that predominates along this portion of the east coast of Crete. The builders used a wide range of bedrock types for the palace, including (besides the Tripolitza limestone) a soft, easily quarried Pleistocene eolianite (poros) for ashlar masonry, a darker limestone from an unknown source, and a small quantity of soft, marly limestone from small outcrops of Neogene bedrock south of the bay.

The flysch bedrock underlying the palace has been tightly folded to form the ridge, which rises 10–15 m above the alluvium of the valley floor. As at other sites, here the Minoan builders founded their structures on a bedrock type (relatively) easy to excavate, while having close at hand—in fact surrounding the valley—the massive Tripolitza limestone that is a far better building stone than the flysch.

In the New Palace period, when the land surface in this and several other coastal valleys of eastern Crete was some 2–3 m higher (relative to modern sea level), the water table in the Zakro valley alluvium would have been correspondingly lower. It is likely that the surface on which the Minoans grew their crops lies at least 2 m below the fields now cultivated in the center of the valley. Therefore it is possible that the major stream flowing into the valley, which in recent times has been characterized by episodic torrential flood events (one in 1901 is vividly described by Hogarth [1910]), was in the Bronze Age constrained by higher and better-defined banks. That the water table in the valley has risen since Minoan times is shown by the frequent flooding of rooms in the palace and the discovery by Pirazzoli (1980) of a solution notch at a depth of 1 m in the south part of the bay.

The siting of Zakro is notably similar to that of Gournia and Monastiraki: a small bedrock rise in the center of a valley possessing cultivable fields and secure water supplies. This suggests that careful attention was paid to the local landforms and geological resources near a major settlement.

The precise line of the Minoan shore at Kato Zakro cannot be determined without recourse to drilling or coring along the present beach. If the relative rise of sea level has exceeded the rate at which

Figure 44.5   North end of palace and town

sediment has been washed down to the sea by the Zakro stream, then the Minoan shore lies seaward of, and lower than, the present one. If, however, unusually large quantities of alluvium have been deposited in recent millennia—as was probably the case—then the Minoan beach is buried several tens of meters inland.

V. EXCAVATION HISTORY

D. G. Hogarth, 1901, for the British School; N. Platon, 1961–, for the Archaeological Society.

VI. BUILDINGS

EM II   Burials in gorge.

EM III   Scattered settlement remains in the area of the palace and town.

MM I–II   Old Palace with plan similar to that of New Palace, but with longer and wider Central Court, and narrow terraced West Court, bounded by grand house, and northeast gate (later out of use). East wing of palace follows alignment of Harbor Road. Three phases to Old Palace.

Harbor Road. Workshops and metalworking furnace in northeast part of excavated area. Many house remains on slope of northwest hill.

Burial enclosures on slopes opposite palace.

MM IIIB–LM I   New Palace: about 8,000 sq m, with 150 rooms, including lost upper rooms. Central Court about 30.3 by 12.15 m. West side: hall beside Central Court; group of rooms around archive, shrine, lustral basin, treasury, and workshop; three groups of storerooms on the west. North side: kitchen and pantry with stairs to probable dining room over kitchen. East side (much destroyed by farming): royal apartments, including halls and large room with cistern entered by steps. Cistern fed from spring chamber. South side: well and workshops. LM IB: North wall of kitchen reinforced.

Town: houses generally of many rooms (often around thirty), with small storage rooms around a large room with a bench and central support; access from street. Houses arranged in blocks. Streets follow or are perpendicular to contours. On northeast hill, houses incorporate Old Palace structures. Olive oil and wine presses in town, and other places for preparing foodstuffs. Pits in rock near church of Ayios Antonios.

LM IB   Destruction. Abandonment.

LM IIIA2   Partial reoccupation of town on southwest hill.

VII. RADIOCARBON DATE

	B.P.	1σ cal. B.C.	2σ cal. B.C.
MM IIIB/LM IA			
P-1784	2870 ± 60	1154–943	1260–900

VIII. BIBLIOGRAPHY

General

1865   Spratt, T. A. B. *Travels and Researches in Crete* (London) 1:234–36.

1900–1901   Boyd Dawkins, W. "Skulls from Cave Burials at Zakro," *BSA* 7:150–56.

Hogarth, D. G. "Excavations at Zakro, Crete," *BSA* 7:121–49.

1961   Platon, N. "Anaskaphi Kato Zakrou," *PAE* 216–24.

1962   ———. "Anaskaphi Zakrou," *PAE* 161–62.

1963   ———. "Anaskaphai Zakrou," *PAE* 160–88.

1964   ———. "Anaskaphai Zakrou," *PAE* 142–68.

1965   ———. "Anaskaphai Zakrou," *PAE* 197–207.

1966   ———. "Anaskaphai Zakrou," *PAE* 142–53.

1967   ———. "Anaskaphai Zakrou," *PAE* 162–94.

1968   ———. "Anaskaphai Zakrou," *PAE* 149–83.

1969   ———. "Anaskaphi Zakrou," *PAE* 197–237.

1970   ———. "Anaskaphi Zakrou," *PAE* 208–51.

1971   ———. "Anaskaphi Zakrou," *PAE* 231–75.

———. *Zakros: The Discovery of a Lost Palace of Ancient Crete* (New York).

Shaw, J. W. *Minoan Architecture: Materials and Techniques, ASAtene* 49:30–34.

1972   Platon, N. "Anaskaphi Zakrou," *PAE* 159–92.

1973   ———. "Anaskaphi Zakrou," *PAE* 137–66.

1974   ———. *Zakros. To neon minoikon anaktoron* (Athens).

Figure 44.6   Houses adjacent to palace

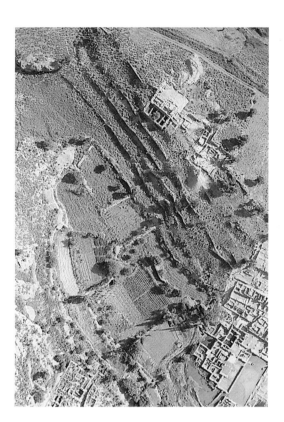

Figure 44.7   House northwest of palace

Figure 44.8   Early excavations on hill (Ayios Antonios) southwest of palace

1975 ———. "Anaskaphi Zakrou," *PAE* 343–75.

1976 ———. "Anaskaphi Zakrou," *PAE* 419–39.

1977 ———. "Anaskaphi Zakrou," *PAE* 421–46.

1978 ———. "Anaskaphi Zakrou," *PAE* 259–99.

1979 ———. "Anaskaphi Zakrou," *PAE* 282–322.

1980 ———. "Anaskaphi Zakrou," *PAE* 297–330.

1981 ———. "Anaskaphi Zakrou," *PAE* 331–66.

———. "Metallourgiko kamini stin Zakro tis Kritis," in *4 Cretological* 1:436–46.

1982 ———. "Anaskaphi Zakrou," *PAE* 320–48.

1983 ———. "Anaskaphi Zakrou," *PAE* 335–47.

1985 Gesell, G. C. *Town, Palace, and House Cult in Minoan Crete, SIMA* 67 (Gothenburg) 137–41.

Platon, N. "Anaskaphai Zakrou," *PAE* 217–62.

1986 ———. "Anaskaphi Zakrou," *PAE* 243–97.

1987 Chrysoulaki, S., and L. Platon. "Relations between the Town and Palace of Zakros," in *The Function of the Minoan Palaces* 77–84.

Frescoes

1990 Immerwahr, S. A. *Aegean Painting in the Bronze Age* (University Park, Pa.) 184–85.

Scripts and Seals

1975 Platon, N., and W. C. Brice. *Inscribed Tablets and Pithos of Linear A System from Zakros* (Athens).

Figure 44.9   Zakro and bay

1976	*GORILA* 1:331–33.
	GORILA 3:147–209.
1977	*CMS* 2.2:381–85 nos. 263–64 (N. Platon, I. Pini, and G. Salies).
1979	*GORILA* 2:97–98.
1982	*GORILA* 4:111–15.
1983	Weingarten, J. *The Zakro Master and His Place in Prehistory, SIMA PB* 26 (Gothenburg).
1984	*CMS* 2.3:339–40 no. 286 (N. Platon and I. Pini).
1989	Kopaka, K. "Une nouvelle inscription en Linéaire A de Zakro," *Kadmos* 28:7–13.

Radiocarbon Date

| 1975 | Lawn, B. "University of Pennsylvania Radiocarbon Dates XVIII," *Radiocarbon* 17:204. |

Geomorphology

1910	Hogarth, D. G. *Accidents of an Antiquary's Life* (London) 78–90.
1980	Pirazzoli, P. A. "Formes de corrosion marine et vestiges archéologiques submergés: Interpretations néotectoniques de quelques examples en Grèce et en Yougoslavie," *Annales de l'Institut Océanographique* 56 Supplement:101–11.
1985	Peters, J. M. "Late Cenozoic Tectono-Stratigraphic Development of Eastern Crete," in *Neogene and Quaternary Vertical Tectonics in the Southern Hellenic Arc and Their Effect on Concurrent Sedimentation Processes. Geologische Uitgaven.* Amsterdam Papers of Geology, series 1, 23, ed. J. M. Peters (Amsterdam) 62–247.

IX. FINDS

Herakleion Museum; Siteia Museum; Ayios Nikolaos Museum.

X. DATE OF PHOTOGRAPHY

May 7, 1982.

GLOSSARY

Alluvium: Silt, sand, or gravel from weathered bedrock and soil sediment that has been transported and deposited by the running water of a stream or river.

Anta(e), in antis: the slightly thickened end of a wall.

Autochthon: a body of rock that has not been displaced from its place of formation by tectonic forces.

Bathymetric: pertaining to submarine topography.

Bioclastic (of sedimentary rocks): made of broken remains of fossil organisms, such as mollusc shell hash or coral fragments.

Breccia: coarse angular fragments of sedimentary, igneous, or metamorphic rocks recemented into a younger rock.

Calcareous: composed primarily of mineral calcium carbonate (calcite).

Chamber tomb: a rock-cut tomb with a burial chamber.

Chert: a hard, brittle sedimentary rock formed primarily of microcrystalline quartz (silica); it may be an original organic or inorganic precipitate or a replacement product.

Cirque: a bowl-shaped depression eroded in rock by glaciers.

Cist: a stone-lined box set into or under the floor.

Colluvium: an unconsolidated mass of weathered rock or soil sediment deposited by unconcentrated sheet erosion at the base of hillslopes.

Conglomerate: sedimentary rock composed of rounded (weathered) pebbles and cobbles cemented together in a matrix of finer sediment.

Country house: a substantial house built in open country or in a village; the ruling house of a locality. Also known as a *villa.*

Dolomite: (1) a crystalline mineral of calcium and magnesium carbonate; (2) the sedimentary rock type composed primarily of that mineral.

Dromos: from the Greek word for road, the passage leading to the chamber of a chamber tomb (q.v.) or Late Minoan tholos tomb (q.v.).

Eolianite: a quartz-rich sandstone, cemented by calcium carbonate, representing coastal sand dunes deposited during recent glacial periods when sea level was scores of meters below its present level. The dunes subsequently were lithified by the natural continuous dissolution and reprecipitation of calcite cement, derived from the marine shell and other carbonate fragments that make up the sands. Quaternary age eolianite is a fairly common rock type around the coasts of Crete.

Eustatic (of a sea level rise): caused by melting of polar ice sheets; it is an absolute increase in ocean water volume and is therefore independent of changes in land level.

Fenster: an area of rock beneath an overthrust sheet (nappe) that has been exposed through subsequent deformation (faulting) or erosion.

Flysch: a marine sedimentary rock facies characterized by thick sequences of nonfossiliferous sandy and calcareous shales and muds interbedded with sandstones and conglomerates.

Foreset beds: inclined sediment layers deposited on the frontal slope of a delta or on the lee side of a sand dune.

Garrigue: an important type of Mediterranean vegetation, as indicated by the different names given to it: *phrygana* (Greece), *tomillares* (Spain), and *batha* (Palestine). Characterized by low, hard-leaved evergreen shrubs, many of them spiny and aromatic.

Gimbal mount: a pivoted device which can keep instruments level in unsteady conditions, as with a ship's compass or a balloon camera.

Grabens: depressed blocks of primarily metamorphic and sedimentary rocks; compare with horsts (q.v.).

Gypsum: (1) the mineral hydrous calcium sulfate; (2) the sedimentary rock composed primarily or exclusively of that mineral.

Horns of consecration: stylized bulls' horns, found in shrines and shown in frescoes on the eaves of buildings. Preserved examples are usually of plaster or stone.

Horsts: uplifted blocks of primarily metamorphic and sedimentary rocks—separated by downfaulted blocks called grabens (q.v.).

Igneous rock: rock formed by the crystallization of magma or lava.

Indurated (of a rock or sediment): consolidated by pressure or cementation.

Karst: a topography characteristic of limestone regions in which most or all of the drainage is by underground channels.

Katavothros: Cretan term for a polje (q.v.).

Klippe: an erosional remnant of an overthrust sheet that is surrounded by the strata beneath the fault plane.

Kouloura: from the Greek word for something round and hollow, the built pits in the west courts of Knossos, Mallia, and Phaistos.

Kouskouras: the Cretan term for the Neogene marls and soft limestones.

Light well: a shaft that lights and ventilates interior rooms.

Limestone: a sedimentary rock consisting of at least 50 percent calcium carbonate; most types of limestone are partly or wholly of organic origin and are composed of the fossilized remains of macroscopic (e.g., molluscs, corals), or microscopic (e.g., foraminifera) organisms.

Lithified: transformed from loose sediment into consolidated rock.

Lustral basin, or basin: an interior room, usually sunken, and probably used for cleansing.

Marl: (1) an unconsolidated sediment mixture of terrigenous mud plus marine or freshwater calcitic mud; (2) the lithified equivalent (also called marlstone).

Megaron: from a Greek word for hall; used in Aegean Bronze Age archaeology for a hall, often with a central hearth, having only one entrance (often through a porch on the axis of the building). Well known in Mycenaean (Late Bronze Age) times.

Metamorphic rock: new rock produced from igneous or sedimentary types by metamorphic processes of high temperature and pressure.

Microfossil: fossilized remains of animals (e.g., foraminifera, raidolaria, ostracods) or plants (e.g., coccolithophores, diatoms) whose study requires the use of a microscope.

Moraine: accumulation of rock debris carried by alpine glacier and subsequently left behind as a depositional landform.

Nappe: a body of rock, often several tens of square kilometers in extent, that has been thrust or folded by tectonism up and over the pre-existing bedrock of an area.

Neotectonism: deformation (folding, faulting) of rock units and sedimentary deposits during the late Tertiary and Quaternary periods of geological time (approximately during the last 5 million years).

Nondestructive (applied to archaeology): The use of methods other than excavation to investigate sites or conduct surveys, often by remote sensing (q.v.).

Orogeny: a major episode of mountain-building tectonic activity characterized by regional deformation (folding and faulting) of the rock strata.

Palace: religious, administrative, economic, social, and cultural center in Minoan Crete.

Peristyle: Colonnade surrounding a central open area; cloister.

Phrygana: Greek term for the vegetation type garrigue (q.v.).

Phyllite: a regional metamorphic rock composed of the minerals quartz, mica, and chlorite plus several accessory minerals such as feldspars, pyrite, or magnetite; developed from terrigenous sedimentary rocks such as sandstones and shales that have been exposed to relatively low temperatures and pressures.

Pier-and-door: see *polythyron.*

Pillar basement, pillar crypt, pillar hall: basement or ground-floor room with pillar(s) to support rooms above. *Pillar crypt* is used for a room that seems to have had a religious use.

Polje: a closed hollow or depression in karst regions, usually flat bottomed and formed by solution of limestone bedrock; it is often partly filled with terra rossa soil (q.v.) and is agriculturally fertile.

Polythyron: Greek word for a room with many doors, referring to Minoan rooms (halls) with walls of pier-and-door partitions making multiple doors.

Poros: a Greek term for eolianite (q.v.).

Radiolarite: a bioclastic sedimentary rock related to chert and composed mainly of the siliceous skeletons of radiolarian microfossils.

Remote sensing: a term applied to the use of instruments at ground level and in airplanes or satellites that create images of the earth's surface by reading electromagnetic radiation either in the visible light spectrum or beyond either end. A method increasingly applied in archaeological surveys and site studies.

Rhyton: Greek word for drinking cup or funnel, with one large hole and one small hole for releasing liquid in a thin stream.

Schlerophyll: hard-leafed vegetation associated with arid climates.

Sedimentary rocks: rocks formed from unconsolidated deposits associated with the sea, fresh water (rivers and lakes), glaciers, or wind activity (sand dunes) that are cemented into sandstone, shale, limestone, and conglomerate, depending on such properties as mineral type and the size of the constituent grains.

Serpentinite: a regional metamorphic rock composed primarily of the minerals serpentine and magnetite, with many other mineral types present; derived from the metamorphism of ultramafic rocks such as peridotite and pyroxenite.

Sideropetra: a term used locally on Crete for any very dense, dark limestone; fragments produce a characteristic "ringing" sound when dropped on a solid surface.

Siliceous: composed primarily of the mineral silicon dioxide (silica).

Soil: unconsolidated mineral matter at the earth's surface that has been subjected to environmental factors such as topography, climate, and biological activity to produce a mixed inorganic-organic material with distinctive physical properties and the capability of supporting plant growth.

Soil creep: the slow but continual surface movement of soil, sediment, and rock fragments downslope under the influence of gravity.

Solution notch: horizontal indentation or undercutting in hard limestone bedrock caused by corrosion at the interface of land and sea; it marks the position of sea level during the period of its formation (decades to centuries).

Tectonic: relating to the geological processes that build up the features of the earth's crust, including those that break, bend, or warp rocks and sediments.

Terra rossa: a reddish clayey soil characteristically developed on hard limestone bedrock in Mediterranean-type climates.

Terrigenous: wastes derived from the terrestrial (continental) environment.

Tholos tomb: from *tholos,* a Greek word for round building, a round tomb with corbeled, vaulted stone walls.

Xoanon: Greek word for wooden cult statue.

The text for this book is Linotronic Janson, with Monotype

Gill Sans for display. The type was set by

G & S Typesetters, Inc.

The paper is 150 gsm. snow white, and the book is bound in

Asahi "T" Saifu cloth. The printing and binding were done by

P. Chan & Edward, Inc.

At the University of California Press, the designer was

Steve Renick,

the editor

Stephanie Fay,

and the production coordinator

Lillian Robyn.